CW01022417

EARLY

NURSERYMEN

Other Books by John Harvey:

HENRY YEVELE
GOTHIC ENGLAND
THE PLANTAGENETS
DUBLIN
TUDOR ARCHITECTURE
THE ENGLISH CATHEDRALS
THE GOTHIC WORLD
ENGLISH MEDIAEVAL ARCHITECTS
THE CATHEDRALS OF SPAIN
THE MASTER BUILDERS
THE MEDIAEVAL ARCHITECT
CONSERVATION OF BUILDINGS
EARLY GARDENING CATALOGUES

edited with translation:
WILLIAM WORCESTRE: ITINERARIES 1478-1480

EARLY NURSERYMEN

WITH REPRINTS OF
DOCUMENTS AND LISTS

by

John Harvey

PHILLIMORE

1974

Published by
PHILLIMORE & CO. LTD.
London and Chichester
Head Office: Shopwyke Hall,
Chichester, Sussex, England

ISBN 0 85033 191 9

Text set in 10pt. Journal Roman
Printed and bound in Great Britain by
BIDDLES LTD.
Guildford and King's Lynn

CONTENTS

		page
LIST OF ILLUSTRATIONS		vii
PREFACE		ix
ACKNOWLEDGMENTS		xiv
INTRODUCTION		1
CHAPTER I	*The Basis of Nurseries — Plantsmanship*	14
CHAPTER II	*Gardener into Nurseryman*	27
CHAPTER III	*The London Nursery Trade before 1700*	39
CHAPTER IV	*The Founding of Provincial Nurseries*	58
CHAPTER V	*A Century of Expansion*	75
CHAPTER VI	*Nurseries Galore*	90
CHAPTER VII	*Culmination and Conclusion*	107
EPILOGUE		128
APPENDIX I	*The Culture of Rosemary in England*	135
APPENDIX II	*Garden Plants, 1375-1400*	138
APPENDIX III	*Rickets' Catalogue, 1688*	145
APPENDIX IV	*Fairchild's Flowers, 1722*	150
APPENDIX V	*Inventories of Nurserymen*	160
APPENDIX VI	*Wills of Nurserymen*	167
APPENDIX VII	*Henry Woodman: Bills and Letters, 1729-33*	171

APPENDIX VIII   *Henry Clark: a Bill and Letters, 1750-71*   186

APPENDIX IX   *William Pendar, 1766-71*   194

APPENDIX X   *The London Firms of 1786*   196

APPENDIX XI   *Shrubs, Roses, Pines and Vines*   201

BIBLIOGRAPHY AND ABBREVIATIONS   209

NOTES TO THE TEXT   211

INDEX   231

LIST OF ILLUSTRATIONS

Plates 1-8, between pages 50 and 51.
1   John Rose (1622-1677)
2   Thomas Wentworth (died 1587) in his garden
3   Grafting in the sixteenth century
4   John Tradescant the elder (died 1638)
5   John Tradescant the younger (1608-1662)
6   Henry Wise (1653-1738)
7   Thomas Fairchild (1667-1729)
8   William Falla (1761-1830)

Plates 9-16, between pages 114 and 115.
 9   Three exotic plants drawn by Henrietta London
10   *Banksia serrata,* the first introduction from Australia
11   *Vaccinium amoenum,* introduced by John Cree
12   *Erica ampullacea,* introduced by Richard Williams
13   *Narcissus tenuior,* raised by James Maddock
14   *Chrysanthemum indicum,* first flowered by James Colvill
15   *Geranium quinquevulnerum,* introduced by John Armstrong
16   *Azalea pontica,* first flowered by Thomas Watson

PREFACE

EVERY GARDENER in the modern world depends very largely upon nurserymen. The services performed by this particular craft, profession or trade are indeed obvious, but tend to pass unnoticed. It would be possible for the owner of a very small garden to keep it stocked by chance gifts of seed or cuttings, and there may still be a few cottagers in remote districts of Britain who do in this way show a few flowers in front, and keep themselves in roots and greens at the back. In almost every case, however, some of the seed sown comes in packets bought in a shop or by post, and plants come from market or plant centre if not direct from the nurseryman.

The ability to buy seed or fresh plants is not merely a matter of convenience. It was an observed natural fact many centuries ago, and set down in writing about 1250 by Walter of Henley, that seed (corn) should be changed every year, 'for seed grown on other ground will bring more profit than that which is grown on your own'. Henley, who had been a knight but entered the Dominican Order and became a friar, was either himself an experimental scientist or put on record the experiments of others, for he went on: 'Will you see this? Plough two selions at the same time, and sow the one with seed which is bought and the other with corn which you have grown.' Over 700 years ago, then, there was a normal trade in seed grains, and the good husbandman was advised against the false economy of saving his own seed. The trade must have embraced several different kinds of seed at least: wheat, barley, oats, rye, and probably also the field crops of peas and (broad) beans.

Exactly how the trade was carried on we do not know, but a good deal of it was based on the surplus produce of great estates and of monastic gardens. Surviving account rolls show that plants, seed and bulbs were bought and sold, and that the sorts included before the end of the 13th century were beans, hemp, onions and garlic, as well as plants or slips of grapevines and of named varieties of pears. These were from the great garden of the Earl of Lincoln at Holborn in 1295-96, and it may be no coincidence that three centuries later the garden of John Gerard was also in Holborn. Tradition, once rooted, dies hard, and certain areas suitable for growing particular kinds of plants are likely to continue in the same use until taken for building.

It is not easy in the medieval records to be sure in every case whether given items formed part of a real trade in seedsmen's and nurserymen's goods, and how far they were items of greengrocery and market gardening including the production of fruit for the table. To some extent this difficulty continues down to relatively modern times, and one of the first matters to explore concerns the various ramifications of the fundamental craft of gardening. This book is an attempt to trace the rise and development of plant nurseries in

x

England in an intermediate period. As we shall see, the first clear traces of commercial nurseries in the modern sense are found in the 16th century, close to the period of the Dissolution of the monasteries. There may even be an element of cause and effect in this contemporaneity. Although there certainly were, at least in and around London, some merchants who sold seeds and plants before 1540, it seems likely that a substantial vacuum was left by the general cessation of specialist gardening on the part of monks, friars and the infirmarers of hospitals.

A good deal is in print on the subject of those English nurserymen who were responsible in the 19th and early 20th centuries for the massive introduction of numerous species of exotic plants. The nurserymen in some cases sent out plant explorers on their own account, and a great part of this adventurous tale has been told. Not very much has yet been said about the less spectacular work of the trade in the country as a whole, as distinct from the few select London firms who supplied the aristocracy and could draw upon large capital. These outstanding leaders of horticultural business stood upon the shoulders of a multitude of lesser but yet worthy subordinates, widely spread throughout England. The London and country trades were in any case complementary, for while the provincial firms had to get new plants and foreign seed mostly from London, the metropolitan businesses were dependent upon many small growers who specialized in raising given varieties of plants or seeds, and who for accidental reasons such as soil and local climate were able to produce improved strains.

The evidence, a little of it in print but very largely in manuscript sources spread through many record offices and libraries, is extremely heterogeneous in character. Only a few business archives in this field have so far become accessible, and those that there are do not begin much before the end of the 18th century. On the other hand, the few known firms of the 17th century became after 1700 a widening flood, and after 1800 a torrent. Whereas it is difficult to discover the names of any nurserymen much before 1650, the difficulty by 1850 is to see the wood for the trees. The bulk of the material which concerns us here comes from those two centuries, and even then it has been necessary to omit – as a general rule – firms founded after 1800. Before that time every part of England had some firms of regional standing able to supply a wide range of requirements. It is then largely with the development of regional businesses, and their relationship with their customers, that this book tries to deal. Inevitably a good deal of the background is general or economic history, but it should be said that the main theme is, as far as possible, biographical and genealogical in tone.

The collection of material would have been completely impossible without the help of a very large number of librarians, archivists, and generous students of garden history. Besides this mention must be made of the fundamental importance of a few earlier books, notably the amazing output of John Claudius Loudon (1783-1843) and particularly his *Encyclopaedia of Gardening* first published in 1822. *A History of Gardening in England,* by Alicia Amherst (later Lady Rockley), which appeared in 1895, is still basic, but to it must be added its worthy successor, encyclopaedic in scope, Mr. Miles Hadfield's *A History of British Gardening*. The *Dictionary of Gardening* of the Royal Horticultural Society has been constantly at hand and (in its second edition of 1956) provides the standard nomenclature of plants adopted here. A great deal of assistance has been derived from the historical works of Miss Alice M. Coats and of Mr. Kenneth Lemmon listed in the bibliography, as well as from two recent books of pioneering character. One of them, by Miss E. J. Willson: *James Lee and the Vineyard Nursery, Hammersmith* (1961), is both a great biography and the first serious history of an early English nursery, accomplished with the highest scholarship. The other, *The Development of Garden Flowers* (1970) by Mr Richard Gorer, covers the whole subject of historical hybridization and is full of incidental references to nurserymen involved in the process.

My indebtedness to the staffs of libraries and record offices has already been mentioned and must here be particularized, though it is impossible to give personal acknowledgments to all of the very many who have contributed material or who have searched their resources at my request. First and foremost I owe thanks to the York City Library and especially to the devoted work by its staff in indexing the York newspapers. In the North I am also deeply indebted to York Minster Library, to the Borthwick Institute, to Leeds City Library and to the library of the Yorkshire Archaeological Society. In London the resources of the Society of Genealogists have been particularly valuable, not least its collection of directories; extensive use has also been made of the unique collection of directories at the Guildhall Library, as well as much else. Most generous help and hospitality have been received from the Lindley Library of the Royal Horticultural Society, from the library of the Royal Botanic Gardens, Kew, and from the libraries of the Linnean Society, the Society of Antiquaries, the Royal Agricultural Society and the Huguenot Society of London. For access to wills over many years I have to thank the former Department of Literary Enquiry of the Principal Probate Registry, and more recently the probate search room at the Public Record Office. As always, a great deal of information has been obtained from the British Museum, in its departments of Printed Books, Manuscripts, Prints and Drawings, and Maps; from the British Museum (Natural History); and from the library of the Victoria and Albert Museum. Outside London the library of the University Botanic Garden, Cambridge; and the Bodleian Library, Oxford, and especially its John Johnson Collection, have been of very great assistance.

A great deal of invaluable local information has been received from the libraries of several of the Greater London boroughs, and for assistance in personal searches I have particularly to thank the staff at the Minet Library and at the libraries of Islington, Kensington, Newington and the City of Westminster. Reference to the many other libraries which have provided information will be found in the notes to the text, but I should specify here the National Libraries of Ireland, Scotland and Wales; the Library of Congress, Washington, D.C.; the library of the Massachusetts Horticultural

Society; the L. H. Bailey Hortorium of Cornell University; and the United States National Agricultural Library. For the ability to borrow many essential works I am grateful to the wonderful resources of the London Library. A large proportion of the records used in this study is in the custody of the archives departments of libraries, public, university, and private; and the majority in county and civic record offices. The number of these repositories precludes individual mention, but my thanks go to the archivists and staff of all these many bodies. In addition to the kind assistance I have received in making personal searches at many offices, I have had the benefit of correspondence from every county record office in England as well as from many others. Several old-established firms of nurserymen have most kindly supplied information, and my gratitude goes especially to Messrs. Caldwell and Sons Ltd. of Knutsford for allowing me to make full use of their remarkable series of early records.

The tale of personal indebtedness is a long one and starts with the members of the Garden History Society, which also deserves mention for its important publications, the former Newsletter and Occasional Papers, and its current Journal, *Garden History*. Separate Acknowledgments are given for permission to reproduce or to quote from copyright material or illustrations. I here express my thanks to those who have contributed in conversation and correspondence:

Mrs. A. Bagot, Messrs. C. B. L. Barr, Harry Battye, G. C. Baugh, Geoffrey Beard, John Bensusan-Butt, Hugh Bilbrough, William Brogden, David Caldwell, William Caldwell, Cecil E. R. Clarabut, Miss Alice M. Coats, Messrs. W. A. B. Crowder, R. G. C. Desmond, Miss Joan Edwards, Mr. A. O. Elmhirst, Dr. L. K. Elmhirst, Dr. F. G. Emmison, Miss R. J. Ensing, Professor J. Ewan, Mr. Trevor Falla, Dr. and Mrs. E. A. Gee, Messrs. J. S. W. Gibson, J. S. L. Gilmour, John Goodchild, Richard Gorer, Arnold Greening, Miles Hadfield, Dr. and Mrs. Ivan Hall, Miss B. Henrey, Messrs. C. R. Hudleston, T. Jaine, Douglas Johnson, Mrs. R. K. Judges, Messrs. R. E. Latham, Francis Leeson, Kenneth Lemmon, Dr. Eileen McCracken, Messrs. W. G. Mackenzie, Stephen Marks, Miss M. Mauchline, Miss P. Minay, Professor A. R. Myers, Mr. and Mrs. David Neave, Mr. Terence Maule Oliver, Dr. D. M. Palliser, Messrs. B. F. J. Pardoe, Hugh Phillips, K. H. Rogers, Mrs. K. N. Sanecki, Miss Irene Scouloudi, Messrs. Colin Simms, Maurice Smith, Ken Spelman, Dr. W. T. Stearn, Messrs. F. W. Steer, R. A. Storey, Dr. Christopher Thacker, Messrs. M. F. Thick, Graham S. Thomas, Dr. Joan Thirsk, Dr. E. C. Till, Messrs. G. F. Verdon, Ronald Webber, H. J. Welch, J. R. Whitehouse and Miss E. J. Willson.

I am grateful to my publishers for their care over the design and production of the book; and to my wife, who has helped at all stages and has read the whole of the proofs.

John H. Harvey

Postscript While this book has been in the press several relevant additions or corrections have come to light:-

p. 35   In 1351 Robert de Goldesburgh (probably Goldsborough near

Knaresborough, West Riding) took up the freedom of York as a 'herberur.' He presumably specialized in pleasure gardens like Roger le Herberur (p. 40). Goldsborough is only 15 miles from York and next to the Templar, later Hospitaller, preceptory at Ribston, afterwards home of the Ribston Pippin. In the Park were formerly enormous specimens of oriental plane (over 100 feet spread) and black mulberry, traditionally brought back by returning Crusaders.

p. 54   The drawings mentioned in George London's will have disappeared, but three drawings by Henrietta London survive at Badminton in an album (MS. D.4.11) mainly by Daniel Frankcom (ff. 2, 108, 109). One sheet (f. 108) illustrating three plants from South Africa (identified at Kew as *Heliophila coronopifolia, Cotyledon decussata,* and *Nemesia strumosa*) is here reproduced (Plate 9) by the kindness of the Duke of Beaufort.

p. 65   Though the catalogues of 1775 remain the first to show prices in print, a list of c. 1754 marked in ink with prices of shrubs and trees has recently come to light (J. Harvey in *Garden History,* II No. 2, Spring 1974, 34-44)

p. 67   Tree nurseries for the supply of hedging plants in many varieties were already common in 1748, when the Swede Pehr Kalm commented: 'In England there is the advantage that nearly in every town and large village there is one or more nurseryman, whose principal occupation is to sow and plant the seeds of a number of different kinds of trees . . . so that they can sell a number of all kinds . . . for a reasonable price . . . When a farmer wishes to lay down . . . a new hedge, he goes . . . and buys of him as many 1,000 shoots as he requires . . .' (*Kalm's Account of his Visit to England,* translated by Joseph Lucas, 1892, 316)

p. 84   Mr Hugh S. Pocock informs me that a pedigree shows Lewis Kennedy (1721-1782) as son of Thomas Kennedy who died on 21 July 1721, a few days after his son's birth; and suggests that Lewis Kennedy, gardener to Lord Wilmington in 1731, was the later gardener to the Duke of Bedford at Woburn who committed suicide on 6 October 1743 (*Gentleman's Magazine,* XIII, 1743, 543). Thomas Kennedy came from Dumfries, and on 14 November 1714 married Amelia Gregg or MacGregor.

p. 88   For Hugh Ronalds (1759-1833) see now J. L. Gilbert in *Journal Kew Guild* for 1972 (1973), IX No. 77, 127-29

p. 89   The grandfather of John Willmott (1775-1834) was lord of the manor of Kelshall and High Sheriff of Hertfordshire in 1683 (by kind information of Dr A. J. Willmott)

p. 99   The firm of Wood at Huntingdon and Brampton already existed by 1733, mainly supplying hedge-plants (Huntingdonshire Record Office, Wood & Ingram extracts)

p. 104   In 1822 Wells, Somerset, had the nurseries of Robert Giddings in New Street and Robert Holloway in Queen Street (Directories)

p. 112   A bill for seeds supplied by William Vickers senior in 1831 to Ralph Richardson esq. of Greenfield Hall, Flintshire, was receipted by William Vickers junior (Flintshire Record Office, D/KK/457, kindly communicated by the County Archivist)

ACKNOWLEDGMENTS

ACKNOWLEDGMENT is here made of permission to reproduce or to quote
from copyright material:
Her Majesty the Queen for Plate 6 and for her gracious permission to use
material from the Royal Archives; His Grace the Duke of Beaufort for Plate
9; the Most Hon. the Marchioness of Cholmondeley for Plate 1; the Rt. Hon.
the Earl Fitzwilliam for Plates 2 and 3; the Rt. Hon. the Earl of Harrowby for
Appendix VIII (B); Mrs A. Bagot for Rickets' account (p. 56); Messrs
Caldwells of Knutsford for access to the records of their firm; Professor
Joseph Ewan for the Hanbury catalogue (quoted p. 96); Nigel L. Swinburne
esq. for Plate 8; the Ashmolean Museum, Oxford, for Plates 4 and 5; the
Borthwick Institute, York, for many wills; the Botany School, Oxford, for
Plate 7; the Trustees of the British Museum; the Buckinghamshire County
Record Office for John Claxton's letter (p. 72) and Appendix XI (B);
Cambridge University Botanic Garden for Cobbett's catalogue (p. 133);
Durham County Record Office and Captain G. M. Salvin for Falla's letter (p.
126); the Garden History Society for Appendix I; the Gateshead Public
Library for Appendix VII from the Ellison Papers; the Gloucestershire
Record Office for Appendix VIII (A); Gloucester City Library and Diocesan
Archives for John Berry's will (p. 73); the London Library for Appendix IV
and Appendix X; the National Library of Wales for material from the
Bettisfield and Wynnstay MSS.; the Northamptonshire Record Office for
John Whittingham's account (p. 94); the Nottinghamshire Record Office for
material reproduced in Appendix V and for Appendix XI (A) and (C); the
Public Record Office, the Greater London Record Office, and the Cheshire
Record Office for the wills in Appendix VI; the Royal Botanic Gardens, Kew,
for Plates 11-16; the Royal Horticultural Society for Appendix III; the
Westmorland Record Office for the letter from Clark & Atkinson (p. 117);
the Wiltshire Record Office for John Cottrall's letter (p. 98) and for
Appendix IX from the Savernake Papers; the Warden and Fellows of
Winchester College for material from the College Muniments; and the
Yorkshire Archaeological Society for the Kiveton Park memorandum (p. 67).
Plate 10 is from an engraving in the author's collection.

INTRODUCTION

MUCH CONFUSION EXISTS, and has long existed, in regard to the different branches of gardening. As with other arts and crafts, a long period of generalized activity led gradually to specialization. The one word gardener for several hundred years did duty for many men of various skills and often of diverse social standing. At the professional end of the scale, as it were, was the landscape gardener or garden designer, who might well be the same person as the chief gardener to some noble estate. A few gardeners with exceptional botanical knowledge also took a high position. Beneath these in general estimation but nonetheless commanding high pay, were a great many chief gardeners to the county gentry. The strictly commercial aspect was divided into the two main divisions of nursery and market gardening: the nurseryman dealing in living plants and the market gardener in crops off plants. Further specialization in fruit and in flowers took place: the fruitist or orchardman had mastered the mysteries of grafting and raised new varieties both for sale as grafted trees and as picked fruit for the table. The florist for a long time tended to be a nurseryman specializing in the raising of new varieties of a limited range of bulbs and fibrous-rooted plants, which became known as Florists' Flowers. In the earlier 'classical' period these were the Tulip, Hyacinth, Ranunculus, Auricula, Polyanthus, Carnation and Pink, but fresh introductions gradually widened the floral scope.

In so far as florists and orchardmen were concerned with the raising of varieties for sale as live plants and trees, they were nurserymen and, though some remained specialists, it was usual in the provinces for the same firm to deal in a wide range of products. One of the most important branches of the trade became the production of forest trees in great numbers. At first this was for planting avenues and parks as showpieces, but in the course of the 18th century a wave of 'improvement' swept over the country. Many of the landed nobility and gentry vied with one another in planting large expanses of wasteland and mountain slopes with thousands of trees, deciduous and coniferous. This phase of our history, one which has left its mark on the landscape in spite of later felling and replanting, lasted for about a century from 1760. There had been planting for a century and more before that, but on a smaller scale whose demands could be met mainly by the creation of private nurseries and sowing of seed. The national importance of the commercial nursery, so far as trees were concerned, was a relatively late development.

Following on the heels of the trade in forest trees came the era of exotics. Ever since the 16th century there had been important introductions of plants from distant lands, in an ever increasing flood. A few of the plants such as the Lilac and 'Syringa' (*Philadelphus*) soon became common and more or less naturalized. The same thing happened, among trees, to the Horse Chestnut and, in a somewhat mysterious way, to the Plane. For the Oriental Plane, as introduced from Turkey and the Middle East, did not become a common tree in this country, even though it is quite hardy here. A new form, now called the 'London Plane', appeared, possibly as a result of accidental hybridization with the American Plane or Buttonwood after this too had reached Europe. Among flowers the Tulip, also from the Ottoman Empire, and the Auricula from the Alps received a great deal of attention and passed into general currency. Individual scientists and landowners began to organize the introduction of more species, and towards the end of the 17th century this brought in a good many new plants of all kinds. As yet, however, the number of sorts grown in any one trade nursery was quite small. As with the vogue for planting trees, it was mainly after 1760 that there began a mounting tide of competition in exotics. The king's mother at Kew, the Princess Dowager of Wales, set the fashion, and nobility and gentry followed suit.

For some time a large proportion of the new introductions came from the British colonies in North America and from other temperate lands. The heated greenhouse was still a long way from perfection and it was only towards 1800 that sub-tropical and tropical plants, needing always to be kept under glass, were acquired in large numbers. This movement also was one that lasted for about a hundred years, to be gradually replaced at the end of the 19th century by a fresh vogue for hardy plants and particularly outstanding flowering shrubs. In the meantime several other fields were being explored. To some extent these fashions were contemporary, but each had its own heyday. Before 1800 there came many introductions of new bulbs from the Cape of Good Hope, and for about a generation these, along with Cape heaths and geraniums (*Pelargonium* species), became the playthings of wealthy amateurs. At the same time began a parallel interest in hardier herbaceous plants for the open garden, and as an offshoot of this some introduction of alpines and the consequent development of the earliest rock gardens. After lying fallow over a long period, hardy herbaceous and alpine plants were to become the mainstay of the modern garden, dominated by William Robinson's famous book of 1883, *The English Flower Garden.*

It is not the purpose of this book to pursue the story of the nursery into this modern era, or indeed later than the middle of the last century. In fact there was a notable turning point rather earlier than that, practically coinciding with Queen Victoria's accession in 1837 and Robinson's birth in the following year. Whereas there had always been humble cottage gardens, the range of plants grown in them had been strictly limited. Until after 1775 there was nothing that could be called a popular demand for new introductions, and it was not until the railway age set in that it became possible for a very large widened middle class to make demands which led to real mass production of trees, plants and seeds. The changes, stage by stage, are reflected in two noteworthy ways. Firstly, and this was a simultaneous development in the North of England and in Scotland in the year 1775, came the issue of priced catalogues. Secondly, the issue of catalogues by leading firms all over the country became regular and frequent, and within a few years prices show a downward tendency. This is the more significant in that it ran contrary to an upward movement of prices generally. Then a few large nurseries, among the first being the firm of William Falla at Gateshead in County Durham, took the initiative in definite price-cutting: certain lines were offered for considerably less than the standard prices general in the trade. A still wider public interested in growing plants was created by this increased accessibility. Finally came the immense increase in the number of nursery businesses, from about 1800 onwards.

It is even possible to get a roughly quantitative notion of the speed of change from the number of surviving catalogues. A recent survey of what can be found in public libraries and record offices shows that between 1675 and 1850 about 300 lists and catalogues of seedsmen and nurserymen are readily accessible. Of these only 100 represent the first 125 years, and 200 the last fifty; but 110 of those appeared in the 14 years 1837-1850 inclusive. Many more firms were in existence, issuing lists more frequently; and a greater number of copies of individual catalogues have survived. The spread of nurseries of significance, from the few main centres represented before 1800 to practically every town in the country, can also be traced in the printed directories. Outside London these began in 1780, and they became general around 1825. In that period it becomes possible, for the first time, to identify virtually the whole of the trade. There is still a good deal of difficulty over undifferentiated entries of 'gardeners', but as time went on the directories made a clearer distinction and their entries can be checked and confirmed from other sources.

It will never be possible to state with any approach to accuracy the total number of trade nurseries in existence before 1800, but figures giving some idea of relative numbers can be reached. It has first to be grasped that the trade as a whole comprises three distinct forms of business, often coalescing in the hands of the same firm. Essentially these three types may be expressed as Plants; Seeds; Bulbs. The trade in living plants has always been that of the nurseryman in the stricter sense; but he might to a limited extent raise his own seeds of vegetables and flowers, and also act as middleman between private specialists in seed-raising (e.g. of strains of flowers) and the public. The seedsman proper, on the other hand, was usually a merchant pure and simple, centralizing supplies bought from individual raisers at home and abroad, and selling both to local firms and to the public direct. Until quite modern times practically the whole of the seedsman's trade was concentrated in London, and particularly in the City and Liberties. Provincial firms of 'seedsmen' bought all or most of their stock from these great firms of seed merchants, and this applied even in Scotland. From the late 17th century at any rate, the principal seedsmen in Edinburgh simply bought wholesale from the London firms, and sold by retail, as did the smaller provincial shops all over Britain. We are not here concerned with this extensive retail trade in seeds, which was quite often combined with the business of corn chandler or grocer and provision merchant.

A wider problem, however, has to be faced at the outset. How far were the trades of nurserymen and seedsmen, even at the highest level, completely independent? There is a good deal of evidence to suggest that the practice of nursery-gardening was for a long time a by-occupation rather than a full-time trade. Similarly, the earliest London seed firms seem to have grown out of more general businesses with a wider scope. Thus Robert Hill, who in 1631 supplied garden seeds to John Winthrop junior, for the colony in Massachusetts, was a citizen and grocer of London with a shop known as the Three Angels in Lombard Street, where he died in 1649. The proprietor of the first seedsman's business whose catalogue has come down to us, William Lucas who died in 1679, described himself in his will as a 'milliner'. Yet by c.1677 he held a full stock of seeds and also a wide range of trees and plants, though in regard to the latter he presumably depended on various nurserymen in the suburbs. Since he left a gold ring of the value of 10s. to 'Each reall member of the Society or Clubb of Florist' he was undoubtedly keenly interested in horticulture and not merely a merchant, but there is no means of assessing the proportion of his income derived from the garden trade. The fact that his sister Jane, whom he appointed his sole executrix, was the wife of Peter Vandenancker, suggests a possible link with Holland, but this is mere speculation.

Quite apart from such evidence of the trade being joined with other businesses, the various branches of commercial horticulture are found differently connected. In the smaller country towns it was usual for the main business in seeds to be carried on by a local nurseryman, while in larger places there might also be combined seedsmen and florists, who dealt retail in seeds but also in Dutch bulbs imported (either direct or through London wholesalers); and perhaps also in cut flowers. In other cases the shop might deal in fruit, possibly the produce of a nursery orchard. The permutations and combinations have to be worked out in each case and there is no universal rule. Yet it is reasonably certain that at all times after the middle of the 17th century it was unusual for a nursery to be combined with a market garden of any size. Only the marginal trades of fruiterer and florist (in cut flowers) were likely to be carried on with those of general nurseryman and seedsman. The growing and sale of vegetables to the retail greengrocers or to the great markets such as Covent Garden, and the specialized production of salads, cucumbers, melons, pineapples, asparagus and the like, were almost always completely apart from the practice of nurserymen.

Bearing in mind these limitations, it is possible to obtain a rough idea of the extent of the whole nursery trade at different dates. Although the word 'nursery', applied to a seed-bed for plants, goes back at least to 1565, the commercial implications of 'nurseryman' do not appear until a hundred years later. The *Oxford English Dictionary* gives 1672 as the first occurrence, though Leonard Meager in *The English Gardener*, published in 1670, referred to his friend 'Captain Garrle' (Leonard Gurle) as 'a very Eminent and Ingenious Nursery-man'. The word 'florist' in the sense of a specialized breeder of bulbs and other flowering plants, had occurred by 1623, but 'seedsman' is not recorded of a trader in seeds until 1678. As we have seen,

William Lucas was actually in business as a seedsman in the 1670's, and we can undoubtedly place the beginnings of the garden trade as we think of it in the middle of the 17th century. The 'great Nursery between Spittle-fields and White-Chappel', occupied by Gurle, was already 'a nurcery and garden plott' by 1643 when the freehold of the area was acquired by the Montagu's, later Earls of Halifax. Gurle (c. 1621-1685) and his predecessor as Gardener to Charles II, John Rose (c. 1622-1677), seem in fact to have been the first two English nurserymen who operated in a big way.

In 1688 John Woolridge (or Worlidge) added to the third edition of his *Systema Horti-Culturae, or The Art of Gardening*, first published in 1677, the complete standard catalogue of seeds and plants as sold by Edward Fuller in the Strand, Theophilus Stacy without Bishopsgate, and Charles Blackwell in Holborn. In the fourth edition of 1719 he added Francis Weston who, like Fuller, did business in the Strand. There is a strong presumption that there were in 1688 only the three major firms of seedsmen in London. Woolridge also printed the catalogue of plants sold in 1688 by George Rickets 'at the Hand in Hogsden (Hoxton) without Bishopsgate, London'. Rickets, after the death of Leonard Gurle in 1685, was certainly the most important of the older nurseries, though he was rapidly being overtaken by the colossal joint enterprise at Brompton Park. By 1691 the significant gardens of the London area were 28 in number and of these at least five were commercial nurseries: Brompton Park, and the gardens of Rickets, William Darby, and one Pearson, all at Hoxton, and of Clements at Mile End. Casual references in the literature, and the chance preservation of bills, show that in the decade 1690-1700 there were not less than ten other nurseries of some standing in greater London, making fifteen or more in all. At that time there were hardly any significant nurseries in the provinces, though at the remote village of Kinlet in the south of Shropshire (near Bewdley, Worcs.) John Rea had maintained a nursery for well over half a century before his death in 1677. At Oxford Thomas Wrench senior had been established in Paradise Gardens by 1648 or earlier, perhaps mainly as a market gardener; and at York the Friars' Gardens were probably a nursery before 1665.

For the London area the next 'census' becomes possible about 1730, when the Society of Gardeners published their *Catalogus Plantarum*, a union-catalogue of trees, shrubs etc. for sale in the gardens near London. The Society included Thomas Fairchild, who had died in 1729, and fourteen more gardeners, and five others signed the preface. Once again it is possible to swell the total from other sources, which show that there were at least ten other nurserymen operating in and around London at this time. There were also five or more substantial firms of seedsmen in the city. In the provinces there were by this time important nurseries at Colchester, Exeter, Newark-upon-Trent, Oxford, Pontefract, and York, where at least four firms were in being. Minor centres were Crewkerne in Somerset, Mansfield in Nottinghamshire, Morpeth in Northumberland, and Tytherington near Bristol. The first large nursery in the neighbourhood of Gateshead, Co. Durham, was to be founded in 1734 by George Dale. The total number of firms was probably much greater, but surviving bills suggest that it was not until after 1730 that the great estates transferred their accounts from Brompton Park and other London firms to regional nurserymen.

After only one more generation, by 1760, the whole picture had changed. A century after the Restoration, the accession of George III marked a notable epoch in many ways, and not least in gardening. In and about London there were at least thirty large firms of nurserymen and a dozen seedsmen, and another forty nurseries of importance were scattered across the country, mostly in the north-western half of it. It is of interest that all the great early nurseries, except that at Oxford and those in London and the south-east, lay along or beyond the line of the Fosse Way. As in the Roman period, so in the middle of the 18th century, this oblique line from Exeter to Lincoln by way of Bath and Leicester marked the approximate limit of 'striking distance' from London. Beyond this line the hard facts of economics precluded the transport of luxuries except for those of great wealth. Near the ports this rule was somewhat modified by cheap coastal shipping, but the facts of geography and existing communications placed a premium upon self-support in the remoter half of England. Hence there was substantial development of nurseries in that region during the mid-18th century, to cope with a growing demand which could not otherwise be supplied. In all there were probably about a hundred nurseries in the whole of England and Wales by 1760, but this disregards minor businesses of quite local interest, and the many specialist florists.

An independent calculation of about 1760 is available, giving the approximate numbers of gardeners of all kinds, professional and commercial, in England and Wales. A proposal was made that the London Gardeners' Company, founded in 1605 but limited to a circuit of six miles around the City of London, should be expanded to cover the whole of the country. The aim was to improve standards by eliminating seeds and plants of poor quality, such as the Gardeners' Company had power to seize and destroy within their legal limits. The approximate totals likely to be incorporated under such an extended charter were estimated to be 10 garden designers, 150 noblemen's gardeners, 400 gentlemen's gardeners, 100 nurserymen, 150 florists, 20 botanists and 200 market gardeners. The whole of professional and commercial gardening was thus regarded as involving about one thousand principals besides their employees. Since the names of over forty nurserymen and seedsmen at work in the London area in 1760 are known, and about as many again in the rest of the country, it is likely that the estimate of a hundred nurseries is roughly correct. The florists, though some of them were horticulturists of outstanding importance, generally had businesses on a small scale and of mainly local concern.

Another thirty years marks the transition to modern times. The year 1790 saw, with the opening of the Oxford and Banbury Canal, the start of the trunk system of water transport linking all the great centres of population. Overtaken by the much speedier system of railway communications less than sixty years later, it was nonetheless the completion of the canal network that most markedly altered the horticultural scene. Even the partial systems of canals that had been brought into use before 1790 had begun the process of cheapening the supply of plants to a noteworthy extent. In 1775, as we saw, came the first priced catalogues, issued by provincial nurserymen in England and southern Scotland. An era of competition leading to sharp price-cutting was ushered in, and in spite of the inflation due to the Revolutionary and Napoleonic wars, effected a transformation to mass production and general availability before the reign of Victoria began in 1837.

In the meantime, the volumes of the *Universal British Directory* had covered the whole country during the 1790's, putting on permanent record the names of all garden firms of any standing. In 1786 John Abercrombie, as an appendix to *The Gardener's Daily Assistant,* had published detailed lists of the nursery gardeners in and within eight or ten miles of London and of London seedsmen. After making allowance for duplications in each list, where partnerships are listed under more than one name, there are 58 nurserymen and 35 seedsmen, but again there is duplication, and probably not more than 84 really separate firms in all existed. Most of the firms are well known, but as many as 10 of the nurseries and three of the seed shops (one of which duplicates one of the 10 nurseries) cannot so far be traced in the general directories of the period. The presumption is that these were firms of relatively slight or purely local significance.

The Abercrombie lists (see Appendix X), in spite of the inequalities of standing of the firms included, provide valuable evidence of the extent of the trade by this time. Even though there must have been a substantial margin of market gardeners who were doing a little nursery business as a side-line, and of corn-chandlers (as Abercrombie explicitly states) whose shops also furnished 'general supplies of garden seeds etc.', there remains a nucleus of not less than 40 firms of major standing, of which about a dozen were seed merchants or seedsmen only and the rest nurserymen or appearing in both lists. So far as nurseries occupying substantial grounds are concerned, the picture can be amplified by evidence of a different kind coming from a period about ten years later. For approximately the same London area a Scottish surveyor, Thomas Milne, was between 1795 and 1799 producing a detailed map of land-use. On this he marked every field and plot of land and distinguished its form of occupation. By different letters and colours he distinguished, not merely Arable, Meadow, Pasture, Common and Woods, but also Marsh, Hop Grounds, Market Gardens, Nurseries, Orchards and Parks. Putting together the detailed information from Milne's map as to the positions and areas of nurseries, with what can be found from the directories and other sources of the period, we get a fairly precise total of 45 firms in the area of 18 by 14 miles covered by Milne, with about five other firms outside this but within a 25-mile radius, some fifty significant firms in the whole London region. In the rest of the country, that is to say England and Wales, there were not less than 150 other firms of standing, making a grand total of 200 at the opening of the 19th century.

These firms differed enormously in size and influence. Of those in the

London area only 13 were thought worthy of mention by Daniel Lysons in
1811, when he published a general account of the plant trade. By 1822, when
J. C. Loudon published his *Encyclopaedia of Gardening*, there were 36 firms
in Greater London regarded as worthy of mention; in 1824 Pigot's *Directory*
named 24 nurserymen and 29 seedsmen (a total of 53) in London; and in
1836 there were 39 London nurserymen and seedsmen in Robson's *Classifi-
cation of Trades*, though this fails to include a number of known firms.
Accidents of compilation, and probably subjective estimates of importance,
played their parts in blurring the edges of the available information. All the
same, a reasonably consistent picture emerges of the growing size of the
trade. Not merely was the demand for plants greatly increased, and from
almost all levels of the population, but the number of different species in
cultivation was expanding by leaps and bounds. The age of deliberate plant
exploration had set in, and botanists and nurserymen's assistants vied with
each other in risking their lives to discover new species in all parts of the
globe.

By a curious accident, or 'as if by magic', another stage in development
was clearly marked by the year of 1837 which was that of Queen Victoria's
accession. In that same year there appeared the first of the regular annual lists
of seeds issued by James Carter,[1] and four years later, in 1841, the list in
sheet form was transformed into a booklet of 32 pages. Here again, in 1841,
The Gardener's Chronicle was first published, the earliest weekly in the field
of gardening newspapers. From this time onwards the number of nurseries of
every kind gets out of hand, and the detailed information available becomes
unmanageable. With a longer perspective, historians of the future may be able
to give a full account of the nursery trade in and after Victorian times. It is at
this point, however, that we shall bring to an end the tale of early nurserymen
in England.

Most appropriately, there is a summary of the horticultural trades available
for 1839, covering both London and the provinces. In that year a remarkable
little book, *The Floral Calendar*, was printed for private distribution. The
compiler was Commander James Mangles, R.N. (1786-1867), himself a
traveller of distinction and a man of wide interests and connections. With his
brother Robert Mangles he was much involved in the introduction of
Australian plants in particular. The importance of his little book of 1839 lies
very largely in its lists of London and provincial nurserymen. For the London
area Mangles listed 19 nurserymen 'whose gardens are within the distance of a
convenient morning's drive, and whose collections will amply repay the
amateur for three or four visits during the season'. He names also 11 of the
principal seedsmen in London. In 1839, therefore, the London trade
consisted of 30 principal firms. In most cases a certain amount of information
is added on specialities, with a separate list of 'nurserymen celebrated for
particular classes of plants'. A few of these were remote from London: Wood

1 Though Carter had already, in 1835, issued a list of flower seeds as
agent to Messrs. Ramann & Möhring, Gleichenthal near Erfurt, Germany.

& Sons of Maresfield (Sussex), noted for Roses; Page of Southampton and Miller of Bristol, for 'New Holland' plants; Lucombe & Pince of Exeter, for Heaths, etc.

Valuable as it is, this information on the London area and the outstandingly famous firms is eclipsed by Mangles' other compilation, a list of 'some of the principal nurserymen, seedsmen, florists, etc.' in Britain. After allowing for a couple of mistaken duplications, there are approximately 120 firms in England, and eight in Scotland, included, besides those on the London register. For the whole of England, therefore, there was in 1839 a trade consisting of at least 150 principal firms. Another hundred, perhaps many more, can be traced in directories and from miscellaneous sources. Many of these firms were then of relatively slight importance, but some of them were to grow in stature as the years rolled on, and all contributed to the amazing horticultural riches of England in Victorian times.

So much for the scope and size of the nursery trade in the two centuries from its effective start under Charles I to its culmination in the reign of Victoria. It is worth stressing that even then only three hundred years had elapsed since the first serious trickle of plant introductions had begun under Henry VIII. To all intents and purposes this was a new form of business, practically unheard of in the Middle Ages (in spite of serious concern with forestry and the growing of field crops and medicinal herbs). This trade, like others, was an offshoot of the age of discovery, of exploration, of world trade, of colonial expansion and of imperialism. Although in part concerned with plants of utilitarian importance, the whole phenomenon of plant exploration and plant raising depended mainly upon aesthetic factors in garden design and appreciation of nature, as well as on the instinct for collecting. Even in that respect, collections very often served primarily scientific ends, and made possible the immense progress in botanical science which accompanied the outburst of gardening.

The fact is, and it is a fact not hitherto adequately recognized, that a great deal of botanical knowledge is owed directly to nurserymen. It is a fiction largely based on modern social and academic attitudes that draws a hard-and-fast line between the 'scientist' on the one hand and the 'tradesman' on the other. The two different functions exist, of course, but they are, and in the past very often were, exercised simultaneously by the same individuals. It is easy to see why this should be so when we come to consider the composition of the nursery trade. The question of importance is: who were nurserymen? Not merely as a 'class' or stratum of society, but as individuals, who were they in a biological and genealogical sense. Naturally this is a question to which there is at yet no completely satisfactory answer. Even more than in many other occupations, there is a serious lack of documents. As a category of tradesmen, nurserymen seem to have been averse from preserving their records. Records of trade, consisting of ledgers, cash-books, stock-books day-books of orders, files of correspondence, memoranda on plants, certainly existed. In a very few instances some part of a given archive has been preserved, though the fact that this preservation has most often been due to the bankruptcy of the firm concerned suggests that the surviving documents may not be entirely typical. Almost all the material of this kind that has so far come to light belongs to the 19th century or, in the very few earliest examples, goes back a little way into the eighteenth. It may well be that more documents will emerge and, if so, really detailed studies will become feasible.

At the present we can only set down a few main landmarks, characteristics of the plant trade seen as a whole down to about 1850. The first point, and one of vital importance, is that gardening of all kinds tends to run in families. It is not necessarily a question of descent in the male line, for many firms have descended to nephews rather than to sons, and the name has changed. But the trade was very largely concerned, in the two centuries which are our particular province, with a numerous but strictly finite number of kinships, rather than families in the ordinary sense. The second point, which is a biological function of the first, is the high degree of longevity observed among nurserymen and, for that matter, among botanists and distinguished gardeners generally. In periods when the general male expectation of life at 21 was less than 60, it was common for gardeners (in the widest sense) to attain 70, 80, 90 or in a few cases to pass the century. Although this may reflect to some extent the benefits of a placid life spent largely in the open air, the instances of extreme longevity in a number of botanical and horticultural families leave no doubt that there must be a genetic factor. Examples of this will be seen as we go along.

In a different field, it is generally observable that the plant trade was concerned with quality. Regrettable exceptions apart, it can be seen that seedsmen and nurserymen set themselves the task of producing sound plants which would satisfy the customer. Even before the days of extreme competition, the penalty for poor germination or the deaths of plants and trees was rapidly seen in a stagnation of trade. The most nótorious case of this concerns Brompton Park, in a flourishing condition in 1714 at the death of George London and retirement of Henry Wise, but within a few years left behind in the race owing to the incompetence of their successors Joseph Carpenter and William Smith. The number of recorded bankruptcies in the trade tells a similar story: many nurserymen were to conscientious for their own material good, or else spent too much time on scientific research, on plants and culture, and too little on business methods. It is sad that material rewards seldom attend upon high character, but some consolation that noble personality is at times recognized. It was written of Thomas Osborn of the Fulham Nursery, shortly after his death in 1872: 'it was his gentleness that made him so greatly beloved. . . . I never remember hearing from his lips an unkind expression or a harsh judgement and in business matters his sense of honour was so high that he seemed ever diffident in pushing his own interests lest he should injure friends or rivals in the trade.'

We are faced, then, in studying the body of nurserymen in England of the two hundred years 1650-1850, with a relatively small and comparatively homogeneous body of men. Taking the rough calculation of 1760 as a starting point, with its grand total of a thousand principal practitioners of all kinds of gardening, it is possible to add a few more general characteristics. Concerning this body of men we know that a very substantial proportion consisted of immigrants from Scotland. Ever since the Union of 1707, English horticulture has owed a great debt to the northern kingdom. This affected all sections of the trade, though not to the same extent. Few market gardeners in England were Scotsmen, but on the other hand a very high percentage of all gardeners to the nobility and country gentry were Scots. In the prominent firms of London seedsmen there are many names that must have originated north of the Tweed. The two most influential nurserymen of the mid-18th century, James Gordon and James Lee, were both Scottish and so, no doubt, was William Malcolm, one of the very first to issue a scientific catalogue on botanical principles. There were many others.

In spite of a few French gardeners employed by Charles II and later (notably Guillaume Beaumont who worked for James II and at Levens in Westmorland), there were not very many foreigners in the picture. One family of leading seedsmen, Minier, was of Huguenot stock; the greatest of the nurseries dealing in rare exotics was founded by one German, John Busch, and continued by another, Conrad Loddiges. The Ordoyno family of Newark-upon-Trent is said to have descended from a Netherlander who came with Sir Cornelius Vermuyden to drain the Fens in the 17th century. Here and there an Irish name appears, such as Kennedy or Flanagan, but these are a very small minority. Apart from the Scots, most of the remainder, both of gardeners and nurserymen, were English and, as far as can be ascertained, of English descent.

It is too early to generalize on the origins of the Scottish immigrants, though some of them certainly came from the counties just beyond the Border, the Scottish portion of the ancient kingdom of Northumbria. This may have some significance when considered in relation to the geographical distribution of the more important English horticulturists. The contribution of the northern and north-midland counties to botany and horticulture is a very substantial one: from Northumberland came our first serious botanist, William Turner (c. 1508-1568), our most famous landscape gardener, Lancelot 'Capability' Brown (1716-1783), and the founder of Britain's largest historical nursery, William Falla (c. 1739-1804). Yorkshire was the origin of the great botanists Thomas Johnson (c. 1605-1644) and Hewett Cottrell Watson (1804-1881), of William Kent (1685-1748), one of the founders of 'English Landscape', and of several dynasties of great nurserymen including the family of Telford, who came to York from the West Riding towards the end of the 17th century. Nottinghamshire was the source of John Parkinson (1567-1650), of the great gardener Peter Aram (c. 1660-1735), and of several of the earliest families of provincial nurserymen. John Gerard (1545-1612) was born at Nantwich in Cheshire; Moses Cook came from the Lincolnshire marshes.

In very many cases birthplace and parentage are unknown, or the individual concerned was a Londoner, with all that that implies of probably remote origins. Apart from Scotland and the North the West Country made a notable showing, starting with Henry Lyte (1529-1607) of Lytes Cary in Somerset; John Rose the King's Gardener (c. 1622-1677), born at Amesbury, Wiltshire, the son of a yeoman copyholder; and Thomas Fairchild (1667-1729), of Aldbourne in Wiltshire. It is unnecessary to go into further detail, but enough has been said to show that the botanical and horticultural world is and always has been largely rural in basis, even though its trading aspects are necessarily bound up with cities and the greater towns and markets. It was within this rural culture, dominated by the great estates, that the early nurserymen had their being. Apart from the Scots and other immigrants, they followed a pattern of their own. Learning their trade by family training or by apprenticeship to a gardener, possibly the chief gardener to a great estate, they would go on to become assistants to such estate gardeners or foremen in nurseries. In course of time, if their luck held and their savings were sufficient, they would found a nursery of their own or occasionally buy a partnership in one, or in a firm of London seedsmen. Not infrequently they married the daughter or sister of another gardener, nurseryman or botanist. Little by little these actual human relationships emerge, and begin to explain the hereditary factor.

Although the detailed facts are as yet unknown, it seems that we must envisage several main groups of men, those in each group being in some degree related, even if remotely. One or more groups will comprise the Scottish immigrants, another the Huguenots; in England as a whole there were doubtless several important groups with no interrelationships between them. We do know, however, of at least one highly significant group which, like the Huguenots, owed its origin to religion, that of the Quakers. A good many nurserymen were members of the Society of Friends, and their personal relationships are known in the case of the families of Maddock, Goring, Wright and Curtis. Here the association brought together families of northern and southern stock, for while the first James Maddock (c. 1715-1786) originated at Warrington in the south of Lancashire, and had spent some time in east Yorkshire before moving to London, the Curtis family. and its associates came from the north of Hampshire. Maddock, as founder of the Walworth Nursery, and William Curtis (1746-1799) who started the *Botanical Magazine,* were two of the most influential figures in our scene.

Before passing on to consider the historical development of the English nurseries from the 17th to the 19th century, a word must be said of another kind of relationship which underlay many of the nurseries. Wills and other documents concerning nurserymen fairly often refer to members of the great London firms of seedsmen. In some cases it is made explicit that the seedsmen were trustees or guarantors or possibly mortgagees; at other times this seems highly probable. The explanation presumably is that the great seed firms were able to advance money, or to allow credit to a nurseryman who would not otherwise have been able to start, or to continue in trade. Behind the complex network of trade between the different firms, the exchanges of plants of different kinds set off against each other in the books, the buying of seeds and the outlay on the year's supply of imported bulbs, there lay this finer mesh of a financial world which we can trace only in book debts and occasionally through the mention of a famous name.

I

THE BASIS OF NURSERIES – PLANTSMANSHIP

THE TRADE of nurseryman in the modern sense has existed for some three centuries, but the basis of the trade is as old as human culture itself. Whether we regard the story of the Garden of Eden as a factual statement or as a myth is immaterial: gardening in the sense of tending plants has for practical purposes always existed. There is a special skill, craft or knack of making plants grow well – call it Green Fingers or The Green Thumb – which, like most or perhaps all skills, rests both upon heredity and upon education. However acquired, this talent is essential to the furtherance of gardening, to the improvement of plants and to the best production of flowers and fruit. This fundamental ability is plantsmanship.

It is within the experience of everyone in any way connected with gardening that certain persons, perhaps the veriest amateurs, are endowed with plantsmanship of a high quality. Others, even some professional gardeners may lack it. Yet on top of the inherent characteristic itself, once possessed, it is possible to heap up much acquired knowledge. This knowledge is concerned not only with plants of many kinds, but with soils and with climate, even the many varieties of microclimate which have to be discovered in one small garden. Much of this knowledge can be imparted as matter of ascertained scientific fact: the acid or alkaline content of soils, the properties of clay or sand, the special dangers of positions exposed to certain winds, or of frost pockets. Modern discoveries in plant heredity which have led, for example, to the chromosome count, have made possible further improvements to plant stocks without waste of time on endeavour *a priori* fruitless. Conditions of light or darkness, heat or cold, as affecting the germination of seeds or the season of flowering, now begin to be fully understood as they apply to one species after another. Long and patient experiment in each field of enquiry is essential.

Even though not upon the present basis of scientific predictability, such experimentation has provided the basis of all successful gardening through the centuries. Anyone, even if not particularly green fingered, can produce a crop of sorts from a known plant in familiar conditions. This is hardly gardening, and not even very enlightened subsistence agriculture. Almost always this approach can be bettered by some Walter of Henley who arrives with superior knowledge of the way plants behave. It is precisely this capacity to acquire improved knowledge by deliberate and controlled experiment that lies at the root, not only of science in general, but in a very special sense of plantsmanship. Little by little over the centuries, and passed from man to man and from one country to another, this know-how of plants has accumulated.

Real progress has been achieved, and humanity as a whole does now know a great deal more about the best ways to grow plants of all kinds than it ever did before. This is to be expected, since within the last generation or so the botanical exploration of the world has virtually come to an end. There is no longer any real hope of discovery of substantial numbers of species of plants of horticultural importance. From now on we have to make do with what we already have, and by scientific improvement make the best of it. The main channel of progress in this field is likely to remain hybridization, as it has been during the three centuries of nursery gardening. Even before the physiology of plants had been studied, the effects of cross-pollination had been observed and interesting, shapely or well coloured strains picked out and preserved. In this semi-conscious way all cultivated plants have been changed by artificial selection over many centuries. Though an extremely slow process at first, the speeding up of results began to be noticeable after the end of the Middle Ages, in fact at the very same time that the trade of nurseryman took its rise.

It is highly significant that the era of conscious or at least semi-conscious improvement broke out into activity, not in the utilitarian field, but in that of flowers grown for pleasure. Not merely the word 'florist', but the essential concept too, has a priority of half a century over 'nurseryman'. The choice of flowers of exquisite shape and colour, with great capabilities of improvement (as Brown might have said), was an early exercise of aesthetic taste on the part of oriental potentates. It was, after all, an eastern King who drew special attention to the gratuitous splendour of the unimproved lilies of the field. Other monarchs, notably the emperor Babur, took a special delight in the habitat of the many species of wild tulips or, like the Ottoman Sultan Selim II, had tens of thousands of bulbs collected and replanted in his palace gardens. Thus a fashion was set that infected the courts of the West with enthusiasm and led to the long cult of Florists' Flowers not yet ended.

Obviously there had been a tradition of plantsmanship in the countries of western Europe long before the first great wave of plant introductions in the 16th century. So far as Britain is concerned there is no doubt that there had been a much earlier cult of gardening introduced by the Normans in emulation of what they had found in Sicily. That the eastern love of gardens which combined the essentials of trees and water was transmitted to Normandy is proved by the chronicle of the bishops of Coutances. Geoffrey de Montbray, bishop from 1049 to 1093, visited his friends and relatives in the south of Italy and on his return, laden with rich souvenirs, set about building a palace and making a park. This was begun at a date before the Conquest of England in 1066. A large coppice and a vineyard were planted, pools were made, acorns sown and various sorts of forest trees grown to give shelter for deer which were brought from England, presumably after 1066. The same fundamental idea was adopted in England on a grand scale when Henry I enclosed his manor at Woodstock with a stone wall in 1110, and stocked it with a variety of wild animals. Well before this, about 1092, Henry's elder brother William Rufus had visited the nunnery garden at

Romsey on the plea of examining the roses and other flowering herbs. Disregarding the possibility that there may even have been an earlier Saxon tradition of sophisticated horticulture, we can at least be sure that England had a developed plantsmanship before the end of the 11th century.

Although there is little connected medieval literature on the subject of gardening, enough references survive to show that there was cultivation on a fairly high level of efficiency. This can be demonstrated in several different fields: forestry for the regular production of timber required for buildings and ships; the planting of vineyards and orchards for supplying wine and fresh fruit; and the maintenance of physic gardens of herbs needed for medicinal purposes. These were all in addition to normal agricultural production of grains and pulse crops. On a higher level of sensibility was the cultivation of parks and the forming of 'arbours' fenced with climbers and trees and planted with flowers, entirely for purposes of pleasure and recreation. It is true that such pleasure gardening was not general, but it touched the court, monastic houses and colleges, and some of the homes of nobility and gentry. By the 13th century there was even a new bourgeoisie, ridiculed by Matthew Paris in the person of Paulin Peyvre who died in 1251. Peyvre, a jumped-up man who became steward to Henry III, was 'an insatiable buyer-up of estates and an unrivalled builder of manor-houses. . . . he so beset one, named Toddington (Bedfordshire), with a palisade, chapel, chambers and other houses of stone . . . with orchards and pools, that it became the wonder of beholders'. He was reckoned to display 'the wealth and luxury of earls'.

The planting of orchards at royal castles and manors was a regular function of the king's works, and both Henry III and Edward I were kept regularly supplied with apples, pears of several varieties, and nuts. Some of these were doubtless the produce of Crown orchards, but others were bought from Nicholas the Fruiterer, probably an orchardman of the period (1292-93). A century earlier still there was an important orchard belonging to the Earls of Chester in the Castle garden. Ranulph III, 6th Earl (1181-1231), in a charter not later than 1191, granted to William the keeper of his garden and orchard his 'restingtre' as well as the residue of the earl's apples after shaking down (*excucionem*) from the trees of the existing garden and those of a garden to be made in the castle ditch. A long chain of later evidence in account rolls for Chester Castle confirms and amplifies this, showing that the 'resting (perhaps refting) tree' was the principal tree in the garden; what would be termed the stock tree from which grafts would be taken. In 1353, for instance, it was stated that Philip Raby, gardener of Chester Castle, was entitled to the tree and the residue of the apples by ancient custom. It would seem that this apple tree must then have been well over 150 years old, or else that a new stock tree was substituted from time to time. In any case it is clear that there was horticultural continuity from the time of Richard Coeur-de-Lion until the 16th century at any rate, and the garden was not destroyed until shortly before 1745.

The continuous succession of official gardeners at each of the main castles and manor-houses, not only of the king but of the greater nobility, provided the essential body of experimentation needed for scientific horticulture. When we add to these the many gardeners at monasteries, friaries and hospitals, responsible for keeping up a supply of medicinal herbs, it is readily understood that mediaeval gardening cannot have been the victim of superstition and stagnation to anything like the extent that has commonly been supposed. The continuity of a tradition of direct experiment, indicated by the apple orchard at Chester Castle and by Walter of Henley's remarks on corn growing, is once again demonstrated in regard to the introduction of rosemary. This rather tender sub-shrub from southern Europe, famed for its many real or supposed medicinal virtues, did not reach England until 1338, when it was given to Queen Philippa by her mother, the Countess of Hainault (Jeanne de Valois, a princess of the Royal House of France). Since Philippa's son Lionel, duke of Clarence, was born in 1338 at Antwerp, it seems likely that the first rosemary plants actually came to England in the queen's baggage when she returned with her infant son.

The remarkable thing about the importation of rosemary is that its culture must have given rise to difficulties, so that it was thought worth while to set down correct details of its treatment. A treatise of the plant's many virtues is stated to have been compiled at the personal instance of the Countess of Hainault and sent to her daughter, and to many copies of this medical work has been added a horticultural appendix, extending to some thousand words or so. After a description, this deals with the hardiness of the plant, its season of flowering, habit and evergreen character, transplantation, need for shelter, watering and the proper way to take cuttings and to prune it for use. An important implication of the statements made is that they came from direct observation of the plant under cultivation in England — or at least in a northern climate — over a considerable period. The earliest manuscript containing these cultural notes is of the end of the 14th century, and the date of compilation may well be between 1375 and 1390. (See Appendix I).

In rosemary we have the earliest specific instance of the problems attending the introduction of a new plant to English gardens. Here we are told of definite dangers to guard against, and precise methods of giving shelter and water, and just how to plant firmly, as well as exactly how to take and set cuttings. The fact that somebody, possibly Friar Henry Danyel of the Dominican Order (fl. 1379), who translated the medical treatise from Latin into English, and many other medical works, found it worth while to record this amount of horticultural detail, is suggestive. This was not merely a new plant, but one of particular value, and one which might easily be lost in English climatic conditions. The traditional skills of most gardeners would not be able to cope with such a radically different problem from those to which they were accustomed. Hence we may assume that in 1338 it was at least unusual, probably unknown, for doubtfully hardy plants to be introduced from abroad. The date marks an epoch.

However uncommon medieval introductions of plants might be, there is no doubt that they did occur. In a general way the references by Chaucer to various species of trees imply that by his time — he was writing mainly between 1370 and 1400 — the Fir (Norway Spruce), the (Scots) Pine, the Laurel or Sweet Bay and the Oriental Plane were known in England. It does not follow that any of them was common. On the other hand, the account of the ancient plane tree close to Nonsuch Palace described in 1582 or soon afterwards as having its branches supported on posts 'so that many people can sit beneath it' does imply a date of planting not later than the opening of the 15th century in the view of Mr. Miles Hadfield. There seems then to be no reason why it, or a few other specimens, should not have appeared some years earlier still, in Chaucer's lifetime. For the Pine and the Bay there is confirmation in their inclusion, not later than about 1500, in the 'Fromond' list of plants, apparently compiled in Surrey in the neighbourhood of Carshalton or Cheam, very close to Nonsuch. This list mentions also 'Almondez' and 'Peche trese'. Chaucer in *The Romaunt of the Rose* mentions the almond among trees manifestly exotic, such as Pomegranates, Nutmegs, Figs and Dates, but Peaches occur among the 'hoomly' trees along with Quince, Apple, Medlar, Plum, Pear, Chestnut, Cherry, Nut, 'Aleys' (Service), and Bullace. Chaucer's accuracy is borne out by the fact that Edward I had bought peach trees for the garden of the Tower of London in 1275 (see p.40).

The true laurel or sweet bay is a tree, but it belonged also to the category of medical herbs. In that context it was illustrated, bearing its berries, in the splendid John Arderne manuscript of the early fifteenth century. The illustrations seem to be closely related to the text of the book, written by Arderne as a record of his surgical career between 1349 and 1370. He was still living in 1378 when he received a regular fee as consultant from the Infirmarer of Westminster Abbey, so that the infirmary garden there is quite possibly the source of the plants figured. Since in most cases the standard of draughtsmanship is far higher than that of the usual mediaeval figures of plants, identification is generally certain. From this manuscript we can add to the introduced plants Lavender, Lily *(Lilium candidum)*, Lupin *(Lupinus albus)*, Parsley, Rue and Southernwood *(Artemisia abrotanum)*, perhaps also the Christmas Rose *(Helleborus niger)*, Dill *(Peucedanum graveolens)* for 'Anece' (Anise), and Hollyhock. Apart from the lily, whose bulbs were doubtless carried all over Christian Europe at an early date, these were probably brought to England fairly late in the Middle Ages.

On the other hand there is another important source of information, the famous *Feat of gardening* by Master John Gardener. The surviving manuscript is of about 1440, but is thought to represent the subsequent versification in English of a rather earlier prose treatise probably in Latin. Here again we are taken back approximately to the time of Chaucer. Master John was already familiar with Parsley, to which he devotes a whole section, and with Hollyhock, Lavender, Rue and Southernwood. Other plants in his list, regarded as aliens or as introductions of the 16th century, are Borage, Coriander, Hyssop, Paeony, Saffron, Savory and 'Lyverwort', almost certainly *Hepatica triloba*. Saffron, like the Madonna Lily, must have come at some early date as a bulb, while the well known herbs can easily be grown from seed in England. The reason why Rosemary was a special case is that it cannot be grown from seed in northern climates in the open. This was explicitly recorded about 1393 by 'Le Menagier de Paris' as the statement of gardeners, when writing instructions on gardening for his young wife and concluding with the method of taking and setting cuttings of rosemary, and sending them to distant parts wrapped in waxed cloth sewn up, smeared with honey and powdered with wheaten flour.

Before proceeding to consider the state of plantsmanship revealed by the Parisian treatise and the roughly contemporary one of John Gardener, it may be as well to dispose of the problem of a few other plants probably introduced during the Middle Ages. One puzzle is that of 'Palma Christi', a term which after the end of the Middle Ages was certainly a synonym for the Castor-oil plant *(Ricinus communis)*. As far back as the 14th century the name occurs in lists of medicinal herbs, notably in the *Synonoma de nominibus herbarum* of Master John Bray (died 1381), physician to Edward III. The difficulty is that it appears as a synonym for other names which are positively identified as Gromwell *(Lithospermum officinale)* and as a 'sunflower' *(gira solis)*; and in some later sources as standing for the Spotted Orchis *(O. maculata)*. Leaving the further question of the 'sunflower' on one side (since the *Helianthus* species are American), we have as a clue only the drawing in the Arderne manuscript, which is compatible with (but not very like) the leaf of the Castor-oil plant. It is certainly unlike any Lithospermum and bears no resemblance to any Orchid. If the drawing does represent Ricinus, seeds sent from the eastern Mediterranean for medicinal purposes must have germinated here.

Another name identified in glossaries as far back as the 15th century is 'Carthamus', the Bastard Saffron or Safflower, generally stated to have reached England from Egypt in 1551. This may well be the 'Cartabus' mentioned as a herb for pottage about 1500 in the Fromond list, and there seems no sufficient reason for doubting that it had arrived some time before that. Finally there are two species of Birthwort (?), 'Astralogia longa' and 'Astralogia rotunda', both mentioned in the Fromond list as herbs for pottage, and both illustrated in the Arderne manuscript. 'Arestologia' is glossed by Bray as 'Smerewort', but in the text of the Arderne manuscript 'Aristologia . . . rownde . . . is clepyd galyngale.' Both plants are described at length, though obscurely, in the Stockholm medical manuscript: the round is said to be 'male', with small white flowers, roots like 'ganyngale', and large leaves of 8 or 9 inches by 4 or 5 inches; the long is 'female', with flowers 'most lyk benys (beans) in colowres', roots like madder, and leaves only 4 or 5 inches long. The Arderne illustration of round 'astralogia' is definitely not English or Sweet Galingale *(Cyperus longus)* and, though not altogether unlike some of the Ginger family which includes the Oriental Galingales *(Alpinia officinarum, Kaempferia galanga)*, these are hothouse plants and utterly out of the question. The long aristologia bears no resemblance to the naturalized English Birthwort *(Aristolochia clematitis)*.

We return to safer ground to consider in more detail the state of practical

knowledge of gardening at the end of the 14th century. For this we depend
mainly on the explicit directions given for cultivation by the Goodman of
Paris and by Master John Gardener. The French treatise mentions some forty
different kinds of plants and for the most part consists of general hints or
'tips' for the amateur gardener, with a calendar of garden operations through
the year, a model for very many later works of the kind. The oak is
mentioned as providing a stump on which ten or twelve fruit trees can be
grafted, and the fruits included are cherry, plum, vine, currant and raspberry.
What we should regard as belonging to the flower garden consists only of
Gilliflower, Lily, Rose and Violet, though many of the long list of herbs are
decorative: Borage, Clary, Hyssop, Lavender, Marjoram, Paeony, Rosemary,
Sage and Savory. The vegetables are Beans, Peas, Beet (apparently for the
leaves only), several sorts of Cabbage, Leeks, Parsnip, Pumpkin, Spinach and
Turnip; with the salads Lettuce, Radish and Sorrel.

The English list is not concerned with fruits other than the grapevine and
omits beans and peas, doubtless because they were field-crops that did not
belong to gardens. In spite of this the total number of plants mentioned is
much greater, amounting to nearly a hundred. This makes certain omissions
the more striking: Marjoram and Rosemary are missing from the herbs,
Parsnip, Pumpkin, and Turnip and Beet from the vegetables; Sorrel from the
salads (though Wood Sorrel is included). The English flower garden apparently did not contain gilliflowers (? carnations, *Dianthus caryophyllus,* or
wallflowers, *Cheiranthus cheiri*), but in compensation it had the Daffodil,
Cowslip, Foxglove, Hollyhock, Honeysuckle, Periwinkle, Primrose, Scabious
and Waterlily. The shortage on vegetables was compensated by a wider choice
of salads, adding Alexanders, Garlic (oddly absent from the Parisian garden,
though often referred to as an item of diet) and Cress. Both the French and
English notes on culture include extended sections on the Cabbage tribe and
on Parsley; Paris also gave hints on growing Beans and Peas, Beet, Lettuce,
Pumpkin, Sorrel, the herbs marjoram and rosemary, and the decorative
Gilliflowers and Violets. John Gardener offered a much more substantial
section on the culture and grafting of trees and special details on vines and
saffron.

The inconsistencies between the list of John Gardener and what we know
from other sources indicate caution in generalizing. It cannot be said that
plants absent from Master John's list had not yet been introduced to England,
for the missing Marjoram and Sorrel are illustrated in the roughly contemporary Arderne MS., and we know that Rosemary, not mentioned by either
of these, had been in the country for two generations at least. What does
emerge from a careful perusal of all these lists and treatises is that each of
them represents only a selection from the total of plants in cultivation at the
time. The Parisian's chapter is an amateur's compilation based on what
'gardeners say' and was intended as a simple do-it-yourself for his young wife.
Furthermore, its comparatively short list is greatly extended by the many
other plants and fruits named elsewhere in his treatise, in connection with
household cookery. Not only garlic, but shallots, cress and saffron occur in

this way, with carrots bought in the market, presumably because it was then as now notoriously difficult for the amateur to grow them well. About a dozen more herbs, mostly on Master John's list, appear and also apples, pears, peaches, medlars, quinces, mulberries and nuts among fruit likely to have been grown around Paris. Figs, Oranges, Pomegranates, Dates and Raisins were all probably imports.

The English treatise is evidently the production of a professional gardener, though somewhat mauled by the later versifier. In sharp contrast to most of the medieval versions of classical treatises on agriculture, grafting and the like, this comes straight from real life and tells us at first hand what went on in the important gardens which were the nearest equivalent to later nurseries. Besides giving a detailed account of the exact way to graft fruit trees upon stocks, covering the graft with clay, then with moss, and binding fast with a hazel-wand, the comment is made that pears should be grafted upon hawthorn. The vine must not be set when an east wind is blowing, and it is best to set it at a time of west wind. Each set or cutting should have three knots or buds, two to be buried in the ground and one left out to grow. The land for vines needs to be manured with dung every year and dung should be spread about them. The vines when growing require to be supported with forked sticks. Forks of the ash-tree are also to be used to stake onions allowed to grow up for seed. The onion seed will show black when ripe and should be ready at Lammas (1st August) if the onions were set or sown in March or April. The seeds should be laid on a cloth and dried in the sun.

The large variety of vegetables included in both the French and English manuals shows how wide of the mark is the common fallacy that medieval people had a poor and unbalanced diet. In regard to 'worts', i.e. the cabbage tribe, John Gardener begins by remarking that 'worts we must have, both to master and to knave: ye shall have mind here to have worts young all time of the year'. This was achieved by sowing four times, in May, July, November and March in land that had been well manured, dug and stirred. Four weeks after sowing the seedlings should be transplanted into 'kind fat land'; two weeks after planting out it will be possible to begin pulling leaves for use. Parsley should be sown in March to grow long and thick, and should be cut in reason as it grows, for flavouring pottage. It must not be allowed to grow tall as this will make it sickly and pale, except that plants left to bear seed should not be cut but left to grow round the year from midwinter to Christmas. It is particularly important to remember that parsley should be sown where it is to remain, and not be transplanted.

The whole of Master John's long list of herbs might be sown in April to be ready by Michaelmas for cooking and sauces. Lastly instructions are given for the proper culture of saffron, which must have special beds well made with dung. The corms are to be set in September, three days before the Nativity of St. Mary the Virgin (8th), i.e. on 5 September. Holes are to be made in the bed with a wide blunt dibble, and three inches deep, for the corms. After this, through the winter, was the time for grafting, from September until April; if properly executed, the grafted trees should bear fruit in the next season after.

Even though the total of species was only about one hundred, *The Feat of Gardening* gave plenty of work around the year, and it has to be remembered that a great deal of time must have been spent on saving and drying seeds of all kinds, not merely those of the onion. No doubt the best gardeners bought seed, or obtained fresh seed by exchange, but in the days before trade nurseries and seedsmen's shops it was essential for every garden to be able to perpetuate itself.

The evidence from the 14th and 15th centuries proves quite conclusively that there was at that time a well developed skill of gardening in the departments of fruit trees, vegetables, pot and medicinal herbs, and flowers, though these last took a subordinate place except for the small bowers and arbours contrived for the recreation of the court and for noble and gentle ladies. There were already varieties of flowers, for John Gardener mentions both red rose and white rose, and the Goodman of Paris names March violets and Armenian violets. It is quite possible that, in addition to the Madonna Lily, one or more species of martagon may have been introduced, primarily for medicinal use. The 'Gladyn' or gladwin, a name covering one or both of the two wild Iris of England, was grown in gardens. Both species were known to John Bray, as well as two that must have been very early introductions. He wrote: 'Iris hath a purpur floure; Ireos a white floure'; evidently *Iris germanica* and *I. florentina.* Continuing, he listed: Ireos, another that is ycleped gladone; it hath a yellow flower like saffron *(I. pseudacorus)*; another there is that is ycleped spatula fetida *(I. foetidissima),* he hath no flower at all. This last statement is of course untrue, but Bray had evidently not seen the leaden flower or the brilliant orange seeds.

What we do not know precisely is the extent to which trees were sown and planted in parks and forests. Certainly there is evidence of sowing acorns as far back as the bishop of Coutances of around 1060, and there is little to be said in favour of the common assumption that English woodland was all natural down to the 16th century. The early forms of certain field-names indicate the widespread existence of nurseries, notably Impgarth and Imp-yard, actually recorded between the 16th and the 19th centuries as an obsolescent equivalent of nursery-garden. An imp was, of course, a graft, a scion, a young shoot or sapling, and the word goes back to the Old English period. Its compounds used as field names go back at any rate to the time of Henry I (1100-1135) and are found from Cumberland and Durham in the north through Yorkshire, Nottinghamshire and Northamptonshire to Essex and Sussex in the south. As we shall see (p.35) one of the monastic gardens at Durham was known as the Impyard or Impgarth and this form occurs also at Farlam near Brampton in Cumberland about 1250 and at Selby, Yorks., in 1319. Impyard, in variant spellings, occurs in South Yorkshire and in Nottinghamshire as the continuing name of particular parcels of ground in several places from the 14th to the 16th century. At Methley in the Aire valley the manorial rolls refer to the 'Impeyards' repeatedly, and on 6 December 1413 it was presented to the court that John Cooke had carried away wood of the Lord (of the manor) in the Impeyards and the firth (frith, woodland), to wit young oaks. This at least is clear proof that the young oaks were a deliberate plantation in a series of nurseries.

The Methley records contain also another relevant word: in 1554 there is mention of a piece of land called 'Okespringe', the Oak Spring or plantation of oaks. Though much confused with the word 'spring' of water, this namesake meaning a wood and more especially one deliberately planted as a spinney or copse, probably underlies at least some grounds known as Spring gardens and the like. Some further evidence comes from the 15th-century rolls of the Master Forester of the Bishop of Durham, suggesting that fenced enclosures were made within which young trees or possibly cuttings were to be grown. The word *virgultum* seems to be used as a Latin equivalent for imp, but this brings us back to a possible ambiguity. Among the words compounded from imp are impcroft, imphaw and impton, where the meaning may perhaps be rather that the enclosing fence or hedge had been formed by planting saplings or specifically osiers. On the other hand it is thought probable that there was an Old English word 'Imping' which meant a place where saplings were grown, a forest nursery in the strictest sense. Field names in this group are not uncommon in Essex and Sussex. Deliberate planting of walnut trees is proved by a manorial presentment of 1403 at High Easter near Dunmow, Essex, when a certain William had destroyed 14 'walnote ympes'. Much later, 'The Impes' occurs as a name for a private nursery garden at Glynde Place in Sussex, in 1705-1717. Returning to Yorkshire we find that Pontefract, later famous for its trade nurseries, had an 'Impecroft' by 1215. Another word implying deliberate plantation is found at Brayton near Selby in 1320, when a field was called 'Rauscorth': *raw*, a row (of trees) and the Old Norse *stordh*, a copse.

In spite of the ambiguity of part of the evidence, enough remains to stress the probability that a great deal of planting, not merely of osiers but of oaks and nuts at least, went on from the time of the Norman Conquest. It is inherently unlikely that a country keen on the grafting of fruit trees in variety would not also plant forest trees, needed as a main building material and source of supply for engines of war. For the present the question must remain open, but the probability is that a certain amount of deliberate afforestation went on, both in the king's and palatinate forests, and in important parks.

The evidence of plant introduction, slight as it is, suggests a fairly steady progress from the Norman Conquest on to the reign of Henry VIII, with quite sudden acceleration thereafter. One would expect that gardening, as an empirical science, would also have continued to make similar progress through the same five centuries. It is stated, however, on quite early authority, that this was not the case. William Harrison in his Description of England, printed in the 1587 edition of Holinshed's *Chronicles*, wrote of gardens and orchards:-

> After such time as Calais was won from the French, and that our
> countrymen had learned to trade into divers countries (whereby they grew

rich), they began to wax idle also, and thereupon not only left off their
former painfulness and frugality, but in like sort gave themselves to live in
excess and vanity, whereby many goodly commodities failed and in short
time were not to be had amongst us. . . . Such herbs, fruits and roots also
as grow yearly out of the ground, of seed, have been very plentiful in this
land in the time of the first Edward and after his days; but in process of
time they grew also to be neglected so that from Henry the fourth till the
latter end of Henry the seventh, and beginning of Henry the eighth, there
was little or no use of them in England, but they remained either
unknown, or supposed as food more meet for hogs and savage beasts to
feed upon than mankind. Whereas in my time their use is not only
resumed among the poor commons, I mean of melons, pompions, gourds,
cucumbers, radishes, skirrets, parsnips, carrots, cabbages, 'navewes',
turnips, and all kinds of salad herbs, but also fed upon as dainty dishes at
the tables of delicate merchants, gentlemen, and the nobility, who make
their provision yearly for new seeds out of strange countries, from whence
they have them abundantly. . . . If you look into our gardens annexed to
our houses, how wonderfully is their beauty increased, not only with
flowers . . . but also with rare and medicinable herbs sought up in the land
within these forty years.'

Harrison may have exaggerated, or applied the facts of his own district in
too sweeping a way. We should at any rate beware of accepting his statement
at its face value. All the same, there is likely to be something in it, and there
is no doubt about the serious slump in the arts and sciences that set in in
England after the usurpation of the throne by Henry IV in 1399. The time of
the Wars of the Roses was in many ways unpropitious, and it is not altogether
improbable that the tide of horticulture did slack off after the period of
Chaucer and John Gardener. But not all can have been lost. In the middle of
the 15th century the poet Lydgate in his *Troy Book* wrote two descriptions
of landscape and garden which give a distant glimpse of English gardening of
the future:-

And all about this mighty chief city . . .
Were fresh rivers of which the water clean
Like crystal shone against the sun's sheen;
Fair plains, as Guido beareth witness,
And wholesome hills full of lustiness
And many a lea and many a lusty well. . . .
Full many a park, full fair and fresh to seen
And many woods and many meadows green
With sundry flowers . . .

. . . Aurora, of heart and whole intent,
With the sweetness of her silver showers
Bedewed had the fresh summer flowers

And made the rose with new balm fleet (overflow),
The sweet lily and the marguerite,
For to unclose their tender leaves white,
Oppressed hearts with gladness to delight
That dreary were . . .
And honeysuckles among the bushes green
Embalmed had environ all the air.

By way of a more serious and factual coda to the story of medieval plantsmanship, let us consider what went on, year by year, in the gardens of Winchester College during the first half-century after it had been occupied by Wykeham's fellows and scholars. The regular series of annual accounts, with only a few gaps, shows just what was done. Since each roll runs roughly from Michaelmas, the years here stated, after the first, are those of the latter of the two seasons included. In 1394-95 a total of 1s. was spent on herbs to be planted in the garden, and an unnamed gardener *(ortolanus)* had two yards of ray cloth costing 1s. 10d. and two yards of coloured cloth costing 2s. 8d. In 1396 four ells of 'Westmale' were bought for collecting and keeping the garden seeds (1s. 10d.); 1 lb. of onion seed was bought (9d.); garlic was bought for planting (4d.); the gardener's fee for the year was 16s.; one long cord for measuring the garden cost 2s. 6d. — a very costly item, implying that it was knotted or marked in some way. Packthread *(pacfilum)* for measuring the garden in 1397 cost only 1d., and besides the fee of 16s. to the gardener there was another of 10s. to his man working the whole year because of making the garden ordained anew. In 1398 one Henry Knyght was paid 5s. a quarter for two quarters as surveyor of the workmen in the garden and elsewhere. In 1399 7s. 6d. was spent on various seeds and seedlings (or cuttings; *plantulae*) for sowing and planting in the garden; Thomas Dayesye (Daisy? !) the gardener had 13s. 4d. for the year. More *plantulae* for planting in the garden cost 1s. 6d. in 1400, and William the gardener was paid 16s. An unnamed gardener had the same fee in 1401, and seeds were bought for the quite large sum of 4s. 2d. The accounts for two years are lost. In 1404 labourers were working on clearing and weeding for 57 days at 2d. a day (9s. 7d.) and John Spryngold had 9d. for three days at 3d. a day spent working in the garden and cleaning the walks *(les alures)* in the bower (le Bour); John Swayne the gardener got 13s. 6d. for three quarters and four weeks. In 1406 rods (or osiers; *virgae*) were bought for 'Rosemondesbour' (8d.); William Gardyner had £1 for his fee and a reward of 6d.; next year he had the same fee but no more. In 1408 a new knife was bought for cutting and trimming the hedges in the garden (1s. 8d.), with an ell of linen cloth to make an apron for the gardener (5d.); two labourers weeding in 'Olemondes bour' for 6 days received 2s. 2d., and William Gardyner again had £1.

More little plants or cuttings for the garden were bought in 1410 (4d.), as well as rods (or osiers) for the 'Raylyngis' in the garden (4d.) and the gardener again had a stipend of £1. In 1411 a large sum, 3s. 4½d., was spent on seeds, with 1d. for rods for 'Raylynges'; Philip Gardener had the usual fee of £1. Presumably the same man, Philip Frebern, gardener of the College, was paid 13s. 4d. for three quarters in 1412. The gardener of 1413 was John Bishop, paid £1 and a reward of 6d.; the wife of William (?) Bishop had 4s. for weeding. In 1414 the gardener had changed again, John Park taking the fee of £1; in the next year, 1415, the name is given as William Park, and 9d. was spent on rods and branches *(in virgis et ramullis)* for 'Railynges' within 'Rosemondesbour'. For ten years from 1416 to 1425 the gardener, still at £1 a year, was John Polwegge, except for the whole year 1418-19 when it was Richard Smyth — had Polwegge gone on pilgrimage, perhaps combined with some plant-hunting? In 1417 a shovel and rods were bought for 'Rosemund' (8d), and in 1418 a little cord was bought for measuring the walks *(lez alurez)* in the garden (4d.) and rods were bought for making 'lez traylyngez' in the garden. More rods were bought for 'lez raylez' in 1419 for 3d. with 18 cartloads of rubbish for raising the walks (2s.); John Thoumbe was paid 5s. for 5 weeks spent working in the garden about 'Rosamondesbour' and making other walks there. In 1425 William Carpenter and his mate worked three days making a new gate to 'Rosemoundes Bowre', the carpenter taking 2½d. a day and his mate 1d. After this the work continued in the same routine, but the gardener changed rather frequently: John Benet held the post in 1427-31; Nicholas Ferrok in 1432-34; John Atte Watyr in 1435; Nicholas Drake in 1436-40, including the last quarter of the year; John Helyar or Helier took over for the remaining three quarters of that account and was still gardener in 1448. Yet again in 1437 a garden line was bought, this time specified as containing 14 'vemys' or fathoms (84 feet). All this may seem a chronicle of very small beer, but it shows that the learned fellows appreciated a pleasure garden as well as the onions and garlic off the kitchen plots. They were prepared to spend money on it, and on measuring cords and lines to set it out according to plan and make it neat. In warm fine weather they doubtless read in their bower, probably sitting on raised seats of turf around the outside margin, within the Railings so often repaired. It may even be that the word 'alures' — raised in 1419 with 18 loads of rubbish — actually means these raised seats: Dulce Domum indeed.

LONG BEFORE the emergence of the nurseryman carrying on a full-time
business, the supply of plants undoubtedly lay in the hands of the professional gardeners. As was pointed out at an earlier stage, the trades of
nurseryman and seedsman were by-occupations, carried on along with some
other work. With the development of the seedsmen we shall deal later, but
must first dispose of the rather scrappy evidence regarding the supply of
plants down to the time of Henry VIII. Although it is well to guard against
undue projection backwards of later practices, there can be no harm in noting
that the practice of royal gifts to distinguished subjects was common form.
This applies at all periods and in all countries. Here we have a specific
instance of 1561 when Sir William Cecil (1520-1598), the later Lord
Burghley, was laying out gardens around his new mansion at Burghley near
Stamford. It is known that Cecil depended for his architectural advice upon
Flemings, and his gardens profited from his contacts with Antwerp and with
Paris. Nevertheless, he was assured that the Queen's gardener at Greenwich
would provide all the plants he could, and recommended to send for lavender,
spike, hyssop, thyme, rosemary and sage. If Greenwich could not supply his
needs, more might be had from Hampton Court and Richmond. This must be
seen as standard practice and can be extended in imagination, *mutatis
mutandis*, down through all strata of society.

Even before this, however, there had been at least the elements of a
nursery trade in the London area. The royal gardens themselves were stocked
in part by purchase from gardeners who were in at least part-time practice as
nurserymen. Accounts for works done for Henry VIII at Chelsea after he had
taken over the manor which had belonged to Westminster Abbey, c.1543,
include:

> To Henry Russell of Westminster, gardener, for 2 banks of Rosemary by
> him bought to be set with in the King's Garden at his manor at Chelsea
> price 13s. 4d.; for 6 borders of lavender price 26s. 8d. And to him for 3
> load of 'Calesse' sand for the great bowling alley . . .

So that it was possible, not merely to buy plants in large quantity from a
gardener in trade, but also to obtain from the same source gardening supplies
such as sand of special quality.

The gardening activities of Henry VIII are indeed relatively well documented by the publication of the immense calendar of Letters and Papers of
his reign. Two records in particular prove that the king was keenly concerned

with the improvement of fruit right up to the end of his life. Only a week before his death, a receipt was given for £20 by sir Jehan Le Leu, priest, on 21 January 1547. This was to be employed in bringing 'trees and sets of sundry kinds out of the realm of France'. The other record concerns the passport for Jean Le Leu, priest, described as the king's gardener, 'whom your Majesty sendeth presently into France for certain trees and grafts'. The context shows that kinds of apple trees were particularly, though perhaps not exclusively, the object of the journey. Who then was this priest-gardener?

The answer is that he was the same man already well known to horticultural history by the name of John Wolf, an anglicization. The version 'Le Leu' must be an English clerk's attempt at a phonetic spelling of 'Le Loup', i.e. the Wolf, for the activities of Wolf and his standing at Court are identical with those of the plant-finder of 1547. The old story was that 'the apricot-tree was first brought to England from Italy, in the year 1524, by Woolf, gardener of Henry the Eighth, who it appears introduced several valuable fruits about the same period'. It is likely that '1524' is simply a mistake for 1542, since 'John Wolf' comes on the scene only in 1538. Described as a Frenchman, priest, or clerk, he seems to have been a horticultural expert brought in largely to design the new pleasure gardens for Henry's palaces. He was granted an annuity for life of 20 marks (£13. 6s. 8d.) on 5 March 1538, and had already received wages of 20s. in February of that year. On various occasions he was called 'planter of grafts' and 'maker and devisour of the King's arbours' or layer-out of gardens *(confector viridariorum)*. He appears as continuously in the royal service, taking his annuity and also occasional rewards, until 1542, after which he may have gone abroad to seek plants.

It is a sad commentary upon the lopsided survival of information that the one thing we know of Wolf as a personality concerns not his horticultural but his theological competence. In 1538, shortly before the final dissolution of the monasteries, the abbot of Woburn made a declaration in which he recalled a conversation on the subject of the New Bible in English. Talking with 'sir John, Frenchman, maker of the King's arbours' the abbot had asked him: Do you Frenchmen take the bishop of Rome for Pope? Yea, marry, said he. On the problem of texts not translated according to the Latin of the Vulgate, inducing errors, he said Christ was called 'a carpenter the son of the carpenter'. The abbot told him this was not so, showing him the text *faber filius Marie*; but 'he said it was otherwise in the French'. Though we are left in the dark as to details of Wolf's work as a gardening expert, he was certainly concerned with the making of the new gardens at Whitehall and at Hampton Court, where galleries or cloisters of more than one storey surrounded alleys, grass plots and flower beds, with sundials, fountains, and pleached alleys.

Considerable sums were spent on these new gardens, but it is difficult to sort out the costs of the associated architectural work from the strictly horticultural. Just a fortnight before Henry VIII's death he had authorized expenditure of £60 upon the new gardens and orchards at Greenwich, one of the major palaces; but a great deal was going on at the smaller royal manors as well. Bills of 1546 show that at Greenwich the gardener was Philip Enys, taking board wages of 4d. a day and employing two men under him at pay of 7d. a day each. Anthony Talwyn, or Tawvyn, keeper of the King's garden in Southwark, also employed two men at the same rate, and in December 1546 bought 3,000 'red rossiers' at 3s. 4d. the thousand, and 1,000 slips of damask roses for 6s. 8d. John Gardener, the keeper of the King's garden at West Horsley in Surrey, took 30s. 4d. a quarter for his own wages and had four labourers mowing the grass alleys and orchard in summer. In the quarter to Christmas he had weeders 'picking and weeding out leaves out of the knottes of the privy garden and of the mounte garden and out of strawberry borders and "roseers borders" (rose beds)'; and over and above his wages took 22s. 6d. for his livery due at Christmas. There is nothing to show where the plants and slips of roses were obtained, but they were bought, not provided from some other royal garden or nursery.

It might be thought that this great activity was a mark only of the concluding years of the reign, but in fact the interest of Henry VIII in gardens had manifested itself from the start. In November 1510 the sum of £20 was allowed to John Reigne or Reygny, gardener, for the making of an orchard at Hanworth in Middlesex. About the same time £50 was paid to John Brome of Eltham for finishing a brick wall round the orchard. The king's concern in these cases was mainly for a supply of fresh fruit, and throughout the reign handsome rewards were given to gardeners and others who came bringing fruit, salads and the like. Privy purse payments of 1529-30 include 6s. 8d. to the gardener of Beaulieu (New Hall, Essex) for bringing roots and herbs and the same amount again for bringing strawberries, when he was named as Jasper of Beaulie the gardener. Apart from special rewards Jasper was paid wages of £3. 0s. 10d. a quarter as gardener of the great garden at Beaulieu. This shows that he was one of the select class of leading gardeners in the royal service, getting pay of 8d. for every day in the year, as well as livery and other perquisites. Later on he was further rewarded for bringing artichokes ("archicokkes"), cucumbers and other herbs to the King.

Another and possibly even more important gardener was Lovell of Richmond, whose full name ultimately emerges as John Lovell. Lovell is first heard of in 1519 when he was already the head gardener at Greenwich, but his retainer was only £3. 0s. 8d. a year. By 1528 he was at Richmond, Surrey, and was specially responsible for supplying the King's table with fruit, nuts, flowers and sweet waters, i.e. distillations. Filberts, damsons, grapes and pears were among the produce for which he was rewarded. His career lasted until 1550, when a second John Lovell, his son, was granted for life from the death of John Lovell the late office-holder, the post of surveyor and keeper of the orchard within the manor of Richmond, and the office of keeper of a garden called the Queen's Garden and the lodge pertaining to it within the manor and town of Richmond. Fees of £6. 1s. 8d. were payable, and in 1555 the younger Lovell had a further grant of £4 a year to pay for 'the weading, sanding, sayling' etc. of the garden and 'orteyard' of the king and queen (Philip and Mary).

Another notable gardener of the period was John Chapman, of Kingston-upon-Thames, master gardener to Cardinal Wolsey from 1515 and taken over by the King after Wolsey's downfall in 1529. Chapman was probably an instance of the gardener who was also in business as a nurseryman on his own account, for plants bought for Wolsey's garden at York Place (later White-hall), Westminster, in May 1515 were put under the heading of 'Erbs provided for my lord's garden by John Chapman'. Before Henry VIII's visit to Wolsey, Chapman had working under him four gardeners taking 6d. a day, eight labourers at 4d. a day each, and 22 women as weeders taking 3d. each for the day. Chapman also obtained a considerable collection of garden tools: a wheelbarrow for 1s. 3d., a mattock (1s. 7d.), hatchet (8d.), hedgehook (7d.), line (6d.), shovel (4d.), three sieves (1s.), three trays (1s.), a rake (4d.), a watertub (10d.), two waterpots (2d.) and brooms (1d.). It is uncertain whether he himself supplied plants and seeds which appear in the accounts for York Place and Hampton Court, or whether he obtained them elsewhere, but at any rate a wide variety of vegetable and herb seeds could be had: Anise, Caraway, Carrot, Coriander, Cucumber, Leek, Melon, Onion, Parsley, Sage and Thyme. The flower gardens already contained pot plants by 1515, for 1s. 4d. was spent on the carriage of 2 loads of 'pottes for the erberes' at Hampton Court. Chapman was succeeded about 1533 by Edmund Griffith or Gryffyn, but was living at Kingston as late as 1539. He had been a bailiff of the town in 1528-29 and was evidently a man of substance.

Each of the royal gardens had its own gardener, though some of these men may not have been of much importance. We know of Robert Pury of Wanstead in Essex, taking £4 a year in 1528-32; of William Rutter at Windsor, at the same rate of pay; and of one Walsh or Welshe at Greenwich between 1530 and 1537. Richard Mounteyn, who took £2. 5s. 6d. for his wages at Christmas 1545 as keeper of the King's garden at St. James's, was doubtless of much higher standing. The unusual Christian name of Mountain Jennings, the later chief gardener to the first Earl of Salisbury at Hatfield, invites speculation as to a possible relationship. One is also bound to wonder if there was more than a rather weak pun in the alternative name Didymus Mountain used by Thomas Hill, author of the first printed book on gardening in English, *A most briefe and plesaunt treatyse* . . . of 1563. Had the name Mountain a definite propaganda value in this context in the middle of the 16th century?

It is notorious that Thomas Hill's treatise, like much of Gerard's *Herball* at a later date, was plagiarized from continental sources. There is no doubt that the whole period was one of much direct indebtedness to developments in France and, perhaps to an even greater extent, in Flanders. Certainly many of the Protestant refugees, both from France and the Low Countries, took up gardening of some kind when they reached England. A great deal of this was market rather than nursery gardening, though the increasing interest in florists' flowers at a rather later date owed much to immigrants from the Netherlands, particularly to those who settled in Norwich. Even in the time of Henry VIII there was a trade in seeds from Flanders and, it would seem, especially from Antwerp. In 1546 a correspondent wrote from Antwerp to Lord Cobham that on his return: 'I will bring you seeds'. This was, of course, the work of a private agent; but in the same year a routine police search of lodgers near the river produced in the course of the search of St Katherine's by the Tower: 'Gerom Somme de Broke, Fleming, 58, and his son Jacob de Ayde, lodged there three weeks tarrying sale of garden seeds and other things which he brought'. In this instance there is a clear implication of a normal visit for a regular form of business.

Before proceeding further it may be desirable to say something about the value of money in the 16th century and earlier. It is quite impossible to give any precise equivalent in terms of the present day, and any translation into decimal currency would be actively misleading. None the less, the costs of staple commodities and the normal wages paid to artisans and labourers do enable us to reach a general mental picture of what prices meant. In 1934, at a time when prices were very low for this century, the late Dr Coulton produced an impressive series of figures which showed that one then needed to use a multiplier of 40 to bring reality to the sums of about 1300-50. By 1950, after the rise in prices due to the war of 1939-45, it was necessary to multiply again by about 2½, giving an overall multiplier of 100 to bridge the gap 1350-1950. For the later Middle Ages, the correct figure seemed then to be about 80; for 1500-50 only about 55. All these factors need to be multiplied again, perhaps by three, to bring them down to 1973. Thus a wage of £12 in 1530 might be £2,000 now. On reconsidering some of the daily wages recorded, we can see that this figure is not an utterly wild guess. Skilled gardeners of ordinary status were getting 6d. a day in 1515, and this had gone up to 7d. by 1546: thus from £4. 2s. 6d. rising to £4. 16s. 3d. Assuming a full week of six working days this would mean a pay packet of £24. 15s. 0d.-£28. 17s. 6d. In 1515 weeders, all women, got only half this; unskilled garden labourers took 4d. a day, implying a weekly wage of £16. 10s. 0d. It is very likely that in the 16th century the working day, taking an average of summer and winter, lasted about ten hours, but for many workers there were fringe benefits which to some extent compensated for overtime.

Looking at costs from a different angle, we may assign imaginary values of £10. 6s. 3d. to a wheelbarrow, £2. 15s. 0d. a rake or a shovel, 13s. 9d. a waterpot. Red roses at a price of 3s. 4d. the thousand in 1546 have in this light to be thought of as costing about £27. 10s. Considering a few of the prices for other plants and seeds from the same period, the equivalents reached are not obviously false, even though there are discrepancies here and there. Many precise prices are on record from the period of Henry VIII's works at Hampton Court from 1530 onwards, showing enormous variations in value, no doubt according to size and the particular sort of plant or tree. Young forest trees, oak and elm, could be had at 12s. 6d. a hundred, specified as 'five score to every hundred' (say £103. 2s. 6d.), but apples and pears for the King's Great Orchard, evidently choice varieties, cost 6d. each (£4. 2s. 6d.), and hollies (perhaps variegated or other special kinds) were 3d.

(£2 or so each). On the other hand, the price for Sweet Bay, Cypress, Juniper and Yew was only 2d., which works out at a hypothetical modern figure of £1. 7s. 6d. (£1.37½p). It is possible to test the reasonableness of this hypothetical revaluation by consulting the 1972-73 price list of Messrs Hillier and Sons of Winchester. This gives contemporary prices of the Bay as £1.15, Cypress £1.65, varieties of common Juniper from £1.05 upwards, Yew at £1.15, £1.35 and £1.70. The many varieties of Holly run from £1.15 up to £3.45, but several are offered in two sizes at £1.70 or £2.05.

Not many seeds have prices recorded for measured quantities. There are, however, specific sums available for the two common vegetable seeds, onion and leek. In 1468-9 the Cellarer of Durham spent 16d. on 1½ lb. of onion seed for his garden; in 1515 it was bought for Wolsey at 1s. 8d. a pound, but leek seed was only 1s. For the 15th century the approximate factor suggested is 240 (80 x 3), so that the onion seed at Durham cost something of the order of £10. 13s. 4d. a lb. The later price of 1s. 8d., multiplied only by 165 (55 x 3), works out at £13. 15s. per lb., but that for leek seed at only £8. 5s. At the present day the catalogue of Messrs Dobie and Son shows a variation of price between 20p and 32p per ½ oz. for onion, and between 30p and 36p per ½ oz. for leek seed. At these rates the prices per lb. amount to a range of from £6.40 to £10.24 for onion, and from £9.60 to £11.52 for leek. We can see that we are in fact dealing with figures of the right order, even though the relative price of onion seed has dropped and that of leek risen. It is safe to assume that, whereas mass production has applied to the onion, the leek is not now of the same importance as a staple vegetable as it was four centuries or so ago. It is worth stressing that the assumed factors were calculated primarily in connection with the building trade and did not include material derived from horticultural sources; hence this is in no sense a circular argument.

What emerges from the study of the accounts and other miscellaneous documents is that, even before the sixteenth century, plants and seeds were bought (see p.40). By the reign of Henry VIII there was certainly an organized trade, at least in the London area, and the gardeners who sold plants also did business in requisites. Some, possibly most, of these men were only in part-time trade. The instance of John Chapman rather suggests that gardeners in distinguished service might also — perhaps with the help of wife and family, or even of paid assistants and apprentices — be in business on their own account. This is, after all, precisely in line with what is known of other occupations. As far back as the 14th century, perhaps even earlier, noted master masons who served the King or other distinguished clients as architects, would also have their shops. When a craftsman of standing had got beyond a certain point he was paid a retainer based on every day of the year, but was not expected to devote the whole of his life to the job. Master gardeners may not have ranked quite as high as masons or carpenters of the top grade, taking yearly fees based on 8d. rather than 1s. a day, or thereabouts, but it seems that the same principles applied. Only in this way can we explain the quite substantial variety of plants and seeds which actually were bought, for the gardens of royal and noble manor-houses and of monasteries great and small. The occupation of nurseryman did exist, but was swallowed up as a single facet of a gardener's career.

Considering the widely accepted view that English gardening was in a very primitive state during the Middle Ages, it is remarkable that the number of gardeners was so great. We have seen that, in a period of little over 50 years, Winchester College employed no less than 15 different named gardeners, all of sufficient standing to get an annual fee as well as clothing and other perquisites. In such cases, of course, the men got their board with the other servants in the College Hall. Apart from the gardener himself, other men were hired at varying rates of pay, labourers getting 2d. and semi-skilled men 3d. On a far smaller scale, all this tells the same story as the very detailed records of the work done for Wolsey and for Henry VIII more than a century later. Though a great deal of research will have to be done to bring out the details, it is already evident that gardening was an important occupation between the 12th and the 15th centuries, and that its practitioners were by no means nameless serfs provided with shovels.

It is time to reconsider, along with the generalized view that England was devoid of sophisticated gardens in the Middle Ages, the more explicit statement of William Harrison quoted above (p.23). We have seen that, so far as lists of plants survive, they indicate that an extremely wide range was grown. The emphasis was a quite different one from that to which we are accustomed, but the practice of gardening was broadly based. The flower garden, of roses and other herbs of beauty, already existed in the 11th century; as a specialized form it was greatly improved under royal patronage. Henry I from 1110 onwards was creating both a park and a pleasure garden at Woodstock, and this set a fashion which underlies all later horticulture in this country. The pleasance of Everswell, acquiring the name of Rosamund's Bower, was the pattern set for the next three or four hundred years. Even though limited in scale, the medieval 'garden enclosed' offered scope for design and for plantsmanship. Trees, climbers such as honeysuckle, roses, lilies and the taller herbs, were displayed in a setting of turf and edgings of aromatics. On the greater estates and at the royal manors there was also, beyond the limits of the private pleasure garden, a far wider expanse of parkland such as that described by Lydgate in the *Troy Book*, and earlier implied by Chaucer's references to scenery and to trees of many sorts.

Harrison regarded the taking of Calais in 1347 as the start of a decline into idleness at home due to profitable trade abroad. It is far from certain that there is any historical truth in this, and it is at best liable to present the age of Chaucer in a false light. Even admitting that there was a decline after 1400, it must be stressed that one of the first acts of Henry V's reign was his creation of 'Le plesans en marys' at Kenilworth, a summer pavilion or banqueting house surrounded by its own moat, away from the Castle beyond the great lake. It is, therefore, quite impossible to regard the famous Banqueting House of Henry VIII's Nonsuch as a pioneering venture. On the contrary, England can boast of a continuous tradition throughout the Middle Ages and early

modern times, based upon ancient precedent in the East and derived by the
Normans from Muslim Sicily and providing a western analogy to the kiosk of
Persia and Turkey.

The continuity of ideas in gardening, even though reinforced from time to
time by fresh introductions from overseas — both of ideas and of plants —
must have owed a good deal to the tendency towards hereditary office. We
saw that, in the middle of the 16th century, one John Lovell succeeded
another at Richmond, but the principle goes back to a much earlier date. In
the reign of Henry I the king's garden at Havering in Essex, later to become
known significantly as Havering atte Bower, was kept up along with the
paling of the park there by one Salomon. He received a fee of 1½d. a day, and
the office descended to his son Ralf fitzSalomon and to his grandson
Geoffrey, who was still in charge in the reign of John, well after 1200.
Furthermore, it would seem that the position was held even later as an
inheritance of the family. The name, Salomon, of the first of these royal
gardeners, might quite conceivably indicate an eastern origin, though nothing
can be built on this. On the other hand, foreign influences were brought to
the Queen's Garden at Langley in Hertfordshire in 1289, when Eleanor of
Castile returned from Aquitaine with several gardeners from Aragon. This is
of particular interest since the kingdom of Aragon remained, even as late as
the 16th century, under far more directly Moorish influence than did Castile.
It was to Aragon that a Spanish queen would send for the best gardeners, and
it may be presumed that they would be of the highest skill then to be found
anywhere in Europe.

The royal manor at King's Langley must, indeed, have been an important
horticultural centre. Queen Eleanor had in 1280 obtained grafts of the
Blandurel apple for the orchard there, and at the same time a new garden was
being made and planted with vines. There is a mention in 1297 of the
gardener's house in the vineyard, and the queen's garden at Langley was still a
place of recreation for Richard II's queen, Anne of Bohemia. Another garden
at Langley, next to the church, was handed over to the Dominican friary
established in 1308. This close association of a royal manor with a Dominican
friary may have particular importance in view of the translation by the
Dominican Henry Danyel of the treatise on Rosemary. At any rate it was in
his time the practice of the king, Richard II, to read the Hours daily
according to the Dominican use, and to have Dominican confessors. The
association of royal homes with houses of religion had been a commonplace
since Saxon times, and provides at least a partial explanation for the spread of
horticultural knowledge. The royal manor of Kingsbury beside Dunstable,
with its garden of nine acres, was another foundation of Henry I, and became
closely associated with Dunstable Priory which, in 1204, received the garden
as a gift from King John. The immediate and constant links between the
Palace and Abbey at Westminster hardly need stressing, but a less obvious
connection was that at Gloucester. The royal castle there had no space for an
adequate garden, so that when in 1277 the queen mother, Eleanor of
Provence, was living there, the adjacent priory of Llanthony allowed her to

have a bridge made so that she and her ladies could take exercise in the prior's garden.

It may be assumed that in almost every case there was a garden, or at least an orchard, at a royal castle or manor, and there were usually several different gardens at each of the greater monasteries. At Durham the cellarer grew vegetables for the convent in a garden known by 1337 as the Ympyard or Impgarth, and there were also separate gardens of the Infirmarer and of the Hostillar. The latter, according to an account of c.1331, had his garden dug for sowing hemp (cannabis!), and also paid for pruning branches in the park at Shincliffe the considerable sum of 11s. 3d. This implies a definite concern with forestry as well as with gardening in the more limited sense. Outside royal and monastic circles there were important parks and gardens belonging to the greater nobles, but surviving documents are few. The garden of the Earl of Lincoln in Holborn is famous, thanks to a surviving account, and that of Richard, Duke of York, at his castle of Clare in Suffolk, is known from a tantalizing reference of 1450-51 to the new paling about 'le Maydengardeyn' there. A good deal is known of the magnificent gardens planned around the new castle of Thornbury built for Edward Stafford, third Duke of Buckingham, but their date has mistakenly been placed around 1502. In fact the correct reading is 1520, when the duke's gardener John Wynde was given 3s. 4d. reward 'for his diligence working and making knotts in the said duke's garden'.

Even were the evidence for a widespread practice of gardening confined to royal and monastic sources, it would be enough to prove very substantial horticultural activity throughout the period from the Conquest to the Reformation. But the records show more than this. At York, for instance, both gardeners and fruiterers entered the freedom of the city from the first half of the 14th century. Mostly their surnames indicate a Yorkshire origin, as in the case of the first of the gardeners, Gilbert de Ilkeley, in 1334-5, though a year later Philip le Fruter was described as of London. Other gardeners, besides those who took up the freedom, are mentioned in the almost complete list of householders in the Poll Tax of 1381. Though not numerous, the fact that some gardeners found it worth while to pay substantially for the right to exercise their craft within the corporate limits strongly suggests a major element of trade in their work. This may, of course, have lain mainly in market gardening and the supply of fresh vegetables, salads and fruit. There were other gardens besides those of the gardeners, such as the one with two vineyards attached at Clementhorpe in the southern suburb, belonging to John Isabell of Micklegate. Isabell, a prosperous cook, was presumably proprietor of an eating house in the main street and very likely served wine made from his own grapes. He died in 1390, desiring in his will that he might be buried at the Dominican friary.

It was the large garden of this friary, extending to more than an acre of ground, that was later to become one of the most influential nurseries of provincial England. Whether there was any real continuity in the horticultural use of the land is a problem which may never be solved, but this example is not unique. In York alone there were nursery gardens also within the former precincts of the Franciscan friars, of St Mary's Abbey, and of St Andrew's Priory in Fishergate. Other instances occurred at the Nuns' Gardens in Chester, close to the Castle (see Appendix VI); at the Charterhouse outside Coventry; in the Chapel lands at Gateshead; the precinct of the Franciscans at Hartlepool; and at Oxford in the Paradise Gardens which had belonged to the Franciscan friary. It is probable that there were other cases of such use. This may perhaps indicate merely that such walled enclosures were let to best advantage as commercial gardens, but there may be more to it than that. It is well known that in the latter part of the Middle Ages there was a tendency for monastic lands to be let out on lease, and quite conceivably some of these walled gardens were held by market gardeners and nurserymen before the Dissolution.

Even if this development had not actually taken place before 1540, it might well be that such existing gardens, stocked with fruit trees or medicinal herbs, could best be exploited by their new owners as 'hortulan grounds', to adopt the descriptive phrase of the Doncaster nurseryman-botanist Samuel Appleby. In the end the tide of building has swept over these gardens, but for as long as three centuries in the case of the (Dominican) Friars' Gardens at York, horticultural use continued. It is likely that, so far as there may have been such continuing cultivation of ancient gardens, it remained unspecialized for a century or more. Certainly at Oxford the Paradise Gardens, which became the leading nursery, had earlier been worked by Thomas Wrench (fl. 1664-c.1719), reputed 'the best Kitchen Gardiner in England'. Wrench's widow in 1720 married Thomas Tagg, who had worked in the gardens, and the later developments as a nursery were due to three generations of the Tagg family. Thomas Tagg in 1725 told Thomas Hearne that he had seen the old receipts which showed that Paradise Gardens had been leased for £7 a year, while he was then paying nearly £40. On the other hand he paid his workmen a total of £700 a year, so that the turnover must have been large.

During the latter part of the 16th century and most of the 17th the emphasis would generally have been on market gardening, supplying fresh vegetables, salads and fruit to London, Oxford, York and the other greater cities. So far as nursery gardening was practised it would have been as a profitable side line, supplying grafted fruit trees of the sorts kept, and disposing of any surplus of seedling plants and seeds. Sharper specialization set in during the second half of the 17th century, and seems to have been almost complete soon after 1700. This was not merely a question of commercial convenience. The fact was discovered, and was being consciously exploited by James Gordon at Mile End before 1750, that plant nurseries should be on relatively poor ground. This encouraged strong growth, essential for the best plants, but was diametrically opposed to the needs of crops. Market gardens are placed for choice in rich alluvial soil, very heavily manured, and are not primarily concerned with hardiness or long life of individual plants. As time went on the separation became absolute, except for quite small local gardens where the two trades could conveniently be handled together.

The separate trade of the plant nursery developed, therefore, from that of the unspecialized gardener, but in two different ways. The first of the great nurserymen known to us by name, the founders of Brompton Park and their immediate predecessors, had generally been the chief gardeners of great estates, or in charge of royal gardens. These men were essentially professionals, and commonly were skilled botanists according to the standards of their day. Secondly came the development of nurseries by market gardeners who had amassed a substantial capital by successful trading, and then launched out into the more fashionable branch, which besides offered far greater opportunities for social advancement. Many of the early nurserymen of the first category, though they sold plants for profit, were gentlemen in the strict sense that they belonged to families of the lesser country gentry, or in the courtesy sense that they came from the upper yeomanry who were in any case rapidly becoming assimilated to the gentry of ancient stock. The men of the second category made an important contribution to the phenomenon of the rise of the middle classes from the ranks of the lesser rural yeomanry and the urban artisans.

The love of flowers combined with curiosity regarding the nature of plants, brought together men from different walks of society. In a general way the exchanges between men of some distinction, regardless of social class, can be seen in many entries in the diaries of John Evelyn and of Samuel Pepys. In a few cases they met nurserymen and gardeners. Many more, of course, are incidentally named by the early botanists and authors of herbals and gardening books, such as Gerard and Parkinson. Yet we do not so far know a great deal of the personalities of the horticultural world before the Restoration. What can be said is that even before the outbreak of the Civil War there had been the first signs of a social interest in the subject. In 1637, if not earlier, there was a florists' feast at Norwich, for it is known that the play of *Rhodon and Iris* was acted for the assembled company. From the will of William Lucas, already quoted, it is evident that there was a well established London Society or Club of Florists by 1679, and it is said that the regular holding of florists' meetings in the London area was due to Nathaniel Rench of Fulham (1682-1783), one of the great horticultural centenarians. Since it is said that the meetings were held 'about the end of the seventeenth century' it is probable that the reference is really to Nathaniel's father Thomas Rench, who died on 31 March 1728 'in the 98th year of his age'. In middle life he could well have taken part in founding the society to which Lucas belonged.

Again according to Loudon, who was at great pains to collect tradition on the subject, there were florists' meetings and also meetings of gooseberry growers in Lancashire and the adjoining counties by 1740, if not earlier. It was presumably at a meeting of one such society in Cheshire that a sermon was preached on 18 April 1732. The sermon, preached by William Harper at Malpas 'at a Meeting of Gardeners and Florists', was printed in London the same year. Eight years later it was Charles Lamotte, D.D., Chaplain to the Prince of Wales, who gave a sermon on 12 August 1740 in St Martin's Church in Stamford-Baron 'at a Meeting of Gentlemen Florists, and Gardeners'. This was printed locally in Stamford, and it should not be forgotten that St Martin's was the parish of Burghley House and Park, or that it was at this very time that the Prince of Wales was taking the decisive step towards the formation of Kew Gardens. Meanwhile there was in London the important Society of Gardeners, perhaps an offshoot of the Club of Florists, that met at Newhall's Coffee-house in Chelsea and in 1730 had published part I of the *Catalogus Plantarum.* As a union catalogue, naming the species held in the major nurseries around London, this was a remarkable venture, even apart from its scientific and horticultural importance.

The coming together of gentleman florists and gardeners was a symptom of great significance and developed still further the human and scientific exchanges which had already shown themselves in the preceding century. The archives of the Ancient Society of York Florists, complete from its foundation in 1768, show by the actual signatures on the roll the almost complete coverage of society by the keen interest in flowers. At the frequent shows the judges were usually noted gardeners such as the botanist Robert Teesdale (the younger), from Castle Howard, or nurserymen like John Telford junior of York. But the membership included knights, baronets and lords of great estates as well as professional men and minor shopkeepers. There was also a Society of Florists at Leicester, flourishing through the 1780's, and doubtless many more, but the early history of most of these local bodies is obscure. It is known that the Exeter society, after a good start, became divided by the new snobbery early in the 19th century, and an attempt was made — though happily defeated — to remove the tradesmen from its ranks. By that time, however, the great Horticultural Society had been founded in London, and succeeded in bringing together almost all enthusiasts for the subject, high and low. That national culmination of earlier local and partial endeavours, was shortly to bring to a close the relatively primitive stage of development which is the main subject of this book.

THE LONDON NURSERY TRADE BEFORE 1700

IN A GENERAL WAY the development of gardening has now been followed through the Middle Ages. At the present stage of research it is a period well provided with tantalizing hints but of which no real history can yet be written. Only in the reign of Henry VIII and at the period of the dissolution of religious houses do we begin to find nurserymen who are identifiable personalities, and the first links in a chain of continuous histories of individual firms or of particular plots of garden ground. The reason for this change is not simply that medieval gardening was more primitive, less sophisticated, than that of the Tudors. To a great extent it reflects the fundamental fact, known to all genealogists, that the parish register of baptisms, marriages and burials was instituted in 1538. Our ability to identify precisely the personalities of all ranks of society, and not just those of the nobility, depends to a preponderant extent upon the parish register, imperfect instrument as that very often was. It is quite true that many families can be traced as far back as the 13th century by means of wills and entries in court rolls of manors, but these are exceptions. The itinerant artisan in many trades, including the craft of gardening, has always been difficult to follow from one part of the country to another. Even modern nurseries are moved, still more the smaller grounds of early times.

As we have seen, there is at least a strong suspicion that some commercial nurseries were founded in the walled gardens of monasteries and friaries, let out on lease to lay tenants in the period of decline in medieval religion. Even if this were not the case, or not common, there is no doubt that the walled gardens of the former religious precincts did, from the Dissolution onwards, become exceptionally valuable for the production of fruit and vegetables, as well as of plants. In one case we know that a particular precinct played an important part in the improvement of a food-plant, though not exactly how or when. This was the production, intentional or by accident, of the rounceval pea in the garden of the hospital of St Mary Rounceval, so called because it was a cell to the abbey of Roncesvalles in Navarre.[1] The hospital precinct, of about three acres, was at Charing Cross, more or less on the site of Northumberland Avenue.

Westminster necessarily bulks large in the early history of the subject, not only because of the royal palace and the great abbey, but on account of the many town houses, with their gardens, of the greater nobles, bishops and abbots. Nowhere else in the country can there have been so great and so

1. For the monastic contribution to horticulture, see also p.59

exacting a demand for fruit, vegetables, flowers and trees for pleasure grounds. Even at an early date there must have been a wide field for specialization, and it may be that we can detect a trace of this as far back as the reign of Edward I. In 1275 he was paying a wage of 2¼d. a day to one Roger 'le Herberur' who had been gardener to his father Henry III. It may well have been this man or a son of the same name, who in 1298-9 received £1 from the King 'for repairing the Arbour (*Erbar'*) and levelling and for digging turf and carrying, and for work in all things, at task', i.e. at an agreed sum for the job. This was part of the work of fitting up York Place (the palace of the archbishops of York on the site of the much later Whitehall) as a royal residence after a serious fire in the Old Palace of Westminster. The Roger of 1275 and earlier, and the Roger of 1298 and later, whether the same man or no, belonged to the category of head gardener. On the other hand there was also a William Gardiner (*Gardinarius*) in 1274-5 who seems to have been largely a nurseryman. In 1274 an earthen wall 17 perches (280 feet 6 inches) long was made round the royal garden in the Tower of London, and thatched with 800 (bundles) of reed. Timber and rods were bought to support the grapevines in this garden, and the payment went through William the gardiner.

In the following year William was paid for a considerable variety of plants for the King's gardens and orchards: 100 cherries (1s. 6d.), 500 willows (or osiers) for 4s. 6d.; 4 quinces and two peach trees (*picher'*) at 6d. each; 3d. for gooseberry bushes (*greseiller*); 1s. for a quart (*quarter'*) of lily bulbs; another peach tree (*pescher'*) for 6d.; and peony roots (*rad' pyen'*) for 2s. Payments to others for plants, lily bulbs, and different kinds of seeds prove that there must have been a substantial horticultural business in Westminster from this time onwards, though very little can be said about the men concerned until after 1500. Firmer ground is reached with the Henry Russell who, as we have seen, was supplying Henry VIII with plants for Chelsea in the 1540's. Russell's will has survived (see Appendix VI) and, though it does not throw any light on his trade, indicates a man of some standing and 'servaunte unto the Kinges majestie' by 1539. He died ten years later in the reign of Edward VI, and there is some significance in the fact that he appointed Thomas Casy of London, gardener, to whom he owed a debt of £4, to be overseer of his will. He was buried at St. Margaret's on 12 September 1549.

The first historical London nursery is disclosed when we come to piece together the available scraps of information on the Banbury family. The first of them known to us at present is John Banbury of St. Margaret's Westminster, basketmaker, who died in 1561. It seems likely that basket-making included the growing of kinds of willow and osier for making the baskets, for when John made his will in 1560 he directed his son Henry (then only 20) to 'plante and grafte for the behalfe of his mother (Elizabeth) and he to have the third part for his labour'. This indicates a family business in plants, probably carried on near Tothill Street as we shall see. Some prosperity is implied by the bequest to Henry of 'a bedstede a bolstar a matteris a fetherbed a pillow a payre of shetes a covering and a stone mortar iiij Tabull napkins and a tabull clothe a quart pot a pint pot a dishe a platter a sauser a Candelsticke and the paynted clothes that hangeth in the chamber the tester of a bed and the long cheste and xl. s.' Henry had been christened in St. Margaret's on 10 February 1540, and was eventually buried there on 20 February 1610. In the meantime he had become, by 1597, that 'excellent graffer and painful planter, Mr. Henry Banbury, of Touthill street neere Westminster', praised by Gerard for the many varieties of pears and apples which he stocked.

Henry Banbury seems to have been married more than once, and had a numerous family, but when he died his eldest surviving son Arnold Banbury (1598-1665) was only twelve. Presumably Henry's widow Margery was able to carry on the nursery and to train up Arnold, who was still noted for fruit trees in 1653. On 15 December in that year he receipted his account for £5 16s. 6d., with £1 more for packing and carriage to Chester, for trees sent to John Percivalle in Ireland. The trees, despatched on 17 December, included 12 apricockes, 6 May cherries, 4 'Read Woman' necterines, 2 'Man' peaches, 2 'Nuttmege' peaches, 2 Newington peaches, 2 'Malagatoones', 2 Portugall peaches, 2 Cornation peaches, 2 violett peaches, 6 Winsor pears, 3 'Summer burgamotts', 3 winter burgamotts, 6 'Boonecrittones' (Bon Chrétien), 4 black pear plums, 4 Mussell plums, 2 Queen Mother plums, 2 Premordin plums, 2 white amber plums, 2 'Damazene' plums, 2 white date plums, 2 'Red pescod' plums, 2 Turkey plums, 2 'Oysterly greene plumes'. His bill described him as of 'Tuttell' Street, so that in all probability the same nursery continued through three generations for about a hundred years.

Banbury was only one of three leading growers of fruit trees named by Gerard in 1597. The last of these was described as 'a diligent and most affectionate lover of plants Mr. Warnar neere Horsey downe by London', and Gerard adds the cryptic comment: '(but beware the Bag and Bottle)'. Whether this was a notorious tavern, or a rival plant-centre selling trees of uncertain sorts and poor quality, will perhaps never be known.[2] The place-name has been misinterpreted in modern versions as 'Hornsey Down', but is in fact the correct old form of Horsleydown in Bermondsey, just across the Thames from the Tower of London. There was garden ground there until the middle of the 18th century, but neither the taxation of 1593 nor other local records reveal any inhabitant named Warnar or Warner. He may have been either John Warner esq., (died 1615) or William Warner, citizen and haberdasher (died 1628), both of St. Olave's parish in Southwark. The first of the three fruit-growers, however, is an identifiable and historic personality. Gerard states in one place that 'the greatest varietie of these rare Plums are to be found in the grounds of Master Vincent Pointer of Twicknam, before remembred in the Chap. of Apples'. Referring back to his discussion of Pears and Apples we find that 'many sorts . . . are growing in the ground of Master

2. It is a remarkable coincidence that there was a Bag and Bottle Alley on the north side of Old Street, close to the nursery of John Millen (died 1635) described below (p.44).

Richard Pointer, a most cunning and curious graffer and planter of all manner of rare fruites, dwelling in a small village near London called Twicknam'. The discrepancy over the Christian name may be a printer's error, never corrected. In fact we know that the nurseryman was Vincent Pointer alias Corbet, father of Richard Corbet (1582-1635), bishop of Oxford and eventually of Norwich. Richard Corbet was born at Ewell and in fact the parish registers of Twickenham do not contain relevant entries. It was at Twickenham, all the same, that Vincent Poynter alias Corbett made his will on 27 January 1603-4; he did not die until 1619.

The will, which left handsome bequests to the poor of Twickenham and £500 to his son Richard when 25 years old, is evidently that of a wealthy man, and the testator describes himself as 'gent.', a qualification not lightly used in the 16th century. The residuary estate to go to his wife Bennet, who did in fact survive him, included plate and jewels and copyhold lands in Twickenham and Isleworth. We have in the case of Vincent Pointer a clear instance of the man of standing who became a nurseryman, rather than the reverse; and as we go on will find that the description of gentleman, not merely at the end of a successful career, is paralleled from time to time. Pointer's will included another bequest of some interest, £1 to Robert Crofton. The Crofton family were Twickenham and Whitton people, and when Moses Glover made his large survey map of the Hundred of Isleworth in 1635 he marked several large parcels of ground as 'Mr. Croftons Nursery'. From entries in the registers it seems likely that this was Robert Crofton, born in 1603, the son of another Robert Crofton of Whitton who may well have been Vincent Pointer's friend. The map also marks an area of about 6 acres belonging to the bishop of Norwich, Dr. Corbet, showing that Pointer's son retained property in Twickenham until the year of his death.

Although there may have been many smaller nurseries, not only near London, but all over England, it is probable that new and rare varieties could most easily be had from the three grounds named by Gerard. We know that the Tothill Street nursery continued to be of importance for more than fifty years. That of Vincent Pointer may have been continued by one of the Croftons after Pointer's death in 1619, though it is likely that the significance of Twickenham, just across the river from Richmond, lessened after Queen Elizabeth's death in 1603. What happened to the Horsleydown nursery we do not know, but its disappearance could indirectly reflect the end of royal interest in the Tower as a residence. New influences replaced the old, and the charter granted to the Gardeners Company of London in 1605 may well account for the rather later tendency of nurseries to cluster around the city in the inner suburbs from Clerkenwell to Whitechapel. There is nothing to show that the Company's first Master, Thomas Young, was of outstanding influence on the trade.

Before turning our attention to the beginnings of the City trade we have to consider another aspect of that of Westminster. Gardeners need not only fruit trees but also flowers, and the greatest florist of the time was Ralph Tuggie. As an historical character he emerges as a parishioner of St. Margaret's, husband of Catherine, by whom he had nine children baptized between 1621 and 1632. He died intestate and was buried on 6 March 1632-3, his gardens being carried on by his widow and later by his son Richard Tuggie (1626-1670) after Catherine had died in August 1651. Apart from John Tradescant the elder, John Parkinson, and the botanist Thomas Johnson who revised Gerard's *Herball*, Tuggie was evidently the leading plantsman of his age. As a nurseryman pure and simple he reigned supreme. Parkinson in 1629 especially praised him for his work on carnations, saying that the most beautiful tawny variety he ever saw was with 'Master Ralph Truggie' and that he 'must needes therefore call *Master Tuggies* Princesse, . . . the greatest and fairest of all these sorts of variable tawnies, or seed flowers'. Parkinson illustrated another kind, 'Master Tuggie his Rose Gilliflower'. Four years later Thomas Johnson, in revising Gerard's *Herball*, referred to the sorts of Colchicum in 'the gardens of our Florists, as M. *Parkinsons*, M. *Tuggies*, &c.'; to Auriculas ('Beares eares') in 'the gardens of Mr. *Tradescant* and Mr. *Tuggie*, . . . at this present furnished with very great varieties of these flowers'; and again to the carnations or Clove Gillofloures. Concerning them he advised the amateur at the time of the year to 'repaire to the garden of Mistresse *Tuggy* (the wife of my late deceased friend Mr. *Ralph Tuggy*) in Westminster, which in the excellencie and varietie of these delights exceedeth all that I have seen; as also hee himselfe whilest he lived exceeded most, if not all of his time, in his care, industry, and skill in raising, encreasing, and preserving of these plants and some others; whose losse therefore is the more to be lamented by all those that are lovers of plants'.

The name of Tuggie lived on, and in 1665 was included by John Rea in his list of 13 Leather Coats or buff Auriculas that 'yet remain and retain the names of those that raised them'. The names were Beasar, Collin, Humphries, Lance, Looker, Meracow, Mow, Mullar, Randoll, Rickets, Tradescan, Tuggie and Turner. We can identify several of these with certainty and others with a fair degree of likelihood, though not all were necessarily florists in trade. Collin was perhaps the Pierre Collin, a French vine-dresser brought to Hatfield in 1607, possibly anglicized into Peter Collins, who from 1617 to 1630 was head gardener at Syon House. Looker was pretty certainly Roger Looker, the prime founder of Brompton Park Nursery. Mullar was the Moulart who in 1654 supplied iris, colchicums, jonquils and fritillaries to Sir Thomas Hanmer and the James Moullar, 'flowerist' of Spitalfields in Stepney, who died in 1666. Rickets was doubtless George Rickets, of whom much more will have to be said; Tradescan may have been either the father who died in 1638 or the son (1608-1662); Tuggie also could mean Ralph or his son Richard; Turner might be the John Turner, gardener of St. George's, Southwark, who died in 1662. (Plates 4,5).

The generation that had elapsed between the death of Ralph Tuggie and the publication of Rea's *Flora, Ceres and Pomona* was the lost generation of the Civil War. Horticulturally the main result was the rise of mercantilism under Cromwell and the introduction from the Continent of improved methods and crops in commercial gardening. The rapid increase of population in inner London put an end to the nurseries of Westminster, which had to migrate further westwards or across the Thames to Lambeth. For a generation more the main centre of trade swung to the other end of the capital, until the success of Brompton Park brought the principal concentration of nurseries to the parishes of Kensington and Chelsea. To Chelsea also migrated the chief medical garden of the London area, which had been at Westminster and indeed was the direct continuator of the great Infirmary Garden of Westminster Abbey with its five centuries of monastic experience of plants. It was on 10 June 1658 that John Evelyn 'went to see the Medical Garden at Westminster, well stored with plants, under Morgan, a very skilfull botanist'. This was Edward Morgan, who in the previous year had been associated with Thomas Gilbank and Richard Tuggy as signatories to a letter printed by William Coles in *Adam in Eden*. In January 1638 Edward Morgan had been one of the witnesses to the will of the elder Tradescant, and he remained in charge of the Garden until c.1678. We may suspect that, simply because he did not write books, Morgan has received less than his due meed of fame.

Even before the Civil War the move towards the northern and eastern suburbs of the City had begun. Parkinson in 1629 mentioned 'the great bearing Cherry of Master Millen' as 'a reasonable great red cherry', and concerning plums had more to say concerning this orchardist. All the sorts of plums worth naming, wrote Parkinson, 'the choysest for goodnesse, and rarest for knowledge, are to be had of my very good friend *Master John Tradescante*, who hath wonderfully laboured to obtaine all the rarest fruits he can heare off in any place of Christendome, Turky, yea or the whole world; as also with *Master John Millen* dwelling in Olde Streete, who from *John Tradescante* and all others that have had good fruit, hath stored himselfe with the best only, and he can sufficiently furnish any'. Johnson in 1633 went into greater detail, and from his scattered remarks an outline list of Millen's stock can be deduced. 'Such as are desirous of them (Goose-berries) may find them with Mr. John Millen, living in Old-Street'; 13 kinds of peaches and six nectarines, choice ones, 'are to be had from my friend Mr. Millen in Old-Street'; of apricots Mr. Millen had five sorts. Not only most of the best pears were to be had from Millen, but in his 'nursery are to be found the choisest fruits this kingdom yields'. Most of the best plums and cherries also could be furnished by the Old Street Nursery.

The Millen family of Old Street was quite well to do, as is shown by the wills of John Millen the elder, who died in October 1635, his widow Elizabeth, who died in the summer of 1637, and of their two sons John Millen the younger (c. 1610–died June 1639) and James Millen who died early in 1642, leaving only a widow Margery and a daughter Elizabeth under age. Nothing is said of their gardens or other real estate, but the elder John Millen had personal property valued at £62. 2s. 10d. Since the south side of Old Street was already fairly heavily built up, it is likely that the nursery was on the north side, and this is confirmed by the fact that James Millen's property included rows of houses along the north side, somewhere in the neighbourhood of the present Central Street and Ironmonger Row. James had been left half of his mother's estate, which included almost everything left by John Millen senior, so that part of the nursery may have been in the 'one acre called Irish Feild on the north side of the Pesthouse'. James also had a lease of six acres of land, partly in St. Giles without Cripplegate parish (which included Old Street), partly in Islington. What is highly significant is that John Millen the father and both of his sons styled themselves gentlemen, like Vincent Pointer-Corbet of an earlier generation, and Moses Cook at a later date.

The Civil War, the relentless spread of London's houses, and the dying off of the generation of nurserymen known to Parkinson and Johnson effectively put an end to the period which might be called post-medieval. The first notable nurseries of a new age had possibly started a little before the outbreak of the war, but in most cases are heard of only after the Restoration. It is probably a symptom of the effective transfer of power from the royal Court at Westminster to the merchants of the City that the outstanding gardens were, for about thirty years, an East End phenomenon. The move to Shoreditch had begun under Cromwell, for in 1653 William Harman, gardener near the Falcon there, was recommended to John Percivall in Ireland (purchaser of fruit trees from Arnold Banbury) by his cousin Samuel Percivall. The precinct of Hoxton in Shoreditch parish was soon to become the home of a group of relatively small but crucially important nurseries. But first we have to consider the founding of what was certainly the largest London nursery through most of Charles II's reign. This was 'the great Nursery between Spittle-fields and White-Chappel' kept by Captain Leonard Gurle. A nursery already existed there in 1643, when Gurle was about 22 years old according to his age declared as 55 at the time of his second marriage in 1676. The name of the occupier of the 'nurcery and garden plott' is not stated and all that is certain is that Gurle must have been well established by 1660.

Though described as the great nursery, it was probably not really large by later standards. As far as can be judged from the available maps it covered most of the block north of Old Montagu Street between Brick Lane on the west and Greatorex Street on the east, stretching back to Princelet Street on the north. Allowing for some building up of the frontages this probably constituted a garden of about 12 acres, quite likely the biggest in the country at the time it was formed. Like the earlier nurseries of Pointer, the Banbury family and Millen, the Whitechapel Nursery was primarily for the supply of the best varieties of fruit trees. Before 1661 Captain Gurle had produced the improved hardy nectarine which he called by his own name spelt backwards: Elrug, later smoothed to Elruge. In 1670 Leonard Meager in his book *The English Gardener* described 'Garrle' as 'my very loving friend' and as 'a very Eminent and Ingenious Nursery-man, who can furnish any that desireth with any of the sorts hereafter mentioned; as also with divers other rare and choice Plants'. The list printed is only of named varieties of fruit trees, and it was indeed choice fruit that Gurle supplied to many customers including the Earl of Bedford, stocking the Woburn orchards in the 1670's. Some years earlier

he had stocked the gardens of Lord Allington at Horseheath Hall, Cambridgeshire, charging 5s. each for peaches, 4s. for nectarines, 1s. 6d. to 2s. 6d. for
apricots or grapevines, 2s. for pears upon quince stocks and 1s. each for
plums 'one with another'. The White 'Figge' cost 5s., but the 'great bleu figge'
only 2s. each. Some other prices can be filled in from a Woburn bill of 1674,
where French pears cost 2s. 6d. each, cherries 2s. but the Nonsuch cherry
2s. 6d., quinces 1s. 6d. and apples, like plums, 1s.

It was, however, in adding 'other rare and choice Plants' to orchard trees
that Gurle was a pioneer. In 1672 he was sending to Sir Roger Pratt for his
gardens at Ryston Hall near Downham, Norfolk, not only pear trees, but also
the best Dutch Limes (£6 for 40), half a dozen laurustinus at 1s. each, 20
spruce firs (£2. 10s.), 30 cypress (£1), and two barberries for 4s. Purely
ornamental flowering shrubs were two white and two red double woodbines
(9d. each), six 'Whit Jassamyes' for 4s. and two Persian 'Jassamyes' (really
Persian Lilacs) costing 3s. each. Seeds and a box for them, amounting to
11s. 10d., completed the order, and show that Gurle had already reached the
position, normal ever since, of nurseryman and seedsman. Five years later he
achieved the highest rank by becoming gardener and keeper of the royal
garden in St. James's Park to Charles II, on the death of John Rose. This
important office carried with it emoluments of £240 a year for life, as well as
£320 a year to maintain the garden. Gurle died about the same time as the
King, in the spring of 1685, administration of his goods being granted on 2
April to his son William Gurle. It is not clear how long the Whitechapel
Nursery was carried on, but the area was long known as 'Gurle's Ground' and
in 1719 part of it was still occupied by Martin 'Girle' who may have been
Leonard's eldest son by his first marriage, the 'Martin son of Leonard Girl'
baptized on 4 November 1641 at St. Olave's, Southwark; his younger brother
Joseph, baptized on 6 August 1644 at Whitechapel, gives us a hint that the
father may by then have taken over the nursery. Leonard Gurle was buried at
Woodham Walter in Essex, which may have been his birthplace.

Gurle's predecessor as royal gardener, the famous John Rose (Plate 1),
was also a nurseryman, specializing in the the best varieties of grapevine,
which he offered (in his book of 1666, *The English Vineyard Vindicated*) 'at
very reasonable Rates'. Rose was an example of a different type of gardener
from the London gentlemen. His father Stephen Rose (c. 1563-1638) was a
yeoman farmer of Amesbury in Wiltshire, and John as the younger son
succeeded at the age of 16 to his father's copyhold. He must have done well
for himself at an early age for during the Civil War (when he was about 19 to
23) he was able to provide £50 for the King's cause. This suggests that he was
then already head gardener to William, Marquess of Hertford, a noted
Royalist and restored to the dukedom of Somerset on 13 September 1660.
Rose was certainly gardener to the Duke's widow at Amesbury House before
obtaining his appointment at St. James's on 14 October 1661. At first his
office carried only £40 a year, but consisted of the position of Keeper and
Gardener of the garden plotted and laid out and to be found and made in St.
James's Park, and of the garden-house and green-house therein to be erected,

and of all the orange trees and other trees and greens therein to be planted.

This reference to a royal 'green-house' is noteworthy since it comes three years before the word's published use by John Evelyn which is accepted by the *Oxford English Dictionary* as the earliest in the language. That Rose's book owed much to Evelyn (half-concealed as 'Philocepos') is well known, but it is likely that the debt was not one-sided. The wealthy amateur Evelyn certainly must have learned a great deal from the many artists and craftsmen with whom he mixed, and he probably depended far more even than he himself realized upon the skilled plantsmanship of Rose in the compilation of his *Sylva, Pomona,* and *Kalendarium Hortense,* published in 1664. Though Rose himself stated that he had been 'formerly Gardener to her Grace the Dutchess of Somerset', it is known that he had also been keeper of the garden of Essex House and that the Earl (Arthur Capel, 1631-1683) sent him to France to study under Le Notre. He may also have been the head gardener 'Rowse' who was in charge at Woburn Abbey for the Earl of Bedford from c. 1658 to 1661. This would fit closely with Rose's royal appointment and the filling of the post at Woburn c.1662 by John Field and of the position under Lord Essex by Moses Cook in or before 1664. Rose died a wealthy man, leaving handsome bequests to many relatives and friends. He made no reference to his occupation, having attained the rank of 'Gent.', and left a freehold at Ditcheat in Somerset to trustees to apply £30 a year 'to an able and orthodox schole Master to teach 20 boyes Grammar, Writing and Arithmatick Gratis borne in the . . . Towne of Almesbury', with any surplus income 'to a Woeman to instruct the same number of poore Children . . . to reade the English tonge'. 'My loving Friend Mr. William Lucus' was left £20 and was to be one of the Overseers of the Will; he was probably the seedsman already known to us as living along the Strand.

The London seed firms too were coming into being, though little enough is known about them. After Lucas's death in 1679 his business came into the hands of Edward Fuller, the leading London seedsman for some forty years. In May 1678 there was a Mr. Crouch in business as a seedsman at the Golden Ball without Bishopsgate, but nothing is known of his firm. Ten years later, when John Worlidge or Woolridge printed the standard list, it represented the 'big three'; Fuller at Strand Bridge, Theophilus Stacy at the Rose and Crown without Bishopsgate, and Charles Blackwell at the King's Head near Fetter Lane end in Holborn. A fourth business was that of Francis Weston, at the sign of the Flower-de-Luce over against the Maypole in the Strand, in existence by 1694; and a fifth was the famous shop of John Turner, The Orange Tree in the Strand opposite to the Duke of Bedford's house, founded before 1695. Turner was regarded by Stephen Switzer as well versed in the trade, unlike many of his rivals, and he had a long and prosperous career until 1734 or later. After this his shop became that of Charles Minier, the most distinguished of the Huguenot seed merchants, and founder of a series of partnerships which kept the name alive until late in the 19th century: the botanist Robert Teesdale (c. 1740-1804) became a partner in 1775. The Holborn seed shop also had a very long life, being taken over by Nathaniel

Powell (died 1773) and continued under various names until 1830.

It is time to return to the group of nurseries set up in Shoreditch and more particularly within the precinct of Hoxton. This area lay without Bishopsgate, not far from Stacy's seed shop at the Rose and Crown. Before the Civil War there had been at least one important garden, not certainly a nursery, kept by John Noble. Noble was already well-to-do in 1633, when he made a gift to Shoreditch parish church for two sermons to be preached each year against excessive gambling. When he died in 1651 he left the church a further annuity of £1 from land in Cock Lane, and had been in occupation of six acres of garden between Old Street, Willow Walk (Great Eastern Street) and High Street. In a dispute with his former servant, Nathaniel Billings, regarding a lease of three acres of the property, Noble stated that he had left to Billings 'divers very good fruit trees of much varietie, partly against the walls and partly in the open ground, and some bedds also of sparragus'. This land lay close to the City, much further south than the main group of Hoxton nurseries, which were formed later.

The earliest Hoxton nursery of which we have any substantial knowledge was that of George Rickets, at the sign of The Hand, between Kingsland Road and Hoxton Street. Its southern boundary was where Nuttall Street runs from east to west across the block. Its total extent is not precisely known, for in 1672 and 1675 Rickets was buying more property, of which at least three acres was an existing orchard, presumably added to his original ground. By 1665 Rickets was already famous as a florist and his garden must have existed for some time. In 1678 his son James was signing receipts on his father's behalf, which suggests that George Rickets was born not later than c. 1635. He died at a fairly advanced age in July 1706. In 1711 James Rickets raised a mortgage on the property but nothing more is heard of the nursery.

Almost adjoining Rickets' nursery was a smaller one belonging to a Mr. Pearson who was 'accounted very honest' and charged moderate prices. A florist, he specialized in anemones, which he would sell only to gentlemen. This curious touch, related by Gibson in 1691, probably means that he would not sell to the trade. He was presumably the Samuel Peirson senior, gardener of Hoxton, buried at Bunhill Fields on 6 March 1701. He had leases of four gardens and two houses besides his own dwelling and was able to leave the interest on £400 to his wife Frances. His son, Samuel Peirson junior, was running the business by 1700 and, subject to conditions, was to continue it. Perhaps a relative was Edward Pearson of Strand-on-the-Green who died in 1721. In his will of 1719 he mentioned the four grandchildren of his dead brother Richard: two of them, Powell Pearson and George Pearson, were apprenticed to gardeners — the elder to the important Thomas Greening (1684-1757). Their father who died between 1716 and 1719, was Richard Pearson, a schoolmaster of Mortlake.

The western end of Rickets' property stretched to the east side of Hoxton Street, almost opposite to the point where Ivy Lane (now Ivy Street) enters on the west. At some distance to the west of Hoxton Street were two important nurseries, one on either side of an alley at the west end of Ivy

Lane; this was probably a right-of-way on the present alignment of St. John's
Road. One of these nurseries was small but highly specialized, established by
William Darby (died c.1713) about 1677. This garden was taken over about
1718 by John Cowell, from whose book *The Curious and Profitable Gardener*
(1730) a certain amount of its horticultural history can be gleaned. Cowell
called his predecessor Mr. Darby 'a famous Gardener, noted for one of the
first in England who chose the Culture of Exotic Plants', and tells us that
Darby had the nursery for 36 years. Among Darby's plants were a Glastonbury Thorn brought from Glastonbury about 1680, but in 1729 'not much
more than nine feet high'; and the great American Aloe, 'the first curious
Exotic Plant he ever had', bought from Anthony Versprit of Lambeth when it
was already some 20 years old. Later, about 1710, Darby acquired a Cereus
or Torch-Thistle which flowered for Cowell in 1729.

The other nursery was much more famous. It was established or taken over
by Thomas Fairchild (1667-1729) about 1691, for in *The City Gardener*
(1722) Fairchild remarked that he had been 'upwards of thirty years . . . on a
Spot of Ground where I have raised several thousand plants'. It is said that
the nursery was in grounds called Selby's Gardens, implying probably that it
was on the site of an earlier market garden. Fairchild (Plate 7) moved to
Hoxton from the adjacent parish of St. Giles Cripplegate, and may have
belonged to a family settled there but originating at Orwell in south-west
Cambridgeshire. He was, however, baptized at Aldbourne, Wiltshire, on 9
June 1667, the son of John and Ann Fairchild; his father was buried on 21
October 1668. Most of the work for which Fairchild is justly famous, as the
pioneer of hybridization and of horticultural town-planning, belongs to the
18th century and must be left for a later chapter. At this point it remains to
be said that, somewhere in the same part of Hoxton, there was a third nursery
which became the ground of Benjamin Whitmill, Fairchild's 'ingenious Friend
and Brother-Gardener', as well as fellow author, of *The Gardener's Universal
Calendar,* first published in 1726.

Not much can be said of the other nurseries which existed in the London
area before 1700. One Clements at Mile End, visited by Gibson in 1691, is
interesting because of the possibility that his small garden may have formed
the nucleus of the great Mile End Nursery formed by James Gordon after
1742. Gibson said that Clements, whose garden was no bigger than that of
Darby at Hoxton, kept 'a shop of seeds (and) plants in pots next the street',
which was of course the great main road into Essex and East Anglia. In
Lambeth parish and within Vauxhall Liberty was Captain Foster, who grew
striped hollies; in 1700 he was rated to pay 17s. 4d. to the repairs of Lambeth
Church; but in 1703 another rate was levied on 'Captain Foster or Occupier',
rather suggesting that he had by then died or retired from business. Also in
Lambeth, but in the Marsh and Wall Liberty, was the garden of Anthony
Versprit who was another of the early specialists in rare exotics. The 1700
rate, in the moderate sum of 2s. 6d., was levied on 'Mr. Vespright or
Occupier'. Another alleged nurseryman of the time, 'Mordan', is perhaps a
myth. In 1674 Thomas Gilbank, the Earl of Bedford's London gardener,

bought four peach trees which, wrote Gilbank in his account (as printed) 'I had of Mr. Lord Mordan nurseryman . . . '. Almost certainly the 'Mr.' represents 'My' and the source was the gardener in charge of the private nursery of Lord Mordaunt (commonly spelt Mordan) at Parson's Green in Fulham.

Fulham already had trade nurseries, one of which may have been started by Nathaniel Dancer who died in 1657, though this was more probably a market garden. Another belonged to Thomas Rench (c. 1631-1728), who is said to have been an early improver of the strawberry as well as a noted grower of auriculas and one of the founders of the London Floral Feasts. Also in Fulham parish, at Hammersmith, was the important garden of Henry Marsh (1665-1741), another gentleman gardener with a mansion in Frog Lane and a great deal of property in several parishes. Marsh supplied 150 evergreen oaks for Canons in 1719, and was said to have a notable specimen of the service tree in 1730, when he was described as 'a curious Collector of rare and uncommon Trees'. Of another nurseryman, Marshfield of Knightsbridge, nothing seems to be known beyond the fact that he supplied pear trees for Wrest Park, near Shefford in Bedfordshire, in 1693-4.

Yet other nurseries lay close to the Thames above London. The most important of these was one at Putney, in existence by 1654 and carried on by the Hunt family to 1775 and then by three generations of Howey until 1838. Francis Hunt the third (1691-1763) was a member of the London Society of Gardeners and among other things a raiser of varieties of the English Iris from seed. This was described by Cowell in 1730: 'There was a most surprising Appearance of these Plants once raised from Seed, at Mr. Francis Hunt's, at Putney, in Surrey, which were wonderfully esteemed by all who saw them, some of them being marbled with White and Crimson, and others spotted with the same Colours; and, again, others marbled with Yellow, Blue, and White, and streak'd like the Rainbow'. Further up, at Kew Green, was the garden of William Cox senior, who died on 29 December 1704, but the nursery's fame as the source of the improved Hotspur Pea may have dated only from the time of his son William Cox junior (1680-1722). Finally, on the Middlesex bank, Twickenham still had an important nursery run by Grigson, who in 1693-4 was sending nectarine trees to Wrest Park. This may have been William Grigson, with a wife Rebecka and children baptized in 1686-91, or the Thomas Grigson (died 1724) who, with his wife Elizabeth, was raising a family from 1688 to 1703.

Before passing on to a reconsideration of the founding of the Brompton Park Nursery in 1681, it may be as well to look back on the general picture of the trade. We have seen that nurseries providing a fairly wide selection of ornamental trees and shrubs as well as fruit really started with Leonard Gurle at Whitechapel somewhere about 1643 at the earliest, perhaps some time later. Notwithstanding the important introductions from distant lands made in the time of Gerard and Parkinson and rather later under John Tradescant the younger (1608-1662), only a small proportion of the new plants was in general cultivation. It is highly significant that Darby, who did not begin to

Plate 1: *John Rose (1622-1677), Gardener to Charles II at St James's Park from 1661. The painting, by Henry Danckerts and therefore not earlier than 1668 when he came to England, is here reproduced by permission of the Most Hon. the Marchioness of Cholmondeley, who kindly communicates the text of an accompanying note in the handwriting of, and signed by, Horace Walpole: 'Mr Rose, the royal Gardener presenting to King Charles 2nd the first pineapple raised in England. The picture belonged to Mr London the nurseryman.(partner of Mr Wise), whose Heir bequeathed it to the Revd Mr Pennicott of Ditton, who gave it to Mr Walpole, 1780.'*

Plate 2: *Thomas Wentworth (died 1587), grandfather to the great Earl of Strafford, a family picture (perhaps a 17th-century copy) dating from c.1575. It is here reproduced by the kindness of the Rt. Hon. the Earl Fitzwilliam. Wentworth is shown by the artist, John Lavorgne, seated and holding a tree-stock in which grafts have been inserted in sawcuts; another stock is by his left foot; in his left hand are the grafting saw and knife. Behind him, in the family livery, stands the Gardener, holding in his right hand a bundle of grafts and in his left the grafting wedge for opening the sawcuts to receive them. Mrs Wentworth (1537-1592), née Margaret Gascoigne, stands on her husband's left, holding their daughter Elizabeth by the hand. In the background is the old Wentworth Woodhouse with its Elizabethan knot-gardens, and the bare winter trees of the park.*

Plate 3: *Enlarged detail from Plate 2. The picture precisely illustrates the method of grafting described by William Lawson in* A New Orchard and Garden *published in 1618 but representing his experience since 1570.*

Plate 4: *John Tradescant the elder (died 1638), royal gardener to Charles I from 1629, botanical collector and nurseryman. From the portrait in the Ashmolean Museum, Oxford.*

Plate 5: *John Tradescant the younger (1608-1662), who succeeded to his father's nursery at Lambeth and to the office of royal gardener. From the portrait in the Ashmolean Museum, Oxford.*

Plate 6: *Henry Wise (1653-1738), junior partner in the Brompton Park Nursery from 1694 and royal gardener to Queen Anne and to George I. From the portrait by Sir Godfrey Kneller at Kew Palace, reproduced by gracious permission of Her Majesty the Queen.*

Plate 7: *Thomas Fairchild (1667-1729), nurseryman of Hoxton. From the portrait attributed to Van Blach', by permission of the Sherardian Professor of Botany, University of Oxford.*

Plate 8: *William Falla (1761-1830), nurseryman, 'the spade husbandman', of Gateshead, Co. Durham. From a portrait in the possession of Nigel L. Swinburne Esq., by his kind permission.*

stock his nursery until about 1677, should have been remembered as one of the first to specialize in exotics. From the founding of Gurle's great nursery and the death of Parkinson (1650) it took about a generation for the newly won riches, largely from North America, to become accessible, Even later still, when the earliest surviving trade catalogue of nursery stock appeared, that of George Rickets of 1688 (see Appendix III for complete text), the number of available species was not very large.

In Rickets' list the only species that are believed to have been introduced after 1650 are: among Housed Greens, the Yellow Indian Jasmine (presumably *Jasminum odoratissimum*) of 1656; and the Lentiscus (*Pistacia lentiscus*) of 1664; among the Winter Greens, Cedar of Libanus (*Cedrus libani*), formerly assigned to 1683, now to '1670-80' but with greater probability to c. 1650; and Winter Jasmine, certainly not our present hardy species (1844) but almost certainly the tender winter-flowering *Jasminum sambac* of 1665; and among the Flowers, the Blew Cardinal's Flower, *Lobelia syphilitica* of 1665. From the Trees and Plants offered in the seedsmans' list of the same year, also printed by Woolridge, it is possible to add: Terebenthus (*Pistacia terebinthus*) 1656; Azedarach, the Bead-Tree (*Melia azedarach*) 1656; and possibly some 'Laurels' not clearly identifiable. In the basic list which goes back at any rate to c. 1677 (and certainly to William Lucas who died in 1679) there are both Cedrus Libani and 'Cedrus Barmudi semper vivens' (*Juniperus bermudiana*). These had evidently been introduced, not simply as rarities, but into trade, well before the date of 1683 formerly assigned to them.

This question of the time-lag between introduction and distribution is worth following a little further. In the section of Choice Trees and Plants of Lucas' list of c.1677 there are some 30 exotics certainly identifiable. Of these 18 had been introduced before 1600 and only twelve afterwards, ten of them before 1650 and the two cedars later. Rickets' 1688 catalogue contains about 60 exotic trees and housed greens, and of these some 20 were introduced between 1600 and 1650, and five only later than that. Out of about 100 trees and shrubs which flowered with Fairchild in 1722 (see Appendix IV), only 15 or 16 had been introduced after 1680 and of these probably not more than three since 1700. The proportions remain much the same, and show that a trade list was likely to offer very few plants established in England for less than a generation. Apart from the single dubious case of the Cedar of Lebanon, even the leading nurseryman George Rickets produced nothing that had not been in the country for well over twenty years. Henry Wise's list of 1700 or later, adds very little: Canary Bellflower (*Canarina campanula*), 1696; Honey flower (*Melianthus major*), 1688; and the Tulip Tree (*Liriodendron tulipifera*), 1663. The great bulk of his calendar of flowers and lists of trees, apart from natives, were introductions of 1640 or much earlier still. (Plate 6).

The mention of Wise leads naturally to some account, however brief, of the founding of Brompton Park. A great deal has been written on the giant nursery, but too much reliance has been placed on the account given by Stephen Switzer in *The Nobleman, Gentleman and Gardener's Recreation* of 1715. Though valuable for preserving a good deal of first-hand information and genuine tradition, and indeed indispensable for much that is not to be found anywhere else, Switzer's history is imprecise in details and exaggerates the share of George London in the enterprise. The 'Advertisement' of 1681, drawn up by the four original partners, makes it clear that London was the junior partner and that the leading spirit was Roger Looker, the Queen's Gardener. Looker had eight other great gardens in his charge, and was probably a good deal older than the other three men. Looker, who has been confused with his son William, died on 3 March 1685, as appears from the proceedings relating to his unsigned will (see Appendix VI, p. 169). He left a widow Bridgett and bequeathed to his son William Looker 'all my share or parte which I have now in Bromton Parke'. William had been old enough by 1671 to sign receipts on his father's behalf, and Roger was pretty certainly the Mr. Looker who was gardener to the Earl of Salisbury at Hatfield in 1661.[3] Samuel Pepys, returning from Cambridge to London on 22 July, 'come to Hatfield before twelve o'clock, and walked all alone to the Vineyard, which is now a very beautiful place again; and coming back I met with Mr. Looker, my Lord's gardener (a friend of Mr. Eglin's) who showed me the house, the chappel with brave pictures, and, above all, the gardens, such as I never saw in all my life; nor so good flowers, nor so great gooseburys, as big as nutmegs'.

The second partner, Moses Cook (died 1715), is better known to us than Looker from his book *The Manner of Raising, Ordering and Improving Forest Trees* (1676), a standard work reprinted in 1679 and again issued after his death in 1717 and 1724. His eldest son, Captain Edward Cook, and one of his daughters, were born before he moved to Little Hadham, Hertfordshire, about 1663. He was head gardener to the Earl of Essex (Arthur Capel, 1631-1683) at Hadham Hall by 1664, and was working on the Earl's new gardens at Cassiobury near Watford from 1669 onwards. From an anecdote of the effect of salt water on a marsh mentioned in his book, we know that when he was a boy of 14 his father's farm in Lincolnshire was flooded by the sea, and from many other details it is evident that Cook fully shared the scientific curiosity of his time and was a sound observer. Among other things he gives us a glimpse of the problem set by the arrival of completely unknown exotics. 'My Lord (the Earl of Essex) had thirteen sorts of strange Seeds sent him, as I remember, from Goa; I never saw the like . . . I rais'd ten of the thirteen Sorts, tho some of them lay almost a year in the Ground; but I also must tell you, I lost all my ten sorts the first Winter, but one Sort, and that the second, for want of a Green-house: some of them, I suppose, were Annuals'.

In the case of Cook it is the diarist Evelyn who gives us a glimpse of the man. On 18 April 1680 'on the earnest invitation of the Earle of Essex I went with him to his house at Cashioberie . . . The gardens are very rare, and

3. William Looker of Hatfield in 1667 married Joan Smith at St. Martin's in the Fields; doubtless the Mr. William Looker buried at Hatfield on 28 November 1685.

cannot be otherwise, having so skillful an artist to govern them as Mr. Cooke, who is, as to the mechanic part, not ignorant in Mathematics, and pretends to Astrologie. There is an excellent collection of the choicest fruit'. Cook's mathematical knowledge is displayed in the latter part of his book, where he goes fully into the mensuration of timber, with numerous geometrical diagrams and abundant formulae. He must have brought to the Brompton Park enterprise a valuable contribution towards the correct naming of kinds of fruit trees, one of the main objects of the 'mutuall Society or co-partnership'. As Switzer tells us, Cook sold his share in 1689, after the deaths of Looker and of John Field (d. 1687). With part of the proceeds he bought in 1690 the advowson of Sible Hedingham in Essex, and settled it on his son the Revd. Moses Cook (1665-1733), who was rector there for the rest of his life. The father was able to live as a country gentleman, having substantial estates which are named in his will. Though Switzer in his book of 1715 refers to Mr. Cook as 'yet living', he was buried at Little Hadham on 11 February of that year. His widow Ann survived until 1719.

John Field was probably rather younger than Cook, for his nine children were baptized at Woburn between 1670 and 1686. He had been appointed gardener there by the Earl of Bedford about 1662, in succession to the mysterious Rowse who, as was suggested, may have been John Rose. The evidence as to his lovable character and the exceptionally intimate terms on which he and his wife lived with the Earl's family, has been admirably presented by Miss Gladys Scott Thomson in her book *Life in a Noble Household* and very little else is known of him. In the Brompton Park 'Advertisement' of 1681 'Feild' is described simply as gardener to the Earl of Bedford at 'Wooburne Abby' where he seems to have spent the whole of his working career. Even the purchasing of plants was mostly done by his colleague at the Earl's London garden, Thomas Gilbank (died 1684). Since one of Field's daughters was called Margaret, it is likely that the Margaret Field, widow, who was buried at Woburn on 14 June 1720 was the gardener's wife found by the Russells to be an admirable sick nurse and domestic treasure. Only one of the five sons survived childhood, William Field, baptized on 17 August 1678 and buried at Woburn on 10 October 1734. He may well have been the gardener of that name who, in 1733, subscribed to Robert Furber's *A Short Introduction to Gardening.* James Field, gardener at Bedford in 1793, and the John Field who founded the great seedsmen's business (later John & John Field & Co. and Field & Child, at 119 Lower Thames Street) about 1750, may have been relatives.

The fourth partner, George London, was a man of surpassing energy. Switzer, after saying that John Rose deserved especially 'to be remembered for the Encouragement he gave to a servant of his . . . I mean Mr. London', tells us that it was 'common for him (London) to ride 50 or 60 miles in a day. He made his Northern Circuit in five or six weeks, and sometimes less, and his Western in as little time. As for the South and East, they were but three or four days work for him; most times twice a year visiting all the country Seats, conversing with Gentlemen, and forwarding the business of *Gard'ning* in such a degree as is almost impossible to describe'. This account shows that London spent about a quarter of the year on regular tours of the great estates, and this pattern of touring was adopted by most of the major nurserymen of later times, both metropolitan and provincial. As far as the evidence at present available goes, this method of getting and transacting business was an innovation.

From Switzer's account we know that London was trained by Rose, and therefore within the period 1661-77,[4] and it is almost certain that London was older than Henry Wise, born in 1653. On the other hand, London's first marriage, to Rebecca Walkes at St. Botolph's, Aldersgate, in London, did not take place until 9 July 1679. Although he received no legacy from Rose, it is clear that he revered his old master's memory, for he preserved the historic painting by Dankerts of Rose 'presenting to King Charles 2nd the first pineapple raised in England'. There must surely also have been some connection with Rose, born at Amesbury, Wiltshire, in London's possession of a 'large Silver Cup and Cover called the Amesbury Cup and Cover', which he left to his grandson Charles Woodward, the elder son of his eldest child Rebecca, who had married Richard Woodward in 1699. Probably it was Rose who recommended London to Henry Compton as gardener when Compton became bishop of London in 1675 and began to stock the gardens at Fulham Palace with foreign rarities. Certainly London had held this post for some time by 1681, when he was also gardener to the Earl of Arlington near St. James's Park, and at 'two Gardens in Bedfordshire, both new' which he had no doubt designed. It was through London's access to Compton's introductions, largely obtained by means of his missionary clergy, that the great gardener was able to get priority over most of his competitors.

George London had a family of five children, apparently all by his first marriage. The second daughter, Henrietta, was a pioneer of the tradition that nurserymen's daughters became botanical artists. She married John Peachy at St. Botolph's, Bishopsgate, on 16 March 1705/6, and her younger sister Katherine became the wife of Richard Elford at St. Botolph's, Aldersgate, on 12 December of the same year. When London made his will, on 2 December 1713, he left 'to my daughter Henrietta Peachy my needle worke Bedd wrought by her and standing in the Upper roome over my Great Parlour with the Bedding Pictures and Furniture in the same Roome it stands and also my fine booke of the Surrinam Plants in Colours to which is annexed her my said daughters drawings of Plants in Colours containing forty odd Plants from the Cape of Good Hope. Also I give to her . . . the Drawings of the severall fruits in colours bound up in rough leather they being all formerly drawn by her.' The first book, extra-illustrated by Henrietta, was evidently Maria Merian's *Metamorphosis Insectorum Surinamensium* of 1705.

The will recommended his elder son George, still in his apprenticeship,

---

4. London himself in a letter of 1710 tells us that he 'wase Apprentice . . . in the Royall garden' in 1673, when the Double flowered Indian Almond arrived.

'that he will stick to his Trade' and not depend upon the inheritance placed in trust for him, as for his younger brother John London, when they should reach 23. Their father's estate must have been substantial and included farms near Kingston and Long Ditton in Surrey purchased from London's friend and colleague William Talman, who had been a superintendent of the royal gardens and who in 1713 was of Ranworth Hall, Norfolk. There was also 'my interest in Lead or other Mines in Wales called Sir Carbury Price's Mines' and 'my house wherein I now dwell with the Garden and Ground lately taken out of the Woodworke near Spring Garden in St. Martin's in the Fields', as well as the share in the Brompton Park nursery 'in the Parish of St. Margaretts Westminster and Kensington' held in partnership with Henry Wise. This share was left for the benefit of the younger son John. A sum of £400 was left to George Woodward, second son of 'my daughter Rebecca deceased', and £100 each to two grandchildren, the children of 'my said daughter Katherine Elford'. Mr. Henry Wise was left £10 for a mourning ring.

George London died, not in 1717 as used to be stated, but on 12 January 1713/14, only six months after Bishop Compton. London's will requested that he should be buried 'in the parish church of Fulham near the body of my first dear wife Rebecca London', and not more than £40 was to be spent on his funeral. To the poor of Fulham parish he left £5, the only bequest of its kind, so that it would seem that he regarded Fulham as his real home. Rebecca had died by 1706, when London obtained a licence for his second marriage to Jane Bramston (Bramton or Brampstone). The wedding took place on 1 January 1706/7 at St. Botolph's, Bishopsgate, but Jane cannot long have survived. Her family can be identified from the bequest 'to Mrs. Grace Brampstone daughter of Anthony Brampstone of Screnes Essex esq. one small silver Bohea Tea pott a Silver Kinister for Tea, which was formerly my late Wife's Jane'. Skreens in Roxwell was bought in 1635 by Sir John Bramston, Lord Chief Justice of the King's Bench, and for long remained the seat of his family. George London married his third wife, Elizabeth Denton, late in 1710. She brought to the marriage an annuity of £10 and her own goods, which were to revert to her, as well as £100 under the Marriage Settlement, another £100, and an annuity of £50 in lieu of one of £30 settled on her. London's executors and trustees were his son-in-law Richard Woodward esq., his friend William Talman (Tallman) and his nephew Thomas Ackres, gent., presumably father of 'my two Cousins and Godchildren George and Rebecca Ackres' left £25 apiece. For reasons which are not clear, the will was proved twice, first by Richard Woodward alone on 8 February 1713/14 and secondly by William Tallman and Thomas Ackres jointly on 25 September 1717. This double probate is probably responsible for the long-standing mistake as to the year of London's death.

Since Brompton Park was not started until 1681 it took some years to reach eminence. Before 1700 it was mostly large numbers of the commoner trees and plants that it supplied, for example to the Earl of Bedford. The choicer varieties and the latest exotics were obtained from Gurle, from Rickets, from Darby and from Fairchild. What is remarkable is that in 1685, only four years from scratch, Brompton Park could send to Woburn in a single order 200 apple trees, 50 pears, 100 currants, 100 gooseberries, as well as peaches, nectarines and mulberries. The speed with which the new firm got under way on a very large scale is a tribute to the capacity for organization, as well as the plantsmanship, of its founders. Switzer considered that its value was 'perhaps as much as all the Nurseries of France put together'.

It was undoubtedly Brompton Park that both regularized and rationalized the central nursery trade and later, by opposites, provoked the setting up of serious rivals at many regional centres. But the great combine did not have it all its own way, and for a representative picture of what one of the older nurseries could do towards stocking a new garden we may turn to a bill of George Rickets for plants sent to Levens in Westmorland in 1689.[5] It is of interest, not only because it relates to a garden unique in retaining its original layout, but because of the wide spectrum of types of stock which it displays.

	£ s d
22 Peaches & Nectarines	01:13: 0
62 Pears dwarfs	01:11: 0
16 Aple-trees	00:08: 0
4 Mullbury trees	00:08: 0
400 Gooseburys & Currants	02:00: 0
13 Lime trees	00:13: 0
30 Black cherrys	00:10: 0
16 Sycamores	00:08: 0
300 Plants for ye Pallisade	03:00: 0
16 Spanish Firrs	02:00: 0
24 Scotch Firrs	00:12: 0
45 Spruce Firrs	02:05: 0
26 Cypress trees	00:06: 6
25 Yews	00:12: 6
68 Roses	01:02: 8
68 Honysuckles	00:17: 0
50 Martagons	00:12: 6
100 Lillys wtt (white) of Constantinople	00:12: 0
50 Campernello	00:04: 0
200 Good Tulipps mixt	01:04: 0
100 Ranunculus	01:00: 0
1 li. Double Emonies (Anemones)	00:16: 0
100 Double Junquills	00:16: 8
1 li. of French Emonies	00:04: 0
	23:15:10

5. Here reproduced by the kindness of Mrs. Bagot, who drew my attention to this important document.

Recd. Octobr ye 23th *(sic)* 1689
    of Collnll Greyhome by   li   s   d
    the Hand of Mr Wm Beaumont
    in full of this bill twentythree   23:00: 0
    pounds

                       p. me   Geo: Rickets

Several points in this bill are of interest. First is the concentration upon dwarf, that is bush, pear trees, with no standards. This may be due to the fact that the gardener, Beaumont, was a Frenchman. Secondly there is the surprising attempt to grow cypress in the North; thirdly the considerable number of roses and of honeysuckles; and fourth that all the white lilies were to be of the Constantinople or narrow-petalled form. There are also problems of identification. It has sometimes been stated that 'Spanish Fir' was used as a synonym for the Scots Pine *(Pinus sylvestris)*, but here the juxtaposition of two entries at very different prices is a sufficient disproof of this identity. Possibly a variety of the Aleppo Pine *(P. halepensis)* is meant, since Loudon regarded *Pinus hispanica* as identical with *P. pyrenaica* and thus with what is now botanically *P. halepensis brutia;* but whether this was introduced along with the type in 1683 (?) requires to be established. 'Campernello' stands for the Campernelle Jonquil *(Narcissus odorus)*, according to Miss A. M. Coats. Martagons were not necessarily all *Lilium martagon,* since the word was applied to the whole of the Turk's Cap species, and Rickets had indeed mentioned 'Martagons of several kinds' in his catalogue (see p.148). Lastly, this account gives a firm impression of fundamental conservatism in planting. Apart from the Spanish Firs and the Cypress there were no adventures in recent introductions, in spite of the outstanding quality of Beaumont and his paradoxical pioneering of landscape ideas in Levens Park. The garden, though not the park at Levens remained, and remains to this day, a type of the ideal garden of the 17th century.

THE FOUNDING OF PROVINCIAL NURSERIES

THERE MUST ALWAYS have been some gardeners who acted as nurserymen in county towns and through the countryside. The ordinary fruit trees, in the varieties commonly grown, could have been bought in each region without any need to go to London. Again, there must have been a limited regional trade in seeds of the usual vegetables and herbs. In some cases this may have provided a sideline for the corn-chandler rather than for the gardener, but it is probable that both types of business were often in competition. All the same it is evident from the surviving bills of the 17th and early 18th century that the scope for local purchase was extremely limited. Once it became fashionable to grow 'choice' fruit of the latest improved varieties, the country landowners took to sending orders to the principal nurseries in and around London. In the case of exotics a certain amount might be got by private gifts and from contacts abroad and in the colonies, but here again it was necessary for most purchasers to send to London to get what they wanted. This was still, as we have seen, common form until 1700.

This is not to say that no provincial nurseries had then been started. A few were undoubtedly in existence, but we have very little direct evidence as to the nature and extent of their stocks. To gather up the scraps of information which remain we must retrace our steps to the 16th century. It was then that it became usual for most of the greater nobility, with important estates in the remoter counties, to maintain also an 'inn' or mansion in London or Westminster, and very often a secondary estate too within the Home Counties. As with the Russells after the Earls of Bedford had made Woburn their chief residence, keeping up a town house in the Strand as well, so many other great families moved to and fro from one home to another. On their migrations they could carry plants from the London firms to their country estates, or send for them at any time. So long as the trade in special trees and plants was confined to the higher nobility, this process meant that country nurseries were generally not needed.

In any case, great numbers of fruit and forest trees were given and exchanged among friends, from one country estate to another. This was obviously a principal means of acquiring stock in the Middle Ages, and the rarer items had to be sought by patient enquiry at one monastic garden after another. The total number of kinds of plant in cultivation was quite small (see Appendix II), and most of them would be grown in the gardens and orchards of each of the greater abbeys. The decline of gardening after 1400, complained of by Harrison (see above, p.23), may in fact have been due less to overseas trade ventures than to the falling off in religious vocations.[1] The numbers of monks, even at most of the major monasteries, fell considerably, and each house tended to lease out more and more of its estates. This, as we have seen, may have included some letting of precinct gardens to laymen before the Dissolution. Even if this were the case, the position must have changed greatly after 1540.

About twenty years before the end of the old order one of the greatest of the northern nobility caused a book to be compiled of the whole establishment of his household. This was Henry Algernon Percy, 5th Earl of Northumberland, who died in 1527. The household book was begun in 1512, and so gives a clue to the state of affairs in the first quarter of the 16th century. One member of the staff, taking his meat and drink within — that is with the other officers in the Earl's hall, was the Gardener. His duties were described thus: 'a Gardynner who attendis hourely in the Garden for Setting of Erbis and Clipping of Knottis and Sweping the said Garden clean hourely'; that is to say, he was paid by the hour, but had permanent board in addition. He ranked fairly low in order, some way after the minstrels: '. . . Mynstralls iiij (as to say A Taberet A lute and A Rebekk) — Footeman j — Falconers ij — Painter j — Joyner j — Hunte j — Gardynner in House j — Under Allmoner of the Hall j . . .'. We know that this Earl spent a good deal of his time at Wressle Castle, not far from Howden in the East Riding, and luckily this is one of the places where garden work was described by Leland on his itinerary about 1540. 'And so wer (excedingly fair) the gardeins withyn the mote, and the orchardes withoute. And yn the orchardes were mountes *opere topiario* writhen about with degrees like turninges of cokilshilles, to cum to the top without payn. . . . There is a parke hard by the castelle.'

In the time of the 9th Earl, Henry Percy (1564-1632), the chief estates had become Syon near Brentford and Petworth in Sussex, but the Percy interest in gardens was maintained. From Mr. G. R. Batho's edition of the Earl's household papers a good idea can be obtained of the horticultural arrangements. Each estate had its head gardener: at Syon Anthony Menvell from 1590 to 1616, with pay rising from £6 to £6. 10s. and livery yearly; succeeded by Peter Collins (possibly Pierre Collin, see p.43) from 1617 to 1630, at £7 rising to £7. 10s.; and in 1623-27 also another gardener, Nathaniel Bourne. At Petworth there were three members of the surname Seabedge or Sebache in succession, Walter from 1595 to 1608; George from 1617 to 1625; and William in 1628, when he was paid 10s. for 'looking to the Nursery ponds'. The Petworth fee seems to have been only about £2. 10s. a year, but in some years £10 was allowed for 'wages and diet'. The gardening done at Petworth included making a knott in the garden for 39s. 6d. in 1585-87, and in 1598-99 46s. spent on 'seedes and settes', 23s. for 'payling in the walkes', 34s. 6d. for 'mowing the said gardens and walkes' and 37s. 4d.

---

1. In 1675 Moses Cook shrewdly observed that 'the Reason why in *France* they raise more Varieties of Fruit and Flowers than we do, is this; there are many ingenious Men in their Monasteries, and there they being seated as long as they live, there they raise many fine Fruits and Flowers.'

for other works. The total for the year was only £7. 0s. 10d., but in 1607-8 it was £41. 2s. 1d. and in 1617-18 £75. 12s. 3d. In these same years Syon gardens cost £82. 0s. 11d. and £86. 9s. 5d. 'with bees and a benche'.

We are not told where Walter Seabedge bought his seeds and sets, but a little information is on record in the accounts of another northern nobleman, Lord William Howard of Naworth Castle in Cumberland (1563-1640). On 6 September 1618 a reward of 6d. was given 'To Mr Dacre's gardiner bringing plumms', which could mean either fruit or trees; but on 27 January garden seeds were bought for 14s. 6d., and on 12 February '9 artichoak rootes, basket, and porter' cost 21s. These were very substantial sums, and show that the institution of the annual seedsman's bill for supply of vegetables, salads and herbs at least to a great estate was already in being. On 22 November 1619 a sum of 40s. was spent on 'frut trese', and 2s. 'To the gardner's man for bringing the trese'. So far the places where seeds and plants were bought have not been mentioned, but in 1621 'Ysop seed brought from Yorke' cost 1s., and 'Cumming (cumin) seed bought at Carlyle' 8d., entered on 9 and 13 June respectively. Then on 3 February 1620/1 a Mr Gray was paid 7s. 6d. for 'Freight of ellm trees and hampers' and another 16d. for 'Botehire and portage'.

Evidently regional and local sources of supply were becoming organized early in the 17th century, but very few details can be supplied. In most cases surviving household and estate accounts state simply that certain sums were paid to the gardener for seeds or 'for slipps', as in the book of Sir John Francklyn of Willesden, Middlesex, when 2s. 6d. was spent in the fortnight from 3 September 1624. Only slightly more informative is the entry of 2s. paid in 1637 to a gardener of Creake, Norfolk, for slips and seeds for the garden of the Le Strange family at Hunstanton. It is possibly significant that Creake, 12 miles away, is nearly as far as King's Lynn, which might have been expected to be the principal local source of supplies. Certain quite small and obscure villages seem always to have been nursery centres, and this may indicate early recognition of special suitability of soil or aspect. On the other hand it is possible that in some cases the nursery belonged to a private estate, or was a permitted side-line run by an estate gardener.

The fact that in 1621 it was possible to buy some herb seeds in Carlisle, while for hyssop it was necessary to send as far as York (well over 100 miles), leads on to the importance of regional capitals. England has been exceptional among European nations, even as far back as the Anglo-Saxon period, for the preponderant economic position of London. The commercial standing of the national capital has thrust even the largest provincial cities into the shade. Whereas Spain, Italy and Germany have always had many cities of more or less metropolitan status, and even centralized France provided many rivals to Paris, this country offers no parallel. Bristol, Norwich and York have at various periods served as regional capitals for political or social purposes; smaller towns like Exeter and Shrewsbury have been centres and markets for wide districts. Yet in most cases this degree of importance was insufficient to attract nursery gardening until quite late dates, mostly towards the end of the 18th century.

In the present state of our knowledge there appear to be only two partial exceptions to this rule, in the cities of York and Oxford. In both cases the reason for the exception seems to consist in a temporary metropolitan status. It is true that Oxford, from the 13th century onwards, was the academic capital of the country, but this in itself was unlikely to have any direct effect upon horticulture. Indirectly, the founding of the Oxford Botanic Garden in 1621, though primarily for the improvement of the medical faculty, has been of the greatest significance. It was, however, almost certainly the fact that Oxford became the King's capital city during the Civil War that led directly to the very early appearance of nurseries there. To begin with, the grounds involved may have been market gardens as much as or more than nurseries, but there was in one instance continuity of use with what became a really notable nursery.

This nursery was in the Paradise Gardens which, as already mentioned, occupied part of the precinct of the former Franciscan friary. We have seen that by 1725 the garden was run by Thomas Tagg, whose large staff cost him £700 a year in wages, and that his predecessor Thomas Wrench, Mrs. Tagg's first husband, had been reputed the best Kitchen Gardener in England. This Thomas Wrench was the son of Thomas Wrench, gardener, born in Oxford, who took up the freedom of the city on 11 August 1646, paying a fee of £10 and a leather bucket. In 1648 he became a Common Councillor, but paid 3s. 4d. to be excused serving as a constable; in 1649 he was chosen Junior Chamberlain, and served as a Chamberlain of Oxford until 1660. In 1665 he was taxed on three hearths in his house in St. Ebbe's parish. At this time his son Thomas, who had taken up the freedom by patrimony on 12 September 1664, paid for two hearths in a house in the parish of St. Peter's Bayley. The younger Wrench in his turn served as a Common Councillor from 1678 but in 1686 asked to be acquitted of his place as he finds it difficult to make attendance; he paid a fine of £5 to be free from further service. In 1696 he was taxed on ten windows in his house in St. Ebb's, which probably implies that he had now inherited his father's house.

While Thomas Wrench junior was still in charge, the gardens were visited by Zacharias Conrad von Uffenbach during his stay at Oxford in 1710. On 25 September Uffenbach 'went into another garden, called the Paradise Garden. This is almost at one extreme end of the town at an inn, behind which by the waterside are countless little retreats, close to each other, of cropped hedge, where the Fellows drink in the summer. The inn itself is furnished in the same fashion. The garden is otherwise nothing in particular and is chiefly dedicated to cookery, though it has fine fruit trees and yews. Never have I ever seen such a mass of these last together, and they include a complete plantation of young trees.' At Oxford, as around London, the demand for yews was at a peak and provided the most profitable item in ornamental gardening. The fruit trees, as was to be expected, were the other mainstay of the nursery side of the business. The pleasure gardens behind the inn may have been run in connection with the market garden and nursery; this would have been a precedent for several later instances of the running of garden centres as adjuncts to tea gardens around London.

Thanks to the curiosity of Thomas Hearne we know a good deal of the family life of the Wrench and Tagg household. In 1733 Hearne recorded: 'Mr Tagg of Paradise Garden, Oxford, was born 4 Feb. 1694. His wife is E(lizabeth) Tagg, whose maiden name was Hunsdon. She is a Berkshire woman & had several sisters. They were all well bred and their father was a substantial Farmer.' This was, of course, Tagg's second wife. His first wife Anne, the widow of his old master Wrench, had died by 1725, leaving two daughters by her first marriage. Hearne wrote of a Mr Whiteside that he 'hath a great Affection for Miss Debby (Deborah) Wrench, & sees her often. She is the eldest of the two Daughters of the late Mr Wrench and Mrs Wrench of Paradice Garden. She is very pretty, as is also her younger Sister, Miss Molly Wrench. Indeed, Molly is said to be the prettiest, tho' look'd upon as not so good natured as Miss Debby.' The girls' stepfather was married again on 29 April 1726 'in Goosey Church in Berkshire to a very agreeable, good natured young woman, Mrs. Hundson (who hath several Sisters), of Spersholt in that County'. Elizabeth Tagg long survived her husband, carrying on the business with the help of her son James Tagg until she died at 83 on 17 January 1779.

The garden had certainly become an important nursery before 1736, when Thomas Tagg supplied the Earl of Litchfield with trees for Ditchley Park. Large English elms cost 2s. each, others 1s. 6d.; a walnut was also 1s. 6d., but chestnuts, Scotch firs and 'abeals' (white, or possibly black poplars), and an 'apricock' were 1s. each, and Golden Pippins only 2s. for four. The firm continued until the death in 1837 of a second Thomas Tagg, who had about 1815 issued an important catalogue showing that his business was abreast of the times in all departments, including greenhouse plants and Florists' flowers as well as trees and shrubs and the traditional fruit trees. The first Thomas Tagg had rented 'many other places about Oxford' as well as Paradise Gardens, and the nursery must have continued to expand in his son's time, for in 1784 the City agreed that 'the city pound in Paradise is to be taken down since Mr. Tagg wishes to enclose the ground on which it stands near his property'. James Tagg, who entered the freedom in 1751, held many civic offices and had to take part in commissions to assess prices of houses and farm compensation. On 18 September 1773 Jackson's *Oxford Journal* reported that a peach tree full of fruit in Alderman Treacher's garden had recently produced a nectarine. 'Nurseryman Tagg said he never knew such a thing before.' Five years later the newspaper reported that he had been a steward at the annual meeting of gardeners and florists to prosecute robbers, held at the Blue Boar. The problem of crimes against nurseries will recur.

Two interesting questions concerning the Wrench family remain, but to them there is as yet no certain answer. Was the elder Thomas Wrench, probably born about 1620-25, related to Thomas Rench, also spelt Wrench, the Fulham nurseryman, born about 1631? If not, it is a curious coincidence that two near contemporaries of the same name (for the spelling at that period was quite immaterial) should both have been prominent in the founding of modern commercial horticulture. Secondly, what connection was there between Jacob Wrench the son of Thomas Wrench the younger of

Oxford, and his namesake who founded the great London seedsman's firm of Jacob Wrench & Sons, which was at the Three Wheat Sheaves, 126 Lower Thames Street, from about 1750 to 1830 and then in King William Street until 1905. Here identity looks very likely, but has not hitherto been proved.

Paradise Gardens were not the only early nursery in the Oxford district. Ralph Austen (died 1676), of Magdalen College and proctor of the University in 1630, later holder of the offices of deputy-registrary and registrary to visitors, was a prolific writer, especially on the culture of fruit-trees. Shortly before his death he was said to have 'now very lately taken in twenty seven Acres of ground, to enlarge his former Nurseries'. He already had a small nursery by 1652 when he was writing his *Treatise of Fruit-Trees* and described himself as a 'Practiser in the Art of Planting'. Austen was a typical visionary of the Commonwealth period, combining theological speculation and exhortation with the new doctrine of material profit and 'improvement'. Less famous than his contemporaries Samuel Hartlib and Walter Blith, he was more directly concerned with silviculture and horticulture than they, and to some extent anticipated the attitude taken up by Evelyn in his *Sylva.*

With the exception of Oxford, York was the earliest important centre of nursery gardening. In all probability its nursery trade really took priority over that of Oxford, for it was a real capital city for the whole of the North over several centuries. Disregarding the earlier part of the Middle Ages, York was actually made the effective capital of the whole country by Edward I in 1298, during the Scottish Wars. For six years on end the law courts sat in York, and thereafter for 20 years in scattered groups until near the end of the 14th century. With the evidence for the trade of gardener in medieval York we have dealt already (see p.35), and can pass to the 16th century. Outside Micklegate Bar, in a suburban district which remained a favourite for orchards and gardens for the next 300 years, a highly significant lease was granted in 1541. On 25 November a parcel of ground 'lying of the west syde of the dwellyng house of Robert Elden without Mikellythe Barre' was granted to Elden for 21 years, on the condition that he 'promyseth to graft and set fruyt treys of the sayd ground and to leyff them growyng of the sayd grownd at the end' of the term.

The former monastic sites had certainly included orchards and there is some evidence that these continued in existence. In 1560 at the death of Alderman Richard Goldthorp he was found to have held the sites of Clementhorpe Priory and of St. Andrew's Priory; at the latter one close was called The Orchard. The site of the Blackfriars at Toft Green, and an Orchard there, belonged to Alderman Thomas Mosley when he died in 1624. This last orchard must have been at least part of the site of the Friars' Gardens, later to become famous as the first important trade nursery in York. The gardens are shown in detail, and named, on Benedict Horsley's plan of York surveyed in 1694. At that time they were still in the occupation of Matthew Wharton or Quarton, gardener, who was buried on 7 April 1695 at the parish church of St. Martin-cum-Gregory. Wharton's children had been baptized there from 1676 onwards, and it seems probable that he was the occupier of 'ye Fryers' who had been rated anonymously from 1665 onwards. When Matthew Wharton died his only son, Jacob, was 12 years old and the lease was given up, to be granted to George Telford, founder of the famous firm. Jacob Wharton took up the freedom of York in 1713 as a draper, but in fact was a gardener, taking apprentices in that capacity in 1722-26. In 1705 he married Mary Wright of Sowerby, and their son Matthew (c. 1710-1784) became his father's apprentice in 1726 and took up the freedom in 1733. The second Matthew Wharton had his nursery in part of the site of the Greyfriars below the Castle, and with John Bentham was in 1731 paid £3. 19s. 6d. for 47 elms and 47 limes 'planted in the New Walk in St. George's Close', the first part of York's fashionable promenade along the bank of the Ouse.

Wharton was a victim of malicious crime on a grand scale. The issue of the *York Courant* for 20 March 1760 carried the advertisement that: 'Whereas last Night, or this Morning, some Person or Persons broke into a Garden belonging to Matthew Wharton, out of Castlegate Postern, and cut down 463 Elms, from five to twelve Feet high; 335 Cherry Stocks; 4 Damsins; 19 Standard Pears; and cut up Part of a large Flat of Pease growing in the said Garden — Whoever can give notice of he, she or they that committed the said Offence, shall upon Conviction of the Offender or Offenders, receive ten Guineas Reward of Matthew Wharton'. An official notice issued later from Whitehall was inserted in the *London Gazette* on 29 April, offering pardon to anyone turning King's Evidence. This was reprinted in the *York Courant* of 3 June, with offers of a reward of 15 guineas from Wharton, and of £20 from the Common Clerk of York. It does not appear that the criminal was ever caught, but Wharton presumably became disheartened; four years later he left his house between Castlegate Lane and Friar Walls, sold his stock, and gave notice that he was carrying on business at his shop in Pavement. He lived on until 5 February 1784, and was buried at St. Mary Castlegate.

The story of the Telford family and the rise of Friars' Gardens to the most distinguished nursery in the North has been told in detail elsewhere, but a slight recapitulation must be given. George Tillforth, Tilford or Telford, gardener, took up the freedom of York in 1684, the first person of his surname who has been traced in the city. The name is known in the south-eastern part of the West Riding, and there are hints of association with Leeds. George and his wife Ellen settled in the parish of St. Martin-cum-Gregory, Micklegate, and their children were baptized there from 1684 to 1695. At George's death in November 1704 his son George was only 17, and he died in January 1710/11. By this time a younger brother John Telford was turned 21, and it was he who took charge after his mother's death in 1714. In the following year he became free of York and he had a distinguished civic career as Commoner for Micklegate Ward in 1723, Chamberlain in the same year, Sheriff in 1751-52 and Alderman in 1756. Resigning his gown at the end of 1761 on account of ill health, he seems then to have transferred the business to his son John Telford (1716-1770), but lived on for ten years, until 12 November 1771, outliving his son by nearly a year and seeing the firm safely in the hands of his two grandsons John Telford (1744-1830) and George Telford (1749-1834).

The first John Telford won fame when he was described by Francis Drake in 1736, in the classic history of York, *Eboracum*, as 'a worthy citizen, and whose knowledge in the mystery of gardening renders him of credit to his profession; being one of the first that brought our northern gentry into the method of planting and raising all kinds of forest trees, for use and ornament'. Drake (1696-1771), who settled in York in 1718 and became city surgeon in 1727, was later elected F.R.S. and undoubtedly had excellent sources of information. As a general truth, his statement implies that the new fashion of planting came in during the quarter-century 1710-35. We must, however, distinguish between this vogue for planting forest trees, and the earlier wave of interest in extending the northern range of fruit. In the edition of Camden's *Britannia* published by Edmund Gibson in 1695 this earlier fashion was mentioned: 'The Improvements in Tillage at *Rock* (in Northumberland) by John Salkeld, Esq.; and in Gardening and Fruitery at *Falladon* by Samuel Salkeld, Gent. (both in the Parish of Emildon) ought here to be mention'd, as *Fineries* hardly to be equall'd on the North-side of Tyne. The latter is the more observable, because an eminent Author of this Age will hardly allow any good *Peaches, Plumbs, Pears*, &c. to be expected beyond *Northamptonshire*; whereas Fruit is produced here in as great variety and perfection as most places in the South.' We have seen that York actually had vineyards in the 14th century, and the far less propitious town of Northallerton had in 1789 a giant vine growing outdoors. It covered 137 square yards and had a stem nearly four feet round just above the ground. As it was reckoned at the time to be about 150 years old it was presumably planted shortly before the Civil War.

John Telford (1689-1771) can be traced in surviving accounts as supplying seeds and trees to various northern estates from 1729; in 1731 he subscribed to the first edition of Philip Miller's *Gardener's Dictionary* and in 1733 to Stephen Switzer's journal, *The Practical Husbandman and Planter*. He was an improver as well as a nurseryman, for on 24 January 1737/8 the corporation of York 'ordered that *Mr. John Telford* shall have the profitts of the Admittance of Horses at the Knavesmire for one year', for his pains in draining and improving the Common for the benefit of Micklegate Ward, and making it proper for the Horse Races. The Knavesmire had first been levelled and rolled for racing in 1730 and the first meeting was in 1731, but must have been found unsatisfactory because of the sluggish watercourse that ran down the middle of the sward. The second John Telford (1716-1770), who took over on his father's retirement in 1762, carried on a flourishing business but died at 54 'after a long and tedious Illness . . . greatly and justly regretted by all his Acquaintance . . . an eminent Nurseryman and Seedsman in this City. He is succeeded in the business by his sons John and George Telford, who purpose to carry it on in all its Branches as formerly'.

The brothers John and George Telford distinguished themselves by producing what seems to have been the first catalogue of nursery stock to be priced throughout, at any rate in England. It is dated 1775, but may possibly have been anticipated by a few months by the catalogue of Robert Anderson of Edinburgh referred to in his advertisement of 4 February that year as being something of a kind 'never before attempted by any person in this Country'. The two lists, though of the same general type, are evidently quite independent of one another, and struck out a new line in the development and advertisement of the trade. The Telford catalogue has been reprinted in facsimile, with tentative identifications, in *Early Gardening Catalogues,* along with the slightly later catalogue of the rival firm of William and John Perfect of Pontefract (see also Appendix XI.A).

The Pontefract nurseries seem to have started as an offshoot of the local industry of liquorice-growing, and owed much of their success to the position of the town by the Old Great North Road. Although the claim has been made that members of the Perfect family were growing liquorice at Pontefract in the reign of Elizabeth I, they cannot be traced in any local records until after 1700. Among the oldest tombs in the churchyard were formerly those of John Perfect, gardener, 1722 and of Noah Perfect, 1723. Noah Perfect appears as a Pontefract voter in a poll-book of 1708 and so had presumably bought a substantial holding before that date. It was at the end of 1717 that John Perfect was paid £16. 13s. 4d. for limes and elms sent to Studley Royal, while John Aislabie's gardener William Fisher on 3 March following had £4. 17s. 6d. 'for bringing of trees from Pomfret'. A much bigger bill for 'Trees &c.', for £73. 12s. 0d., was paid to John Kirke in 1719, and it is likely that this order was sent from London by the founder of the 'Cromwell's Garden Nursery' in Brompton, hard by Brompton Park. John Perfect, however, received further orders in later years. Aislabie eventually came to regard Perfect's prices as extravagant, and from 1729 took to sending the regular orders mostly to Telford in York.

It is impossible here to follow out in detail the ramifications of the Perfect pedigree over some five generations, until they sold the business in 1810. Several of them were highly regarded as knowledgeable gardeners, and they were subscribers to most of the standard reference books as were the Telfords in York. The second John Perfect (died 1764), Mayor of Pontefract in 1737 and 1754, on 24 July 1730 wrote to Switzer a long letter, subsequently printed in *The Practical Husbandman* for May 1733, giving the fullest details of the cultivation of liquorice. Though disguised by initials, Switzer makes the identity of J. P. quite clear by stating that he was 'a Person well known in the North for his Skill in Nurseries and Planting of all Kinds', and by printing his address, Pomfret. Among the interesting information in the letter is the fact that at the time the common labourers who worked the liquorice garths took one shilling per day and two drinkings, amounting in all to 14d. or 15d. About the same time Perfect was designing a plan for the gardens at Nostell Priory.

The third John Perfect (1717-1762) dying young, the firm was continued by his brother William Perfect (died 1785), some of whose letters survive, either printed or among estates muniments. On 26 September 1759 he wrote to William Banks, the father of Sir Joseph Banks, sending him diagrams of a glass case to strike young oranges in at Revesby Abbey, Lincolnshire. Perfect, in signing 'for brother and self', apologised for the roughness of the sketches as 'we are not draftsmen'. In 1765 the *Museum Rusticum* printed a correspondence on Timothy Grass, which had been praised by (Bartholomew) Rocque of Fulham, but which Perfect, after experiment, thought hardly worth growing. Introducing him to the reader is the statement that he was 'a very justly famous gardener . . . the *Rocque* and *Miller* of the north, and his gardens at *Pontefract*, about a mile from the great road betwixt *London* and *York* are a noble collection of every thing useful and curious in the store-house of the gardener, the nursery-man and seedsman.'

The chance survival of bills and other documents makes it difficult to be sure of the precise period when the great northern estates became mainly dependent on regional sources of supply. For the latest exotics it was always necessary to go to London, or for the provincial nurseryman to do so as intermediary; but for most purposes the period of transition to regional self-support was ending between 1725 and 1750. In 1692-94 the gardens of Temple Newsam near Leeds had to get their seeds and fruit trees sent up from the London area from William Cox, doubtless the elder Kew nurseryman (died 1704) whom we have already met. As might be expected from his firm, 'half a pack of hot spur pese' (2s. 6d.) and '1 qvort of Egg pese' (1s.) figured in the first order. In the course of three years he also sent apricot, cherry, peach, pear, plum, and quince trees, apple trees 'of several sortes' to the number of 116 and then 13 more; also vines, nectarines, and 24 Dutch 'govsbere and Covrrent plantes'. Elsewhere the ancient method of do-it-yourself in a private nursery was still at work.

At Kiveton Park in South Yorkshire, for instance, there was a memorandum made in 1708 of 'ye numbers of Forest trees & Plants in ye nursery Aug. 26th 1708:-

Number of Limes fitt for removing next		limes
Under ye Cikamoores pretty large	13 ⎞	
In ye nursery of different sizes but all	⎬	253
fitt to plant out next season	240 ⎠	
Limes in ye Nursery wch at this time		
twelve moneths season will bee fitt to	--------	200
plant out		
Limes for two yeares season	--------------------	250
Elmes fitt for planting out this season		260
ditto for ye next season after this		050
Cikamores fitt to plant out this season		040
Chesnutts but not yett fitt to plant out		030
Ashes of about 2 yeares growth		120
Oakes of ditto or more		350

There are no forest trees in ye Pond garden quarters
vnless some few Cicamoores
But there are severall young wallnutt trees
some Mulberry trees young
some quince trees ditto there & in ye Nursery

some Cherries trees & many Cherry stocks
some apple trees lately grafted & many crabb stocks
some Pare trees & some pare tree stocks
Ewes & hollies in every quarter of ye Pond garden
& in many places besides as in ye old & new orchard.

In later years Kiveton bought named varieties of apples from John Perfect of Pontefract (in 1744), but the main source of supply for seeds and trees was Francis Noble (died 1756) of Newark-upon-Trent. Noble was already in business as a gardener by 1720, and in 1739 and 1752 was Mayor of Newark. In 1743-44 he was supplying a good selection of roses and flowering shrubs for the gardens at Burton near Lincoln. The Newark nursery passed to his son Michael Noble, who had earlier helped his father in the business. Other early Nottinghamshire nurseries were at Blyth near the Yorkshire border (before 1718); Mansfield (by 1717); and Worksop. At Hodsack Woodhouse in Blyth parish was the substantial garden of William Leeson (died 1722), an inventory of whose stock survives (see Appendix V). The Mansfield nursery was run by William Aram, who was born c.1689 and probably related to the Nottinghamshire gardener Peter Aram (died 1735) who was assistant to George London in Bishop Compton's gardens at Fulham Palace and later gardener at Newby Hall, Yorkshire, to Sir Edward Blackett from 1694, and at the end of his life gardener at Ripley Castle. Henry Cowlishaw (died 1777) belonged to a later generation, but by 1746 was supplying from his ground at Carlton in Lindrick north of Worksop (and close to the site of Leeson's nursery at Hodsack Woodhouse) large numbers of firs at 5d. each for the gardens of Lady Oxford at Welbeck Abbey. Later he sold quantities of larch and Spanish chestnuts. In 1776 John Winter and John Fox, both of Blyth, went into partnership as nurserymen, the ground belonging to Winter but Fox 'to do the Working part as far as he is able'.

Not much is known of other northern nurseries founded before 1760. The claim that Messrs. Matheson of Morpeth go back to a nursery founded there about 1689 has so far proved incapable of substantiation, though Morpeth is an ancient nursery centre as well as the birthplace of William Turner (c. 1508-1568), our first great botanist and reputedly the introducer of lucerne to England. With George Dale, who founded the great nursery at Hebburn Quay in Jarrow by 1734 we shall deal later in considering the firm of Falla. The neighbourhood of Gateshead soon became a centre of nurseries, among them one notable rival to the firm of Dale, later Falla: that of William Joyce (died 1767). In 1754 Joyce was advertising that he had fruit trees, shrubs, seeds etc. 'in Gateshead as cheap as in London' and three years later that, besides the best sorts of Fruit Trees, many sorts of Bulbous and fibrous rooted Flowers, and all sorts of Garden Seeds, he and his son Stanley were selling 'Beach, Ash, Walnuts, Spanish & horse Chesnuts, Hornbeam, Limes, Abeals, Poplars, Birch & Larches, Cedars, Pines and Firs, Oaks, Elms, Plains' and 230 different kinds of Flowering Shrubs and evergreens.

Several other northern centres seem to have got their first substantial nurseries during the second quarter of the 18th century. At Beverley the firm which by the 1790's was Benjamin & Samuel Sigston of Flemingate had taken its rise with John Sigston the elder, free of Beverley in 1733; John Sigston junior took up the freedom in 1760, Samuel Sigston in 1767, Benjamin in 1787. The Ripon firm of Adcock was started by John Adcock of York, free in 1733, son of John Adcock a linenweaver (free of the city 1705). The younger John took an apprentice in York in 1739, but by 1741 was resident in Ripon, where he was still living until 1784. His younger brother William Adcock, free of York in 1740, was a head gardener at Thirkleby and later at Whixley, and in 1768 was a founder member of the Ancient Society of York Florists. More shadowy are the beginnings of the trade in Lincoln, where Robert Gildon seems to have been a seedsman in 1743. At Derby the principal firm around 1800 was that of Joseph Wilson, doing a flourishing trade in the period 1798-1824 and later. In 1827 this was said to be 'the oldest establishment of this kind in the county'; the family of Messrs. Wilson 'have carried on the business with great respectability nearly a century'.

When we turn from the North to the other regions of England a rather different picture emerges. This probably indicates a fundamental distinction of social structure. Whereas York and the greater towns of the North and North Midlands were always relatively broadly based, in most other parts of the country there was no basis of general popular demand to back up the needs of the great estates. The simultaneous production of general priced catalogues in Edinburgh and in York in 1775, reflects the fact that not merely common interests united high and low in Scotland and in the northern counties of England, but that almost everybody was concerned with thrift as a basic virtue and necessity. This appears also as a fundamental factor in the economics of the trade. Thrift might be penny-pinching when it came to cautious shopping around, but it was usually coupled with a strict sense of obligation in paying bills. In going through long series of vouchers of north-country estates it is striking that most bills are receipted within the year, or at any rate within 12 months of presentation. In the case of the Home Counties and much of the rest of England it seems, on the contrary, to have been an ingrained habit to keep tradesmen generally, nurserymen included, waiting even many years for their money. The wonder is, not that so many firms went bankrupt, but that business could be carried on at all.

There certainly were trade nurseries here and there at quite early dates. We know of the activities of John Rea, a country gentleman of Norton's End at Kinlet in the extreme south of Shropshire, who in 1665 had been active in the supply of plants for 40 years, taking his start back to the opening of the reign of Charles I. Rea was a very great gardener, but as a nurseryman chiefly a florist concerned with the specialist flowers, notably the fashionable bulbs. In any case his operations seem to have been closely linked to his work as a garden adviser to Lord Gerard of Bromley. Rea died in October 1677, leaving the nursery to his daughter Minerva who had married the Revd. Samuel Gilbert, chaplain to Lady Gerard and author of *The Florist's Vade Mecum* (1683), long regarded as one of the principal standard works on the subject.

In spite of the importance of the Kinlet nursery, it does not appear to have persisted for any length of time after its founder's death, or to have established a regional tradition. It cannot, however, be a mere coincidence that Ashley in North Staffordshire, little more than a mile from the great mansion of Gerard's Bromley, had an important nursery of fruit trees in 1683-86. Richard Bates, the Ashley gardener, was then supplying Edward Mainwaring of Whitmore with a substantial variety of fruit and also with garden seeds. Mainwaring's list of his fruit trees and vines from Ashley as planted by 1685 includes a high proportion of those varieties which Henry Wise set down some 15 years later.

The special relationship of John Rea's nursery to the important gardens of Lord Gerard and of Sir Thomas Hanmer (1612-1678) was not without parallels. Something of the sort seems to have been associated with Wilton House. In 1677 Anthony Lawrence, who has already been quoted on the subject of Ralph Austen's nurseries near Oxford, mentions this in a passage of considerably wider interest:-

'One said, that if we had one skilful and diligent Nursery-man, who had a complete Nursery of all sorts of good fruit, and of the best Vines that agree best with this Climate, and Mulberry Trees and wholsom trees for the avenues of Cities, Towns, and fair Mansions; That one such Nursery within ten or fifteen miles in all the Vales of these three united Kingdoms, would make all these Plantations spread apace, and amount to the value of Millions yearly. I answered, That it was now doing . . .' Lawrence went on: 'And here I shew, How any Gentleman may freely furnish all his neighbourhood, even Cottages (who cannot send to Mr. *Rose*) with the best Vines. . . . I am sure, that many in Wiltshire, Hampshire, Dorsetshire, and Sommersetshire are obliged and the richer for the famous Garden of Wilton, and for the goodly Nurseries about *Salisbury*. And his Majesties Gardiner, Mr. *Rose*, was an obliging Example for his sale of the best Vines, and the fittest for our Climate.'

Lawrence's letter, from which this is an extract, was contributed to a collection otherwise written by John Beale, D.D., F.R.S., and published in 1677 under the title of *Nurseries, Orchards, Profitable Gardens, and Vineyards encouraged*. Beale too referred to the example set by Mr. Rose in 1666, in offering Vines at reasonable rates, and further on asks the rhetorical question: 'Where are the *Seeds*, and *Seeds-men*?'. To this we know the answer: in London, at the Strand Bridge shop of The Naked Boy, kept by William Lucas, 'milliner'. But it is evident, both from Lucas's treatment of the seeds and plants as a side-issue and from Beale's implication of a felt want, that commercial organization of the trade can only just have begun. Lawrence and Beale, following the line taken by Ralph Austen, evidently expected a widespread founding of local nurseries, and expansion of some already in existence, mostly linked to the gardens of great estates. What happened was quite different. The answer given by history was the founding, four years later, of the immense co-operative venture at Brompton Park. This acted as a blanket and stifled the opportunities for successful local enterprise for more than a generation.

The deaths of Bishop Compton in 1713 and of George London early in 1714, followed by the retirement of Henry Wise later in the year, led to a breakdown in the London monopoly. The inept management of Brompton Park by the new lessees William Smith and Joseph Carpenter, notwithstanding their training under London and Wise, together with the excessively high cost of long-distance transport, at last produced the explosion of nurseries which Lawrence and Beale had expounded. The firms so far traced were scattered very widely. Not very far outside the London area was Colchester (55 miles), which by the latter part of the century had several businesses well established. The oldest of these was that of the Agnes or Agnis family, probably founded by Thomas Agnis who died in 1733, and carried on until 1808 by his son Robert Agnis (died 1782) and grandson John Agnis, who in 1793 was county freeholder and nurseryman and seedsman. His will of 1808 refers to his gardens as The Moores or Moore Grounds in the parish of St. Botolph. This was presumably the tenement and land called Childwell Moor in St. Botolph's which his grandfather had bought from Edward Raynham, since his father Robert had left him the stock in trade and the estate called Childwell with Cross-path Field. Among florists the family of Stow, fulling millers of Lexden next to Colchester, was famous through much of the century. By 1748 John Stow was noted for his auriculas, brought to even greater perfection by Henry Stow (died 1771) within the next 20 years. 'The connoisseurs allowed (these auriculas) to be the finest in the British Dominions, if not in all Europe, some of them having no less than a hundred and thirty-three blossoms upon one stem.' Henry subsequently became 'as famous . . . for fine tulips'. Going deeper into East Anglia, a tree nursery was founded at Woodbridge, Suffolk in 1749 by William Woods. In 1798 John and William Woods, nurserymen, were county freeholders there. Sold by their descendants in 1897 this became the nucleus of the well-known modern business of Notcutts.

In the opposite direction Southampton, 77 miles from London, could get locally grown trees in 1745 when planting of the famous Avenue began at the Cross. They were bought from George Irwin of All Saints parish who by 1743 had a nursery in Giddy Bridge Field on the north of East Marlands abutting on the London Road. Irwin was still occupying the nursery as late as 1760 and was living in All Saints parish after retirement in 1775. Much further off, at Crewkerne in Somerset, a nursery is said to have been started about 1728, probably the firm which was Webber & Pierce in the early 19th century and apparently taken over in 1848 by John Scott to become the Royal Nurseries at Merriott. It has to be admitted that virtually nothing is known of the activities of this western nursery before Victorian times.

Though a good deal more substantial than the early history of the Crewkerne establishment, the beginnings of that at Exeter depend mainly upon the traditional story given by Loudon. Though doubtless correct in outline, the details are hard to reconcile with established dates of the family

of Lucombe, Luccombe or Luckombe. They were another tribe of centenarians, for on 3 March 1758 Mr. John Luckombe died at Exeter aged 105
years, while the William Lucombe who is said by Loudon to have been the
founder died at 98 in 1794. Here again was a case of a nursery business
originating as an offshoot of estate improvement. Thomas Ball, F.R.S.,
planting at Mamhead with evergreen oaks, employed as his gardener William
Lucombe, who by 1720 is said to have started the nursery at St. Thomas's by
Exeter. The business, with a seedsman's shop at New Bridge, Exeter, was
Luccombe & Son by 1795 and had become Lucombe, Pince & Co. before
1828. Robert Taylor Pince (c. 1804-1871) married Anne Lucombe Ford
(1790-1861), who was the granddaughter of the second William Lucombe,
the 'Son' of 1795. The founder may well have been the William Luccombe of
Alphington, two miles south of Exeter and adjacent to St. Thomas's who had
licence to marry Mary Coule, spinster, in February 1715/16; the son almost
certainly his namesake of Powderham, gardener, who was to marry Mary
Bennett in January 1735/36.

The Exeter firm, which later became celebrated for camellias and for the
introduction of rare exotics, as well as for heaths, owed its fame largely to the
happy accident of 1763 that produced the hybrid Lucombe or Exeter oak. The
date, usually given as 1765, was probably two years earlier since 1774 is the year
assigned to a letter preserved among the Lee of Hartwell papers. Written from
Mamhead on 7 September by John Claxton to Sir William Lee, Bart., of
Hartwell, Bucks., this narrates a first-hand story of the tree. 'I took a ride to St.
Thomas's near Exeter to see a new species of Oak called the Luccombe Oak
from the name of the person who first discovered, & propagated it. It is a very
quick grower, the stem straight & tapering, the bark smooth: the wood is of a
close grain, very hard & ponderous: the tree is an Evergreen tho' it sometimes
sheds its leaves in a severe winter or a very bleak exposure; it has hitherto been
propagated only by grafts, having born no acorns, tho' it makes a shew of them
every year. I saw the parent tree which is about five & thirty feet high tho' only
eleven years old, and several of six years growth that were from sixteen to
eighteen feet high. Mr. Luccombe told me that he had sent some young trees for
the purpose of grafting to the North of England, Wales and Ireland; and had
received accounts of their succeeding; this encouraged me to bespeak six plants
which I beg you will do me the favour to accept of: they are to be sent some time
in October (of which I will give you advice) by the Exeter Waggon to Mrs.
Morice's, and I have desired her to forward them to you immediately by the
Aylesbury Waggon. The grafts are not to be made till April, they are to be set on
stocks (of) common English Oak of four, five or six years growth; the stocks
should be cut down very low, almost to the surface of the ground; small cuttings
from two to six inches in length do best. If these plants succeed, as I hope they
will, I can by Mr. Temple's means procure more another year, as likewise some
for Ld. Nuneham if he should wish to have any.' The sending of young trees to
the North is confirmed by the entry of the Devonshire or Lucombe Oak in the
1775 catalogue of Telford of York, and this in turn confirms the earlier date of
1763 for the first seedling.

Bristol was to become a great nursery centre, but there is surprisingly little evidence for the trade until the latter part of the 18th century. In 1480 William Worcestre mentioned the Great Orchard, and Millerd's plan of 1673 names and marks Hobson's Gardens to the east of the church of St. James in the area now between Horse Fair and Bond Street, but there is nothing to show what kind of gardens were maintained. Some ten miles to the north of Bristol, at the little village of Tytherington in Gloucestershire, a small nursery was started in 1714 by John Berry (died 1727). Owing to the fortunate survival of the detailed pleadings in a tithe suit brought against Berry by his vicar in 1721, and of Berry's will and probate inventory, we are given a clear picture of his standing and activities. He must have kept a haberdasher's and general shop in a house with four other rooms as well as a kitchen and outhouse. When he made his will, 'being aged and sick', in 1726, he held both freehold and leasehold properties, some in Frampton Cotterell and in Stowell as well as at Tytherington. His son-in-law James Pullen, gardener, and his eldest daughter Sarah Pullen were to share 'all my moveable Trees at Stowell', while Sarah was to be executrix and was left 'my Silver Tankard, my Silver Cupp, my Silver Spoones with my Clock and Case, all my Shop Goods, Bookes, Booke Debts, all my Fruite Trees, Greene Trees, Flowring Trees and Trees and Flowers in the Home Garden'.

From the tithe suit, in which the vicar claimed that Berry had sold quite large numbers of fruit trees and forest and ornamental trees each year from 1714 to 1721, it appears that fairly precise records had been kept. These showed that Berry had on the average yearly numbers of about 150 apples, 100 pears, 200 to 400 cherries, up to 30 plums, 80 walnuts, and a few apricots, filberts, medlars, nectarines and peaches. He admitted only to very small numbers of bay, cypress and fir, and to average yearly stocks of 100 holly, 50 laurustinus and 350 yew. The preponderance of the yew among ornamental trees is as noticeable in rural Gloucestershire as elsewhere, and shows where profits could be made by the nurseryman on the spot. Berry, though his gardening was a side-line and he was not a wealthy man — the valuation of his personal property for probate, doubtless a good deal below its market price, was £67. 16s. 10d. — was in his own humble way a pioneer of the provincial trade.

A much greater, but later, figure in the development of the trade in Gloucestershire was Henry Clark (c.1702-1778). Like so many others, Clark was a part-time nurseryman, though he began as gardener to Sir William Keyt, Bart., of Ebrington, some two miles east of Chipping Campden. Sir William had succeeded to the baronetcy in 1702, probably the year of Clark's birth, and died in September 1741, by which time Clark had been for some time his steward as well as gardener. He was a man of some education and wrote quite a good hand, but his spelling was atrocious as he himself admitted. In 1753, when he was over 50, he wrote: 'I have lived Long a nouf in the wourld to know a Little of itts ways and Coustombs and not so Long as to forgitt them . . . . I . . . miss but uery few points as I aime at, exsept spelling my meaning wright, which is oing to my misapplying in my youth, forgiue me

that'. This and many other letters by him, mostly written in his capacity of
steward to the (Burnt) Norton estate of Sir Dudley Ryder, have survived
among the manuscripts of the Earl of Harrowby, by whose kindness they are
quoted here (see Appendix VIII).

Most of what is known of Clark's work as a nurseryman is derived from his
long account rendered for plants supplied to Powell Snell, esq., of Guiting
Grange, in 1750-1755. Poor Clark was kept waiting 18 years for the
substantial total of £29. 8s., so that the change of emphasis in his career to
land agency and estate management is easily understood. The range of plants
he held in his nursery was very extensive for the period, and it appears that it
was only bulbs that he could not supply out of his own resources, but
obtained from London. It is uncertain whether the nursery was always at
Campden, for before the autumn of 1752, when he moved to the Court
House in 'Camden', his home had been at Norton, at any rate since soon after
Sir William Keyt's death. In 1759 Henry Clark was paid £23. 10s. for trees for
Warwick Castle, and in the next year £82. 6s. 6d. for 650 oaks, another 365
oaks, 80 North American oaks, and 754 elms for the Park there. It is a tribute
to the reputation of Clark as a nurseryman that the Earl of Warwick should
have patronized him, about 20 miles off, at the same time that he was buying
other trees for the Park from John Whittingham of Charterhouse by
Coventry, only some eight miles away. No reference to Clark's nursery has
been found later than 1760, but he may have kept it up until 1771 when he
suffered a severe illness from which, it seems, he was not expected to recover.
In the next year he gave up the post of steward to the Ryder estates, which
he had continued to hold under Nathaniel Ryder, son of Sir Dudley and in
1776 the first Lord Harrowby. Henry Clark died on 29 June 1778 aged 76
and was buried in Campden churchyard.

A CENTURY OF EXPANSION

IT WAS not only in the provinces that the nursery trade exploded soon after the beginning of the 18th century. Several factors of quite different kinds contributed towards a rapid development around London. Just as the Parliamentarian victory in the Civil War, the rule of Cromwell and the puritan faction had led to the establishment of mercantilism and 'improvement' in agriculture, so did the second Revolution of 1688 introduce a new type of garden patronage. Starting at the top, the new king from Holland, William III, was genuinely interested in gardening and, as was natural, his new kingdom provided a quasi-colonial field for exploitation by the Dutch planters and bulb-growers. The new political outlook, however, tended to diminish the direct influence of the Court and to exalt that of the Whig oligarchy of great families, placed in the saddle for a hundred years. Though mostly English, these families were of rather different stamp and tastes from the ancient aristocracy. One of the richest was founded on the king's friendship by the new Earl of Portland, the Dutchman William Bentinck (c.1645-1709). What might be called the horticulture of ostentation, modelled indirectly on the Versailles of Louis XIV, was produced to suit these men.

A preponderant amount of the money spent went on gigantic palaces, such as Blenheim and Castle Howard, surrounded by the conversion of wide tracts of country into parks and gardens, with canals and waterworks made regardless of expense. Avenues even miles long were planted with thousands upon thousands of trees. The production of trees in such large numbers and capable of being moved at a substantial size, called forth exactly the kind of highly organized plantsmanship that could be provided by London & Wise at Brompton Park. The more specifically ornamental side of gardening was represented mainly by hundreds of yews, trained and clipped. Dutch bulbs filled the parterres in spring, and through all changes of horticultural fashion have continued to do so ever since. Technical improvements in the greenhouse and conservatory were at the same time leading to the cultivation of a wider range of exotics, only half-hardy or definitely tender. In this context the individual importance of Bishop Compton of London, himself a leading plotter of the Revolution, cannot be exaggerated. His key position in the politics of the 25 years before his death in 1713 meant that his advanced interests in rare introductions exerted the maximum possible influence in exalted circles.

Meanwhile, though in a secretive manner, another revolution was being planned, this time in taste. The strict regularity of garden planning in the Age of the Sun King began to appear in England as a strait-jacket. Little by little there grew up a cult of irregularity and a loosening, at first extremely slight, of the bonds of formalism. The surrounding landscape, of mainly natural origin, began to be let in, and paradoxically enough this seems first to have happened under the French gardener Beaumont at Levens, well before 1700. The fascinating story of the many successive stages of development has been told by Mr. Miles Hadfield in his magistral work, *A History of British Gardening,* and cannot even briefly be recapitulated. What it meant in terms of nursery gardening was, firstly, a growing demand for many more species of trees; secondly, for flowering shrubs and climbers; and thirdly for fibrous-rooted, or as we should say, herbaceous plants. There was also some demand for rarities, mainly for greenhouse and hothouse culture, but this was almost entirely confined, for two generations or more, to a few wealthy specialists. The satisfying of the new demands, not adequately fulfilled by Brompton Park after 1714, devolved upon a number of smaller but yet important nurseries founded in and around London.

Only two of the outstanding nurserymen of the old century, apart from London and Wise, survived into the new: George Rickets, who did not die until 1706; and William Darby, who lasted until about 1713. Darby's nursery for four years fell into the hands of a short-term tenant, but then came, about 1717, into the capable management of John Cowell, with much of Darby's important stock. Rickets' business, declining for years before his death, was probably quickly wound up by his son James. The gap was filled by Thomas Fairchild who, as we have seen, established himself in Hoxton about 1691. Fairchild was, it seems, the first nurseryman to be an outstanding botanist, and he remained at the forefront of his profession until his death on 10 October 1729 at the age of 63. Deservedly famous for his pioneering work in deliberate hybridization: Fairchild's Mule Pink of 1717 was his cross between Carnation and Sweet William, he still lacks a really adequate appreciation. In a lifetime shorter than that of many of the famous botanists and gardeners, he nevertheless crammed in work of outstanding importance in many fields. He is especially worthy of honour in that, unlike so many scientists, he had serious moral scruples about what he was doing. The production of new forms, even by the artificial mixing of those created, smacked to him of interference with the plan of the Creator.

It was probably with a view to discharging his soul of impiety that Fairchild in his will left £25 to the Trustees of the Charity Children of Hoxton and the Churchwardens to provide an annual interest of £1 for a sermon to be preached yearly on Tuesday in Whitsun week, on 'the wonderfull works of God in the Creation or on the certainty of the Resurrection of the dead proved by the certaine Change of the Animal and Vegetable parts of the Creation'. His worldly wisdom did not desert him, for this bequest was to revert to the Churchwardens of St. Giles Cripplegate in the event of default. Fairchild's will is of interest in other respects: he desired to be buried humbly 'in some Corner of the furthest Churchyard belonging to the said parish of St. Leonard Shoreditch where the poore people are usually buryed'. To the Charity Children of the parish he left £10, to 'my late servant

John Sampson' £5, to 'my servant Stephen Bert' one guinea. Among the legatees were 'my Cousin Richard Butt',[1] very likely the Kew nurseryman who was to have £30, and 'my friend Mr. Cateby', that is Mark Catesby (1679-1749) who was a witness, left a guinea to buy a ring. There were a number of other fairly substantial bequests to relatives, totalling some £500, and the residue including his lands, goods, Garden Stock and personal estate to his nephew Stephen Bacon. There was one important exception: 'my right and title to a subscription of a Booke belonging to the Society of Gardners subscribed thereto which I gave to my nephew John Bacon'. This clearly indicates that Fairchild was not himself, as has often been alleged, the real author of the *Catalogus Plantarum*, of which the first (and only) part was issued in the year after his death, with his name at the head of the Society.

Fairchild was all the same one of the chief movers of the project, and his own writings were considerable. Besides his well known paper on the circulation of the sap in plants, printed in the *Transactions* of the Royal Society, and his book *The City Gardener* (1722), he contributed quite largely to various periodical works run by Richard Bradley, F.R.S. Among these occasional papers one of the most valuable was the set of lists of the plants in flower in his nursery, month by month from April 1722 to March 1723 (for the full text see Appendix IV). These lists give a more precise idea than any other source of exactly what had been induced to flower and was in effective commercial cultivation. After Fairchild's death his letter of 4 October 1724 on the culture of the 'Lilium Sarmiense or Guernsea Lilie' was printed by Switzer in *The Practical Husbandman* for May 1733. As long afterwards as 1747 'the late Mr. Fairchild's White Lily' was chosen for engraving as Plate 5 of *The Compleat Florist.*

The nursery was carried on for some years by Fairchild's nephew Stephen Bacon (1709-1734), who advertised on 15 November 1729 that he had 'managed his Uncle's Business with Success for these several Years past'. He was a precocious youth for he was still under 21 when Fairchild's will was made, but had attained his majority in time to obtain probate on 13 October 1729. Bacon was a member of the Society of Gardeners in 1730 and in 1733 subscribed to Robert Furber's *Short Introduction to Gardening*, but was dead by the following 7 March, when his wife Mary Bacon obtained administration of his property. The nursery was then taken over by John Simpson, possibly the same man as the John Sampson who had left Fairchild's service by 1729; but it came to an end in 1740 when, on 12 July, the sale of stock was advertised of 'curious flowers and plants of Mr. John Simpson deceased at the Garden of the late Mr. Fairchild of Hoxton'. The Spanish Jasmine of 'Sampson' of Hoxton was engraved as Plate 3 of *The Compleat Florist* in 1747. So ended, after a life of barely 50 years, one of the most influential nurseries in the whole history of British gardening.

1. Fairchild's mother was Ann Butt when she married Thomas Shepherd at Aldbourne in May 1659; after Shepherd's death in February 1664 she was married to John Fairchild on 25 June 1665.

The mantle fell upon some of the other members of the Society of Gardeners. Apart from Fairchild, 14 of them signed the preface of the union-catalogue of their stock, and most were nurserymen of whose careers something is known. Three men were of outstanding fame: the nurserymen Robert Furber (c. 1674-1756) of Kensington and Christopher Gray (c. 1694-1764) of Fulham, and Philip Miller (1691-1771), Curator of the Chelsea Physic Garden from 1722. Among the rest were Stephen Bacon, Francis Hunt and his brother Samuel, of Putney, and Moses James the seedsman, of Stangate, Lambeth. Although the Society did not manage to bring out further parts of the great *Catalogus,* the work of registering the plants in cultivation was in fact continued by the publication of Miller's folio *Gardener's Dictionary* in 1731, and by its many later editions. Miller had already brought out the smaller but none the less important book of 1724, *The Gardener's and Florist's Dictionary.* Furber made a mark by issuing what appear to have been the first book-form trade catalogues in 1727, followed by *Twelve Months of Flowers,* with splendid plates, in 1730, and by *A Short Introduction to Gardening* in 1733.

Furber's nursery at Kensington Gore had probably been founded very soon after 1700, when he was 26; at the age of 32 he married Mary Everton, and in 1722 their son Wiliam was apprenticed to Philip Miller of Chelsea at a premium of £4. Miller remained on close terms with Robert Furber, some of whose lists he printed in his dictionary of 1724. From this we know that Furber was already cultivating and selling the Moss Rose, so that he must have had it almost as soon as the Leyden garden, which listed it in 1720. The Kensington Nursery, partly from its position but mainly because of Furber's skill and enterprise, became the fashionable place for buying plants. Mrs. Pendarves, the later Mrs. Delany, wrote from Upper Brook Street to her sister on 15 October 1730: 'I was this morning at Furber's, and you shall be sent by coach on Monday next (19 October) all the garden things you wanted'. Furber left only a reversionary bequest of £200 to his son; the nursery passed to his assistant John Williamson and continued to be a leading firm as Williamson & Co. and, after 1783, under Daniel Grimwood (c. 1725-1796) and various partners until 1804. Taken over by the younger William Malcolm (1769-1835), and from 1835 by Richard Forrest, the Duke of Northumberland's gardener from Syon House, the Kensington Nursery went on as a mainstay of the trade until the middle of the 19th century.

The other long-lived nursery of those flourishing in 1730 was that of Christopher Gray at Fulham. A great many nurserymen named Gray appear in the London area throughout the 18th and early 19th century; those of Fulham had roots there even before 1700. It has not yet proved possible to disentangle the relationships of these men, and they may have belonged to several separate families. Christopher was not 21 until 1715, so that it is not very likely that he was, as tradition asserts, the man chiefly responsible for saving valuable trees and plants from the Fulham Palace grounds after the death of Bishop Compton in 1713. It is possible, however, that Christopher succeeded to a nursery founded by his father, perhaps William Gray. But it is certain that, if so, this was not the William Gray, nurseryman of Fulham, who was buried there on 17 July 1745, who held part of his gardens simply as a tenant of Christopher. This William (presumably the William Gray junior who in 1724 had commended Miller's first dictionary) left his house in Parson's Green Lane and his stock to trustees, of whom the first was Mr. John Williamson of Kensington, gardener, evidently the ultimate successor of Furber. The chief beneficiary was William Gray's son-in-law Daniel Dunn, who was to pay £30 a year to Gray's wife Mary. The trustees were not to take up or destroy the stock of Plants and Trees, but to maintain the stock to the value of £200 until after the annuity had expired. Christopher Gray's nursery was probably a good deal larger. He was already a man of standing in the trade in 1724, when he was one of those who recommended Miller's first dictionary, and he appears as a subscriber to a succession of gardening publications and in 1741 to the map of ten miles around London issued by John Rocque, brother of Gray's fellow nurseryman in Fulham, Bartholomew Rocque.

Christopher Gray has long been famous for having issued a catalogue in 1740, under the mistaken impression that it was the first of its kind. No copy of this catalogue is now known, but its title was the same as that of one of his of 1755 which does survive, and there is no reason to deny its former existence. It was, however, 13 years later than Furber's catalogues already mentioned. As a highly skilled plantsman Gray was more deservedly renowned. He claimed in 1755 that 'there are a greater Variety of Trees, Shrubs, Plants and Flowers, cultivated in *Mr. Gray's* Nursery, than can perhaps be found in any other Garden, for Sale, not only in England, but also in any Part of Europe'. He provided most of the trees and shrubs planted by Horace Walpole at Strawberry Hill, and Walpole wrote on 8 November 1755 to his friend George Montagu of 'the Hiram from whom I obtained my cedars of Libanus. He is by men called Christopher Gray, nurseryman at Fulham. I mentioned cedars first, because they are the most beautiful of the evergreen race, and because they are the dearest; half a guinea apiece in baskets. The arbutus are scarce, and a crown apiece, but they are very beautiful. The lignum vitae I would not recommend to you; they stink abominably if you touch them, and never make a handsome tree . . . Gray . . . sells cypresses in pots at half a crown apiece; you turn them out of the pot with all their mould, and they never fail'.

Gray died in 1764 and on 15 November was buried at Fulham. His nursery passed to William Burchell (c. 1725-1800) and later to his nephew Matthew Burchell who in 1765 had been apprenticed to his uncle. Matthew's son was the distinguished explorer and naturalist William John Burchell (1781-1863), who was a botanist as well as a great deal else. Yet the Burchells do not seem to have maintained the level of the Fulham Nursery, and it was not again of distinction until after it had been taken over in 1810 by Reginald Whitley (c. 1754-1835) and his partners, Peter Brames (died 1834) and Thomas Milne (c. 1767-1838). After 1833 Whitley took Robert Osborn into partnership, and the nursery went on until 1880. We have already heard (p.10) of the delightful character of Robert's younger son Thomas Osborn (1819-1872). From 1810 onwards Fulham again became one of the great centres for the supply of plants, and Milne in particular was a noted hybridizer.

Several of the members of the Society of Gardeners who were concerned with the catalogue of 1730 have left little or no other mark on horticultural history. John Alston, near Chelsea College; Richard Cole of Battersea, and Obadiah Low(e) of Battersea are mere names, though Low had appeared in 1724 to commend Miller's first dictionary, and a Mr. Alston supplied chestnut trees to the Rev. Joseph Spence at Byfleet in 1749. William Hood, at the Wheatsheaf, Hyde Park Corner, appears again, described as a seedsman, in 1733 when he subscribed to Furber's *Short Introduction.* George Singleton of the Neat Houses was a Physick Gardener, 'very sick and weak in body' when he made his will on 19 June 1735. He left £50 each to his two daughters Sarah and Elizabeth when they should be 20, and all the residue to his wife Hester, who proved the will on 15 December. John Thompson, of The Rose in Chelsea, emerges from the rate books as a personality of slightly more substance. The Rose, on the north-east angle of the crossroads at King's Road and Old Church Street, has been rebuilt and renamed the Cadogan Arms, but does show us precisely where Thompson's nursery was. For this original property on the north side of the King's Road, Thompson was first rated in August 1721; and in November 1723 he paid also for ¾ acre of Glebe Land which he rented on the south side. He continued to hold the original property until June 1740, and the parcel of glebe until December 1750. From 1751 to 1758 his name was marked 'poor' and he was excused payment of rates. In 1733 he had been a subscriber to Furber's *Short Introduction,* but there is no record of any later activity.

To make up for the lack of information on several members of the Society we have records of a number of others who were nevertheless prominent in the London area. Samuel Driver of Lambeth had in 1717 supplied trees to George Lucy of Charlecote, Warwickshire, and in 1724 commended Miller. In 1730 he owed £2. 17s. 6d. to the estate of Peter Mason of Isleworth, to whom we must return. He was probably the father of the Samuel Driver who by 1760 had a nursery in Walworth and in 1777 subscribed to William Curtis's *Flora Londinensis.* The important business built up by the second Samuel was continued by Abraham Purshouse Driver and William Driver, still in business in 1805, and as surveyors in 1812. In 1788 they had produced a revised edition of *The Pomona Britanica*; or *Fruit-Garden displayed,* and in 1794 the *General View of the Agriculture of Hampshire* for the Board of Agriculture. In the *Catalogus Plantarum* the name of Samuel Driver appears as the first of five who were apparently not concerned in the production and may have been only associates. The others were Thomas Bickerstaff, William Welstead, John James and William Spencer, of whom nothing is known, unless James was the well known architect (c.1672-1746) who translated from the French of Le Blond *The Theory and Practice of Gardening* (1712).

Outside the central area there were, besides the Hunts at Putney, a number of firms of note. Adam Holt, at Leytonstone in Essex, paid rates from 1710 to 1729 on a large area of ground near Grove Green, and on a much smaller property as a non-resident until 1733. He was overseer of the Poor in 1718, surveyor of highways in 1720 and 1721, Churchwarden in 1727 and 1728. The parish records call him 'Mr.', a sure mark of standing, and he sent fruit trees as far as West Bromwich Manor in Staffordshire in 1720 for the garden of Sir Samuel Clarke. As a florist he also won distinction by raising the 'Royal Widow' auricula, 'the best of the Painted Ladies' from seed of a striped 'Duke of Beaufort'. The plant was so much esteemed that it sold for ten guineas, as Furber related in 1734 in *The Flower Garden Display'd.* Holt moved to Wanstead, where he died in 1750. The rest of the recorded nurseries of the period were mainly up river to the west of London, generally continuing older establishments which we have met in considering that area before 1700.

The Kew Green nursery, already of importance under William Cox the elder and the scene of improvement in early cropping peas under his son, passed to Richard Butt. This was probably the cousin and legatee of Thomas Fairchild and, in spite of spelling, the 'Mr. Butts' who owed £2. 14s. 9d. to Peter Mason's nursery at Isleworth in 1730. In the period 1731-1750 Butt's nursery included part of Warren Field next to Kew Green, rented at £12 a year, but by 1750 at latest this had been resumed as part of the Kew Mansion House property. In 1749 Richard Butt supplied 700 trees and shrubs to the Earl of Uxbridge for Dawley Lodge near Harlington in Middlesex, for £9. 2s. 6d. More notable historically is the payment of £29. 19s. to 'Butt, for Trees & Shrubs' in March 1751 among the arrears for Kew New Garden outstanding on the death of Frederick, Prince of Wales. Richard Butt was thus one of the original suppliers for the planting of what from that time on became Kew Gardens.

Across the Thames at Twickenham the ancient tradition of nurseries was maintained by Joshua Spyers or Spires, another debtor to Peter Mason in 1730, for £2. 10s. In 1748 he supplied some trees to Horace Walpole, and two years later Walpole paid him two guineas for a survey and plan of the Strawberry Hill estate. About this time Spyers was described as a 'draftsman', and in 1749 he had been a Churchwarden. Evidently a man of some status, he probably made a living by combining surveying and the design of gardens with the running of a small nursery. He may well have been related to Thomas Fairchild's friend Richard Spier of Hoxton, gardener, left £5 and appointed joint executor with Stephen Bacon. Close by, at Isleworth, had been the distinguished nursery of Peter Mason the younger (1680-1730), described by Batty Langley in 1728. Referring to the spruce fir, Langley wrote: 'the only Nursery, that I know of, as has this Tree, with all other Ever-Greens, Fruit and Forest-Trees, Flowering Shrubs &c., in their best Perfection, is that of the ingenious Mr. *Peter Mason,* Nursery-Man at Isleworth . . . who, I dare to affirm, has one of the best Collection of *English* Fruits of any Nursery-Man in *England*; and on whom every gentleman may safely depend of having, not only every kind of Fruit exactly of the right Kind desired, but the very best Growth, and at reasonable Rates'. A fully detailed inventory of Mason's house, and of the stock in his nursery, was taken after his death and has fortunately survived (see Appendix V, p.164).

Batty Langley (1696-1751), himself the son of a Twickenham gardener Daniel Langley, was very well informed as to the best nurseries in the district. Besides Peter Mason and William Cox of Kew, he noted a nurseryman at Strand-on-the-Green as an improver. Another kind of Hotspur Pease, he wrote, 'called and known by the name of *Master's Hots*, (was) first raised and improved by an ingenious Gardiner and Nursery Man of that Name now (in 1728) living at *Strand in the Green*, near old *Brentford*'. This must have been the George Master(s) who, on 4 April 1722, had made the valuation of Cox's nursery stock at Kew, immediately opposite on the south bank. The improvement of peas was very much to the fore at the time, for in 1726 Benjamin Townsend, in his book *The Complete Seedsman*, particularly mentioned the many sorts raised by 'Mr. Knight, a curious Nursery-Man in Bedfordshire, a great Collector of Pease'. These were Knight's Forward Grey Pea, Large White Pea, Amber-coloured, Large Greenish, Large Grey Late, Large or Rounceval Grey, round Black-Eyed, and White or Forty-day Pea. It is tempting to speculate on a possible relationship to the famous gardener and nurseryman Joseph Knight (1777-1855), or on a connection with the later Ampthill Nursery specializing in agricultural and vegetable seeds, of Thomas Gibbs & Co., who flourished 1787-1847.

Also at Strand-on-the-Green was the nursery of Henry Woodman (c. 1698-1758), son of an earlier Henry Woodman of Chiswick who had married Esther Durham in 1694 at St. Martin's in the Fields. He himself in 1728 married Eleanor Compton, of another Chiswick family, at St. Paul's Cathedral. His wife brought him property to add to his own small garden, and Woodman's was a substantial nursery, assessed at £45 in the rates from 1727 to 1737 and thereafter at fluctuating amounts. Early in his career, between 1729 and 1733, Woodman was able to supply large numbers of trees and shrubs to Henry Ellison Esq. of Gateshead Park in Co. Durham. It is possible, but far from certain, that he may have taken over the existing nursery of George Master; this would account for the very large numbers of flowering shrubs he could provide by 1731. In that year he subscribed to Miller's folio *Dictionary*, and though apparently not himself a member of the Society of Gardeners, bought all his seeds from Moses James the Lambeth seedsman, who was a member. Woodman, whether justly or not, incurred the enmity of Stephen Switzer, who succeeded in ousting him from Mr. Ellison's confidence (see the correspondence transcribed as Appendix VII).

Whether or not it was true that any secret commission passed from Woodman to Thomas Woolley, the Gateshead Park gardener, and that the prices charged were excessive, as Switzer bluntly stated, we cannot now judge. But there is independent evidence that the fruit trees Woodman supplied later in his career were of excellent quality. Thomas Hitt (died c. 1760) the distinguished gardener, in his book *A Treatise of Fruit-Trees*, published in 1755, devoted chapter xxvii to 'How to pack up trees so as that they may be carried safe to places remote from whence they are raised'. Hitt advocated the provision of large hampers, especially for trained espalier trees, but he had the honesty to admit that simpler packing was not necessarily harmful. 'I must own that I have received peach-trees and nectarines from Mr. Henry Woodman, of Strand on the Green, in the county of Middlesex, which I planted for the Reverend Mr. Ewer, of Bottisford near Belvoir castle; all of them lived and some bore fruit the first year after planting, tho' they were brought above a hundred miles, and only packed up with straw and matts; they have been planted nine years, and are now strong healthy trees.' Presumably Woodman supplied these peaches and nectarines about 1745 or 1746, and in 1749 'Mr. Woodman' was supplying trees to the Rev. Joseph Spence. Even if Hitt did not entirely approve of the method of packing, which was that normal throughout the period, he could hardly have given a warmer testimonial to the trees themselves. Since Hitt was a native of Aberdeenshire and had spent most of his life as head gardener on several of the best estates within a radius of twenty miles of Newark-upon-Trent, his judgment must be accepted. In any case, Woodman prospered, for when he made his will in 1755 he was able to leave Bank Annuities and other legacies to a total capital value of £1,500, then a very large sum. 'All my Stock on the Ground and in the Ground as being a Nursery Man I give and bequeath to my said dear Wife' Eleanor for her life; the reversion was to go to their son Henry Woodman, who in the event died in 1775, five years before his mother.

Up to now it will have been noticed that practically all nurserymen bore English names, apart from a few manifestly of French Huguenot descent. This was being changed by the consequences of the Act of Union with Scotland of 1707. Scotland became an economically depressed country, and Scots emigrated in large numbers to seek their fortunes elsewhere. In particular, numbers of gardeners from the Lowlands came south to London and found work at great estates all over the country. Just what factors, apart from a capacity for hard work and a better educational system than the English one, made and have continued to make Scottish gardeners so successful is a problem. It is, however, irrelevant to the state of tension and even conflict that grew in English gardening circles as job after choice job fell to 'the lads from the north' as Switzer contemptuously called them. We are not here concerned with these men as gardeners, but as time went on an increasing number set up nurseries with the savings that resulted from their habits of thrift. Although it is impossible in many cases to adduce specific evidence of nationality, evidently Scottish names begin to be noticed, and in the vanguard were two contemporaries who may even have been brothers, Henry Scott and James Scott. Henry had become gardener to Lord Burlington at Chiswick House before 1738, when he was regarded as especially an expert on the culture of pineapples. Having accumulated the capital he was able before 1754 to set himself up with a nursery at Weybridge in Surrey, for which in October of that year he issued a trade card advertising his Pine Apples, Seeds, Fruit Trees, Flowering Shrubs and Green House Plants. It was at Weybridge in the same year that his daughter Martha was born, and there his wife Anne was buried on 7 February 1760.

James Scot or Scott, of Turnham Green, first appears as a subscriber to Rocque's map of ten miles round London in 1741, and he too set up a nursery, probably in the large ground later occupied by Richard Williams of Williams' Pear fame. As almost certain evidence that Scott really came from Scotland we have the fact that James Justice (1698-1763), the Scottish horticulturist, always bought and recommended James Scott's cauliflower seed and had his pineapple plants and a pineapple stove shipped from London to Edinburgh. Scott was also a botanical draughtsman, and produced an engraved plate of the *Sarracenia* or Side-saddle Flower on which Thomas Knowlton (1692-1781), the great gardener, commented in a letter of 23 July 1754.

The nurseries of Henry Scott and James Scott, though quite evidently of substantial size and high quality, were completely eclipsed in importance by those of two Scots whose gardens dominated the rest of the 18th century: James Gordon (c. 1708-1780) and James Lee (1715-1795). Between them Gordon and Lee were responsible for the introduction to Britain, or the effective cultivation, of an enormous proportion of the new plants which streamed in, in an ever increasing flood, from 1740 onwards. A great deal has been written of Gordon and his introductions, and Lee is the subject of a model biography by Miss E. J. Willson. Accordingly little need be said of them here, and in any case they belong essentially to the modern rather than to the early nurserymen. Gordon was lucky enough to become gardener to Dr. James Sherard (1666-1738) at Eltham when Sherard's previous expert, Thomas Knowlton, left about 1730 to take charge of the Earl of Burlington's great horticultural works at Londesborough in the East Riding of Yorkshire. For the last eight years of Sherard's life Gordon had charge of his treasury of botanical introductions, and when his patron died was again lucky. He secured the plum of all horticultural posts in England as chief gardener to the brilliant young Lord Petre of Thorndon Hall in Essex. On Petre's tragic death in 1742, Gordon was able to launch himself into business in a nursery at Mile End, which lasted for 95 years until it was swallowed for building in 1837. By adding a seed-shop in Fenchurch Street to his nursery, Gordon was able to secure a substantial slice of the London trade, and his was by far the most influential firm in the country during the whole of the third quarter of the century. James Gordon turned the business into a company and surrendered control in 1776, and died at Barking, Essex, on 20 December 1780.

In spite of the intensive research of Miss Willson and others, the beginnings of the Vineyard Nursery at Hammersmith remain somewhat vague. The founder, and senior partner to James Lee, was Lewis Kennedy, but he cannot have been identical with the partner of Lee, Lewis Kennedy, who is said to have been born in 1721 and died in the summer of 1782. The elder man was already gardener to Lord Wilmington in 1731, when he subscribed to Miller's *Dictionary*, and still described himself as gardener in subscribing to Furber's *Short Introduction* two years later, and to Rocque's map in 1741. On the other hand he is said to have been already well known as a nurseryman and florist when he took Lee into partnership at a date certainly earlier than 1753 and traditionally put at 70 years before 1813, therefore 1743. There are several confirmatory proofs that Lewis Kennedy was not merely older than Lee but in fact senior partner. On 20 December 1759 a letter from Francis Eyre of Warkworth, Northamptonshire, to his friend John Caryll of Ladyholt, Sussex, enclosed a list of flowers, commenting: 'I dare answer you may purchase of Mr. Kennedy Nursery-Man at Hammersmith the whole (wh. will supply you for Ever) for less than two guineas'. On 21 April 1769 a bill for plants supplied to H.R.H. the Princess Dowager of Wales for Kew was receipted by Lewis Kennedy 'for self and Co.'. The deservedly famous catalogue of 1774 was of 'Plants and Seeds sold by Kennedy & Lee'. The firm remained Kennedy & Lee in the heading of a bill for plants sent to Croxdale in Co. Durham between 30 October 1780 and 6 November 1781. On the other hand the Lewis Kennedy who made a partnership agreement on 29 June and his will on 1 July 1782 and was dead before 15 August that year, was certainly the father of John Kennedy (1759-1842), born 30 October 1759, son of Lewis and Margaret (née Garioch) who had married at Fulham in 1756. We can only suppose that there were father and son, both named Lewis Kennedy, and that the father died only a short time before the son. These Hammersmith Kennedys must in any case be distinguished from the John Kennedy who was gardener to Sir Thomas Gascoigne, Bart., of Parlington House near Aberford in Yorkshire, author of *A Treatise upon Planting* (1777), who died in January 1790; and the Lewis Kennedy (c. 1757-1810) who was later gardener at Parlington.

Two other nurseries were founded, both close to Brompton Park, in the first half of the 18th century. We saw that on 3 November 1719 one John Kirke was paid the large sum of £73. 12s. for trees supplied to Studley Royal for John Aislabie's notable venture in landscape. Unfortunately no detailed bill survives and there is no clue to the source of the trees, except that the number implied is so large as strongly to suggest the London area. There was a nursery in Gore Lane, Brompton, partly within the walls of 'Cromwell's Garden', which in 1820 was said to have been in the hands of the Kirke family 'upwards of 70 years'. Certainly by 1766 Joseph Kirke was paying rates for a nursery in this part of Kensington parish. By 1793 the firm was Mary, William & Joseph Kirke; Mary was the widow of the elder Joseph. The younger Joseph Kirke was in partnership with his brother William in 1805 but seems later to have been sole proprietor; then by 1822 it was Kirke & Son, and in 1836 John Kirke, no doubt the son. The nursery was particularly famous for its grapevines and for fruit trees including 100 varieties of apple.

The Kirke nursery expanded to about 14 acres by 1800; the other now to be described was nearly twice as large. It must have been founded somewhere near 1730, by Henry Hewitt (died 1771) and his brother Samuel Hewitt (died 1793). A bill of 1738 receipted by Henry was for 7s. for 'Four Large Spruce Firrs order'd by Mr. Rea, Gardr. to the Honble Sr. Wm. Stanhope'; evidently the nursery had been in existence for some little time. The Hewitts adopted the method of personal travelling initiated by George London, and obtained large orders from various great estates. Later on, as is shown by some of their books which have survived, they also carried on a thriving trade with the smaller provincial nurserymen all over the country. The firm passed into the hands of Henry Hewitt (died 1791), son of Thomas Hewitt of Welby Mason, Lincolnshire, brother of the elder Henry and Samuel. Later the younger Henry's nephews John and Samuel Harrison were brought in, and lastly, from 1819 to 1833 the firm became Harrison & Bristow. A century of what appears to have been scrupulously honest trading in plants and seeds of very high quality was brought to an end by Samuel Harrison's bankruptcy in 1833.

Before completing the picture of the mid-18th century with a brief account of several other major firms founded by 1760, something must be said of a number of smaller businesses. In addition to the great nurseries there were always some of modest size which were of importance for one or more lines. One such was John Parkinson (died 1719), who turns out to be the Parkinson of Lambeth mentioned as a specialist in evergreens about 1712, by Peter Collinson in his reminiscences of 50 years later. According to Collinson, this Parkinson was regarded as a leading member of the trade, yet nothing else of his career is known. From the early Lambeth rate books, however, he can be identified in the Bishop's Liberty, paying 6s. 6d. to the repairs of the church in 1700 and, in Vauxhall Liberty in 1703, 4s. to a special rate. It is permissible to wonder whether he was a connection of his great namesake of the *Paradisus* and *Theatrum Botanicum,* who had died in 1650. The Lambeth Parkinson died on 14 November 1719, leaving all his real and personal estate to his wife Mary Parkinson for life, with reversion to his daughter Ann Parkinson and 'Hur Aires'. Ann was to have £20 when she attained 21; her sister Mary was cut off with the proverbial shilling. The first witness to the will was Moses James, doubtless the Stangate seedsman we know.

A few nurseries were founded outside London and its inner ring of villages. We have seen that Henry Scott went out as far as 20 miles in settling at Weybridge. In the other direction, Cheshunt in Hertfordshire was recognized as suitable for the trade soon after 1700. When, on 19 August 1725, Robert Lucas of Cheshunt made his will, he described himself — one of the very first ever to do so — as Nursery Man. All his property was left to his wife Elizabeth, who proved the will on 11 March 1733/4. Barnet, on the boundary between Middlesex and Hertfordshire, also became a nursery centre. The principal family concerned was that of Emmerton: Thomas Emmerton of South Mimms, a widower who remarried in 1741, was probably the man who supplied forest trees and roses to John Radcliffe Esq. of Hitchin Priory in 1763, and very likely the Emerton who in the previous year had sent Weymouth pines to Cusworth near Doncaster, Yorks. More famous were the two Isaac Emmertons, described as nursery and seedsmen but chiefly florists. Isaac Emmerton senior (c. 1736-1789) was probably son of an earlier Isaac of South Mimms who remarried in 1740; Isaac Emmerton junior (c. 1769-1823) was the author of *A plain and practical Treatise on the culture and management of the Auricula,* etc. (1815). He and his father before him had then been nurserymen at Barnet for 55 years, which puts the foundation at 1760. Another Barnet nurseryman of the period was Henry Clark who specialized in magnolias and other uncommon shrubs. At his death in the winter of 1782-3 the stock was sold and much of it bought in by James Lee and Conrad Loddiges of Hackney.

Some nurseries were especially concerned with forest trees, and notably with various species of American oaks. Thus Joseph Allerton, nurseryman of the Old Spring Gardens, Knightsbridge, with his home in Brompton Lane, subscribed to *The Practical Husbandman and Planter* in 1733 and on 16 April wrote to Stephen Switzer the editor, sending him a copy of Lawson's 'Abstract of North American Trees'. Allerton commented: 'Some of which, particularly the *Red* or Scarlet-Oak, are what we have now great Quantities in our Plantations'. At Leytonstone in Essex were two nurseries also planting American oaks. One of these was probably the old ground of Adam Holt, refounded by John Hay about 1759 and run by him to his death in 1792. Hay was succeeded by James Hill (c. 1761-1832), and then by Hill's widow Charlotte. In her time the nursery was visited in 1835 by J. C. Loudon, who found that it abounded in a 'very great variety of Red American Oaks'. This was known as the Leyton or American Nursery, near Grove Green. Further south was Holloway Down Nursery, owned by Spencer Turner from about 1751 to his death in 1776. During his quarter-century of gardening he raised the hybrid semi-evergreen oak which still bears his name as *Quercus x Turneri*. Another Leyton nursery by the Lea Bridge Road, was run by Richard Siborn (died 1774) from about 1755, and later by Joseph Hughes, by Richard Siborn the younger (c. 1751-1821) and by James and William Pamplin to 1869.

Among the many small nurseries of Lambeth was one that specialized in the supply of Norfolk willows, kept by Richard North. He subscribed to the first edition of Miller's *Dictionary* as a gardener in 1731, was assessed in Marsh and Wall Liberty at £17 in 1757, and in 1759 was mentioned as former occupier of 2½ acres called 'Shoulder of Mutton Field' near Mayer Lawrence's Charity School in Water Lambeth. At this time he was writing his *Treatise on Grasses, and the Norfolk Willow* (1760), stating that he would furnish sets of the willow to any who might want them. Early in 1766 a correspondent of the *Museum Rusticum* wrote: 'As he (Mr. North) is very lately dead, who may be his successors in his business, or whether they will continue to provide for the demand of sets, I am at present ignorant'. He later wrote again to say that he 'went to Lambeth to inquire, and found that Mr. North had resigned his business for a year or two before his death, to one Mr. Sheilds . . . who is prepared to furnish any quantity of the willow sets . . . I found him very well provided with them, and all the plants which are usual in the nurseries; as well as a good collection of those which are more rare . . . he has an ample stock of the *Carolina poplar* . . . as well as of both the kinds of the mulberry-trees . . . '. This was James Shields or Shiells, who was supplying tree seeds to the Seaton Delaval estate in Northumberland in 1779-81, and who was assessed at £18 for his land in East Place, Bishop's Liberty, Lambeth, as late as 1788. 'Shields Nursery' is marked on John Cary's 'new and accurate plan' of London of 1787.

The year 1760, with the accession of George III, was one of the great turning-points in history, and not least in the nursery trade. The many firms, great and small, founded between 1760 and the king's death in 1820 lie for the most part outside the scope of this book, though a few of them will have to be mentioned at a later stage. There were, however, some great businesses of primary importance that were started a little before this major climacteric, and of which a brief account must here be given. Probably the first in date was the Brentford garden begun by Hugh Ronalds the elder (c. 1726-1788). Loudon in 1822 stated that it had been 'established upwards of a century', but there seems to be no evidence for this. Indeed, Loudon himself in 1834 wrote in the *Gardener's Magazine* that Hugh Ronalds the younger (c. 1759-1833) had died on 22 November at Brentford in the same house in which he was born, aged 74 years. 'The Brentford Nursery was established nearly 100 years ago, by the father of the late Mr. Ronalds . . . .' Loudon went on to comment upon Ronalds' great skill with fruits 'evinced by his *Pyrus Malus Brentfordiensis*, beautifully illustrated by drawings from nature on stone, by his daughter Elizabeth . . . he had great skill in raising flower seeds'. This great book had appeared in 1831, the culmination of a life's work. Much of the nursery was on land in Isleworth leased from the Duke of Northumberland: from the small assessment to Land Tax of £5 in 1780-91, this climbed to £82 which was maintained 1807-29. Besides fruit trees the firm supplied various great estates, including those of the Earl of Jersey and of Lord Ailesbury at Savernake in Wiltshire with a very wide range of plants.

From 1757 William Malcolm was rated for land in Kennington, near the site of the Oval, and his nursery remained there until 1788 when he moved southwards to Stockwell where he had 50 acres and in 1789 had 'just erected a handsome house built with grey stock-bricks, which is most' delightfully situated; on its south-east side are large hot-houses, conservatories, &c.'. Malcolm was one of the pioneers of scientifically botanical catalogues, his first edition appearing in 1771. His son, the younger William Malcolm (1769-1835) carried on the Stockwell nursery until 1815 with various partners, the last being the great Robert Sweet (1783-1835). Almost exactly contemporary with Malcolm's nursery, but on the other side of London, was that started by Warren Luker (died 1784) about 1758. Very likely a descendant of Roger Looker, for the spellings are interchangeable, he was at first a seedsman and cornchandler at The Sun in City New Road, parish of St. Luke Old Street. Several of his children were baptized at St. Luke's between 1758 and 1764. The firm became Luker, Smith & Lewis and opened a nursery under Edward Smith at Dalston in Hackney. This expanded to some 30 acres and as Smiths, from 1785 to 1849, became one of the principal firms of the London area, with over 30,000 square feet of glass.

Two of the greatest of the London nurseries were founded in or about 1760. One of these was the largest in extent and probably the biggest economically, that of John Russell (c.1731-1794) at Lewisham; the other, in Hackney, founded by the German John Busch, later became world famous under Conrad Loddiges. Russell 'raised himself by his skill and industry to a state of affluence rare among nurserymen and, after keeping his carriage and living many years like a gentleman, died of smallpox in 1794 aged 63, leaving property to the amount of £20,000'. By 1811 the land occupied amounted to over 100 acres, in 1822 to 150 acres. In 1811 the annual bill for labour alone was over £3,000 and the nursery was already the largest in the London area; in 1822 the number of hands employed was 70. After 1794 the founder's sons John Russell junior (1766-1808) and Thomas Russell (c. 1773-1810) carried on, with their brother-in-law John Willmott (1775-1834). As John Willmott & Co. and eventually Willmott & Chaundy, the nursery continued until 1860 when it had to close owing to the expiry of the original lease.

The first Hackney nursery of John Busch was in Well Street, and was taken over by Loddiges (? 1743-1826) in 1771. The old grounds were inadequate and in 1787 and 1792 Loddiges obtained gardens to the east of Mare Street. His first catalogue, issued in 1777, was well drawn up and had the unusual feature of being in three languages, Latin, German and English. The 16th edition appeared in 1836 and there were also special catalogues in the later years, of Orchids, Trees, Ferns etc. The business was kept on by Conrad's son George Loddiges (1784-1846), who conducted the firm's beautifully produced magazine, the *Botanical Cabinet,* from 1817 to 1834. Although outstandingly important for its introductions of hothouse exotics, Loddiges also planted an arboretum, begun in 1816, one of the first in Britain. Like the Lewisham nursery, that at Hackney closed down in 1860.

We have seen that from the 1740's the world of plantsmanship was dominated by the two nurseries founded by the Scotsmen Gordon and Lee. Logically enough, the first catalogues of a botanical character were those produced by Gordon about 1770, by Lee in 1774, and by their fellow Scot Malcolm in 1771. The polyglot work of Loddiges followed in 1777, also the year of publication of what seems to have been the first botanical catalogue produced in the provinces, by John Brunton (c. 1721-1803) of Birmingham. As we know, priced catalogues were coming out about the same time, starting in Scotland and in Yorkshire in 1775. It was, then, about the 1770's that the modern era of horticulture began, firmly based on scientific nomenclature, and offering clearly marked goods to the public. But we must not forget that, even around London, there was still room for the little local firm, in the closest touch with its customers. Typical of these was another of Horace Walpole's suppliers, close by Strawberry Hill: Thomas Ashe, a Churchwarden of Twickenham in 1741 and nurseryman also to the poet Pope. Ashe, who lived until 1779, was more than a plant salesman: on Walpole explaining to him that he wished his trees to be planted irregularly, Ashe replied, 'Yes, Sir, I understand; you would have them hang down somewhat poetical'.

NURSERIES GALORE

HUMAN HAPPINESS CONSISTS largely in the pursuit of the unattainable, and this is very true in regard to gardening. It is permissible to hold many different and conflicting views of the real aim of the gardener, but one thing is certain: a garden depends on plants. It is and always has been the function of the nurseryman, under whatever name, to get plants to the gardener. The state of the trade depends, and always must depend, on the efficiency of the nurseryman as a conveyer and provider, a man in the middle between the ultimate natural sources of supply and the consumer, yet a great deal more than a commercial middleman. As has been insisted at an earlier stage, the basis of nurseries is plantsmanship: the ability to get seeds to germinate, plants to grow and above all to flower and fruit; and not simply to do so, but to display the fullest perfection of which the species is capable. If possible the natural beauty of the species must even be enhanced by diligent work, in selection of the best seedlings or bud-sports, by active hybridization and by patient watching of results, even for many years on end.

The more one contemplates these propositions set before the ideal nurseryman, the more astonishing and complex does his programme seem. How is it possible that any single lifetime can include so much acquired skill, so much hard work, so much sheer expenditure of time. Besides, this is not the end: the man who is to accomplish all this has to do it while at the same time running a business which is to provide him, and a large staff, with at least a livelihood. Every plant or batch of plants has to be labelled, if possible with the currently accepted scientific name; but on the other hand it is a business asset which needs to be registered in and out of stock books and also, broken down into individual plants, described in the bills sent out to customers. Complaints from those customers, requests for information and for plants not in stock; negotiations with landlords or agents over the land of the nursery or for expansion; the preparation of catalogues, and of exhibits for floral feasts or modern shows; travel, commercial or scientific, the attending of meetings and conferences: all these have to be fitted in, and most of them always have been fitted into the nurseryman's life, even in earlier and quieter periods than the present.

Not only had all or most of these factors to be faced in the horticultural world of two and three centuries ago: they had to be faced with a background realization of a terrifying threat: that of bankruptcy. This is a feature of life which it is difficult for us to grasp. Living after the passing of the Companies Act of 1862 it is impossible to feel the thrill of horror at the very word which caused it to be written as b . . . . . t; the seriously held view that bankruptcy was a stain upon the personal honour of the merchant involved; the hard fact that the guilty man might very likely spend the rest of his life in a Debtors' Prison. As we have seen, nurserymen sometimes did go bankrupt, and the roll of unfortunates was to grow longer in the harsh period of depression after the end of the Napoleonic Wars in 1815. On the one side a modest share of fame, and an off-chance of fortune — such as John Russell's £20,000 — beckoned; on the other hand there was the risk, even if not of gaol, of a poverty-stricken old age like that of John Thompson of Chelsea, who in his time had belonged to the select band of London Gardeners who held their regular meetings close to his home, at Newhall's Coffee House.

Like all activities in process of expansion, nursery gardening in the 18th and 19th centuries was in danger of becoming top heavy, and competition became more stringent. In a few cases there was bitterness and hard feeling between different practitioners: we have seen an example of this in the unhappy recriminations between Henry Woodman and Stephen Switzer (p.82 and Appendix VII). Yet on the whole it is amazing how much good will, how much generosity towards competitors, there is to be found in the literature. Letters and articles are full of references to rivals who were 'very ingenious friends'; wills commonly reposed trust in or showed gratitude towards other members of the trade. The co-operation of gardeners, florists, nurserymen and seedsmen in societies of various kinds, and the moral compulsion to show good sportsmanship at prize displays, all played a part in promoting the general interest and minimizing friction. Beyond this there was a fundamental unity of purpose and need for combined effort that tended to keep rivalry within limits. All nurserymen depended on each other in some measure, and by the latter part of the 18th century, when detailed working records first become available, the resulting links across the country formed an extremely complex web.

Before going on to consider this network of greater and lesser firms, and their interrelationships, a word needs to be said on the problem of advertisement. This was of several kinds. Until after 1700 personal recommendation, by word of mouth or by letter, was practically the only way of obtaining custom, apart from an immediately local group of clients, or casual passersby. We have read Horace Walpole's remarks on Christopher Gray of Fulham, Mrs. Pendarves' reference to Furber, Francis Eyre's mention of Kennedy at Hammersmith. Such remarks, passed on from person to person in the ranks of higher horticultural society, undoubtedly counted for much. Then after about 1725, most of the country began to be covered by weekly and later daily newspapers carrying local and regional advertisements for payment. It is worth noting that this development almost exactly coincided with the first period of founding of the greater provincial nurseries. It coincided too with the earliest book-form catalogues issued by Robert Furber from the country's most fashionable nursery.

Newspaper advertisement seems to have begun among the London seedsmen rather than nurserymen; the seed shops in the Strand, Fleet Street and elsewhere were, after all, mercantile establishments in the world's greatest city of merchants. Nurserymen were often content to announce only such events as the setting up of a new business, the sale of an old one, the death of a senior partner or proprietor coupled with the assurance that his successors intended to carry on as before; occasionally the sale of an important body of stock. Later there were notices of the issue of catalogues, but it was only after 1800 that this practice, and the incorporation of priced catalogues into the advertising pages of magazines, became at all general. On the whole it is safe to say that in the English provinces the part played by newspaper advertisement during the 18th century was rather slight. On the other hand, a few enterprising men took advantage of the new medium practically from the start. In York the florist Samuel Smith twice inserted in the *York Courant* for 7 and 14 April 1730 a notice that at his Flower Garden without Mickle-gate Bar was to be seen 'a choice Collection of Ariculas, Animonies, Renunculos, Tulops and other Flowers' and that anyone might be furnished with them at reasonable rates. Thirty years later, on 3 June 1760, William Dickinson, gardener at Clifton near York, advertised that he would dispose of 'A Large Quantity of Ranunculuses now in full Blow' by the hundred or in larger numbers.

From the time of Gerard, at the end of the 16th century, there was a fair amount of unsolicited advertisement in books on plants and gardening, of the places where they might be obtained. Generally this seems to have been altruistic and in the best interests of the reader who did not know where to buy. Later there doubtless was in some cases an element of you-scratch-my-back-and-I'll-scratch-yours, but deliberate puffs for a consideration seem to have been unusual. On the other hand, as Mr. Miles Hadfield has remarked, some publications by nurserymen — and one notable case in point is Loddiges' *The Botanical Cabinet* — were undertaken partly as advertisement. On the whole these publications maintained a very high standard, and many of them were landmarks in the botanical knowledge of the time or in horticultural method. Not all of the books of this kind were written by nurserymen as such. Some were the work of head gardeners like John Kennedy of Parlington, who in 1776 published *A Treatise upon Planting, Gardening, and the Management of the Hot-House.* If its purpose was profitable self-advertisement, Kennedy fell far short of his mark for, in making his will ten years later, he apologized to his wife Lucy: 'I am sorrey forten has not favoured me to make an ampler provision for so deserving a wife'.

In drawing a line of division between nurserymen and gardeners we must keep in mind the fact, already mentioned, that individuals moved from one side to the other. While the nurseryman depended quite largely on recommendations from his clients and their gardeners, the clients in turn looked to their nurserymen to recommend to them reliable gardeners. It was in fact a principal part of the social utility of nurserymen that they usually could suggest a suitable well trained man. He, bred up on a nursery, might eventually after years of experience and responsibility on private estates, return to the trade as a partner or set up on his own account. Not all the gardeners recommended were necessarily suitable. John Perfect wrote to Henry Ellison at Gateshead Park on 21 November 1751: 'I . . . am extreamly sorry John Holmes behaved contrary to my expectations which I did not in the least imagine, he return'd back two or three days ago, & by what I have since learn'd he had almost engaged himself in Matrimony to a Young Woman who was his late Fellow Servant in this Neighbourhood wch I apprehend was the cause of his sullenness & leaving Gateshead Park so soon, & for which I have sharply reprimanded him & shall never give him another recomendation'.

It is not surprising that most of the nurserymen who were successful as writers should have been Londoners or more or less attached to the metropolitan area. Apart from John Rea, this applies to the authors of most of the works already mentioned: John Rose, Moses Cook, Leonard Meager, who for a time was foreman at Brompton Park; and also to London and Wise themselves in their translations and adaptations. Fairchild, Whitmill and Cowell all belonged to the Hoxton brigade of nurserymen, Furber to Kensington and Bartholomew Rocque, who issued *A Practical Treatise of Lucern* in 1761, to Fulham. Richard North, as we saw, was of Lambeth; James Lee already established at Hammersmith when he brought out in 1760 his *Introduction to Botany*. Among the first of the provincials to burst into print, though while still a gardener, was Thomas Barnes, who in 1758-59 brought out *A New Method of Propagating Fruit-trees, and Flowering Shrubs*. In 1773 he announced in the *Leeds Mercury* that he was 'fixing in The Nursery and Seeds-Way in Park-Lane, Leeds'. In 1782 he was able to supply seed of four different colours of Sweet Peas (Fine Scarlet, White, Painted Lady, and Purple) to Edwin Lascelles Esq. of Harewood, and later entered into partnership with Ebenezer Romain Callender. The firm issued a very well produced catalogue, not dated but apparently of c.1785-90. Though belonging to the northern type of priced catalogues started by Telfords of York in 1775, it is better arranged and contains full lists of fruit trees and of seeds. The catalogue was issued from The Orange Tree, Briggate, Leeds, where Barnes and Callender still were in 1795.

Apart from catalogues, and those mostly of utilitarian rather than scientific type, not much literary output can be attributed to the early provincial nurserymen. One of the first writers was James Wheeler of Gloucester, founder of a firm which survived well over a century, who published in 1763 *The Botanist's and Gardener's New Dictionary*. George Lindley, who ran a nursery at Catton near Norwich and was the father of John Lindley the botanist, issued between 1796 and 1831 a miscellany of papers and books, culminating in *A Guide to the Orchard and Kitchen Garden*. William Pontey (fl. 1782-died 1831), who had an important nursery in Kirkheaton near Huddersfield and a seedsman's shop in the town, was an expert on trees described as 'the Evelyn of the 19th century' and published *The Profitable Planter* (1800), *The Forest Pruner* (1805) and *The Rural Improver* (1823). Thomas Haynes, of Oundle, Northamptonshire and with a shop in Stamford, had printed a large sheet catalogue, fully priced, by 1802 and published in 1811 *An Improved System of Nursery Gardening*, followed by several other useful works in the next ten years.

It cannot be claimed, therefore, that the provincial nurserymen of earlier times made any great contribution to the literature of their subject. Only Pontey's books stand out as among the most important ever written on the subject of forest trees, and he alone in respect of the stature of his published work can fitly be compared with Evelyn or the other giants of earlier and later times. The silence of the trade, at any rate until well on in the nineteenth century, has quite naturally obscured the part played by these men, quietly getting on with their business in all parts of the country. Clearly the tremendous development of plant nurseries between the middle of the 18th and the middle of the 19th century was a miracle of organization and fulfilled a necessary purpose. Though not part of the Industrial Revolution, it was an accompanying and parallel phenomenon. This is what, as the last section of this book, we now have to study.

It is impossible in the present lack of trade archives to attempt any detailed account of each of the greater firms that, between 1750 and 1800, spread over most regions of the country. In many cases only the merest outline exists of the early history of firms which, later on, were of outstanding importance. Where neither catalogues nor detailed bills survive, it is often impossible to form any impression of the character and size of the firm. Even more tantalizing are the cases where there is just enough evidence to indicate a business of standing, but no details emerge of the partners or the overall period covered. One such case is the Coventry nursery already mentioned as supplying trees for Warwick Castle Park in 1759. The trees included 200 Scotch Firs, 60 Spanish Chestnuts, 8 Larches, 11 Spruce, an evergreen thorn, a Glastonbury thorn, and one each of Norway, Sugar and 'Sir Christopher Wager's' Maple. The last, which should have been described as Sir Charles Wager's, was *Acer saccharinum*. In the same year John Whittingham was paid 14s. 7d. for seeds sent to Mr. Brunton the gardener to Earl Gower at Trentham in Staffordshire; and in 1760 he sent to J. Ashley Esq. at Welton near Daventry, on the order of the Revd. Mr. Maud, the following:-

	s d
2 Swedish junipers	2. 0
1 Vard. Holy 1^s. 1 Evergn. Oak 1^s	2. 0
3 Larches 1^s. 6^d, 3 Weymouth pines, 10^s. 6^d	12. 0
1 Dl. Blm Cherry 1^s, 1 Matt 1^s	2. 0
1 Virginia Scarlet Woodbine	1. 0
2 Trumpet Woodbines	2. 0
1 Spotted, 1 Gum Cistus	2. 0
2 Dl. Blm Thorn	2. 0
	1. 5. 0

Let not a Root of ye pines be cutt nor a Branch, & stake them & the Evergreens as soon as planted

By 1783 John had given place to Charles Whittingham, with a shop in

Much Park Street, Coventry, and this continued until 1793. In 1795 the firm
had become Whittingham & Weare, and from 1803 was controlled by James
Weare, who owned several nursery grounds around the city and in 1824-26
was Mayor of Coventry for three years running. Weare was still living in 1830,
at Hertford Terrace, Coventry. The scanty history of the firm is of interest
for several reasons. So far it is the earliest known nursery in the central
Midlands: the first in the Birmingham district were those of Luke Pope near
Smethwick (c. 1771) and of John Brunton at Perry Hill, with a shop in
Birmingham High Street by 1777. Incidentally this was probably the Mr.
Brunton who in 1759 had been Earl Gower's gardener at Trentham. John
Whittingham the founder was very likely the gardener of that name born at
Shifnal, Shropshire, on 29 June 1696, son of John Whitingham a baker and
his wife Ann; this boy was apprenticed in 1711 to Samuel Chapman of
Shrewsbury, gardener, for a premium of £10. Finally, the Coventry firm
between 1795 and 1813 was transacting business in both directions with the
nursery of Nickson & Carr, later of William Caldwell, at Knutsford, Cheshire,
to which we shall return. William Bettridge, nursery and seedsman, was in
business at Warwick in 1798.

   In northern Yorkshire a nursery was begun about 1760 by Christopher
Thompson at Pickhill, between Thirsk and Bedale. In this case a fair amount
is known and a catalogue of c.1785 has been preserved. This indicates a
standing and stock little inferior to those of Telfords of York, Perfects of
Pontefract, or Barnes & Callender in Leeds. Christopher Thompson very
likely started the nursery about the time of his marriage to Margaret Raper on
24 December 1756. Their second son William Thompson (1759-1811) and his
son Christopher Masterman Thompson, born in 1781, continued the business
until about 1849. The Pickhill Nursery supplied a good deal to Caldwells of
Knutsford between 1804 and 1811, but on the other hand had purchased
from Knutsford in 1792 a collection of plants including 500 seedling Altheas
(i.e. *Hibiscus syriacus*) for 12s. 6d.; 100 Double Rocket (8s. 4d.); 6 'Cutleav'd
Area Theophraste' (Whitebeam) for 3s.; 12 Candy Tuft Shrubby (1s.); 2
Purple Batchelers Button (1s.) and 2 Double Flowering Apple (5s.). Again in
1796 they got from Knutsford 1000 seedling Limes (£1) and 100 Red Cedars
transplanted (£1. 13s. 4d.). Thompsons in 1807 were paid by Samuel Harrison of Brompton a total of £5. 13s. 6d. Possibly the most significant
document in the history of the nursery is a bill of 1775 for seeds etc. to a
total of £7. 3s., including an Orange Tree (7s. 6d.) sent to Lionel Vane Esq.
of Long Newton Hall near Stockton, Co. Durham, receipted for Christopher
Thompson 'by me William Falla'. From this we learn the name of the 'capital
nursery in Yorkshire' where Falla had acted as foreman and bookkeeper for
upwards of ten years before he purchased Dale's nursery at Hebburn Quay in
the autumn of 1781. To Falla's great venture we shall return.

   Typical of a far smaller kind of business, combining a nursery with
planting and jobbing gardening, was that of Richard Simpson (died 1783) of
Tentergate, Knaresborough. He or his son John Simpson must have been the
'Mr. Simpson, Nurseryman' who subscribed in 1776 to the *Treatise* published

by John Kennedy. John had become a member of the Ancient Society of York Florists in 1772 and was still a 'gardener and seedsman' at Knaresborough in 1795. One of Richard's bills for 1763 has survived and is printed in *Early Gardening Catalogues* (p.32). Another Yorkshire firm of local interest was that founded at Loversall near Doncaster by Abraham Crowder, gardener to William Dixon Esq. who died in 1783. Crowder in 1779 subscribed to William Speechly's *A Treatise on the Culture of the Pine-Apple, etc.* which was published at York by Ann Ward, as Kennedy's book had been. Abraham Crowder died in 1831 aged about 97, and was the first of a large clan of Crowder or Crowther, horticulturists in and around Doncaster until after 1850. The most important of their nurseries was that of Abraham's brother Rowland Wood Crowder who in 1789 married Betty Law. Their son William Law Crowder was the father-in-law of Samuel Appleby (1806-1870), nurseryman, botanist and historian of the hortulan grounds of Doncaster in 1866.

Before giving some account of the greater nurseries founded in the last 40 years of the 18th century, mention must be made of a remarkable venture which was in direct competition with trade nurseries. This was the unusual charitable trust set up by the Revd. William Hanbury (1725-1778), rector of Church Langton, Leicestershire. Before obtaining the living, Hanbury had acquired land in the neighbourhood and in 1751 began sowing seeds 'from distant countries, particularly North America'. For some years he sold seeds, then in 1758 propounded his idea of a trust which should run the nursery at a profit as a means of raising funds for the church, for an organ and organist, schoolmaster and other more visionary purposes. At this time his stock was valued at £10,000. In the following year his trustees, 23 in number, were appointed and Hanbury advertised a sale of 'forest trees of all sorts . . . American plants, flowering shrubs, greenhouse plants, etc.'. About 1760 a large sheet catalogue was printed, inviting all Gentlemen 'who will favour the Society with their orders' to direct them to any of the Trustees, to Mr. Hanbury, or to his gardener. A remarkable feature of the list is that it was clearly based on one drawn up alphabetically according to the then Latin names in use, and translated into English without changing the order. Thus, after Acacia we get Maple, Sycamore, Alaternus, Alder, Almond, Tutsan, Holly (of which there were 32 named varieties, '&c.'), Strawberry Tree; instead of Acer, Alaternus, Alnus, Amigdalus, Androsaemum, Aquifolium, Arbutus, and so on. There were 45 kinds of Rose and 13 Oaks, some of which are now unidentifiable by name. One of the most interesting sections of the list is that of herbaceous plants, described as 'Perennial Flowers proper to adorn Wilderness Quarters, Borders in the Flower Garden, Court-Yards, etc.'.

To follow out even what little is known of all the country nurseries founded between 1760 and 1800 would require a book to itself, but the material would be mostly jejune and repetitive. All that can be done here is to pick out a few of the most important developments in each region, beginning with the outskirts of greater London. It has been seen that even before 1750 Colchester had become a centre and that a few nurseries were spreading well out from the ancient nucleus of London, Westminster and the villages in the suburban Thames Valley: to Leyton in Essex, Barnet and Cheshunt in Hertfordshire, long before actual pressure on land made such a move inevitable. The tendency of these businesses was to grow up beside or near the great main roads, and this applies also to the ventures at Turnham Green and Brentford. In Surrey there was a nursery at Dorking run by James Clarke on about two acres of copyhold of the Manor. On Clarke's bankruptcy in 1767 there was a sale of his stock, and the detailed catalogue reveals the degree of expansion in the number of species held, as compared with similar stocklists of 1722-1730. This problem was tackled in a different way at Addlestone near Chertsey, where John Cree (c.1738-1816) from Kew Gardens founded a specialist nursery about 1765 (Plate 11). By 1768 Cree was able to supply the Princess of Wales at Kew with a remarkable list of rarities and new plants not yet named (for the account see *Early Gardening Catalogues*, p. 49). The Addlestone nursery grew larger and under Cree's son, the second John Cree (c. 1800-1858) produced outstanding catalogues in 1829 and 1837.

There had been an earlier nursery in Chertsey parish, but nearly two miles from the site of that formed by the Crees at Addlestone. Most of it was probably held on lease, but a small piece of copyhold land in Gogmore Lane can be traced. It was a garden and orchard of Thomas Cussings, gardener, from 1730 to 1751, when it was bought by Richard Woods (died 1793). Woods was later to become known as a landscape gardener in Essex, from 1768 until his death, but he was already a gardener and probably nurseryman in Chertsey by 1750. In 1759 he was able to fulfil a very large order for shrubs, trees and pineapples for the gardens of Sir William Lee, bart., of Hartwell, Bucks., amounting to over £100, and undertook 12 journeys to Hartwell as well as supplying a design in 1760 for the new Garden, Greenhouse and Pinery. His time charge on journeys was one guinea a day, with 6s. a day for time spent by his clerk and 12 guineas for the design. The plants were sent from Chertsey to Hartwell in a waggon with four horses at a cost of £3. (see Appendix XI. B) Woods was still based on Chertsey while he was providing designs and planting plans for Cusworth Hall in Yorkshire in the early 1760's, a remarkable exercise in detailed landscaping by remote control. Like other nurserymen, Woods was able to recommend estate gardeners, as he did for Hartwell in 1759: 'Mr. Willm Lapidge . . . I know to be a very good gardener, I belive equall to any one of the first Rank in abilitys, and belive to be a down right Honoust Man'. Lapidge had two sons that he would be glad might be 'imployd under himself'. In January 1763 Woods mortgaged his Chertsey copyhold for £160, but was able to pay this off by 1770 when he was already living in Essex. With his wife Hannah, who had had a reversionary interest in the property from the start in 1751, Woods sold the land in 1771. He was then described as 'late of Chertsey, gardner, and now of North Ockenden, Co. Essex, surveyor'.

The career of Richard Woods is of considerable interest for several reasons. His progression from nurseryman to landscape gardener and surveyor, involving abandonment of his nursery, was rather unusual, but probably due to the relatively risky finances of the plant trade. For the £150 or so of his Hartwell account, spread over the period from 10 October 1759 to 22 October 1760, Woods had to wait until 4 May 1761 for final payment, though he had by September 1760 had an advance of £55. 5s. 0d. It is not hard to see why he was driven to raise a mortgage on his little holding in Chertsey Manor. The overheads of running his nursery, able in a single order to supply 120 different species, some in considerable numbers, must have been heavy, and he was subject to the risks of weather and disease as well as of non-payment. In the second place, it is strange that he should have got two remote but important jobs as a designer while still at Chertsey, Cannon Hall and Cusworth, both in the West Riding; yet have otherwise practised almost exclusively in Essex. Finally, Woods' career is one of the few fully substantiated examples of migration.

North of London and beyond Cheshunt there was a Hertford nursery of Charles Bridgeman in 1795 and this or another was the important tree nursery of Robert Murray in the period 1807-1823. Mention has already been made of nurseries in Bedfordshire and that county of poor soil, which undoubtedly had important early market gardens around Sandy, seems to have had local resources as far back as the 17th century. In 1676 John Cottrall or Cotterel (died 1708),[1] gardener to the 1st Earl of Ailesbury at Ampthill wrote 'that those trees for the new garden may be sent, 12 apricockes and Peaches, 7 ploumes standards for the orchard below thear wants 50 trees. My Lady spoke of som trees att Bedford that should be bought their, he desired to know whether they must be had for it is time they weare set'. As we know, Ampthill itself became the rural centre for the firm of Thomas Gibbs & Co. which went on to become seedsmen and nurserymen to the Board of Agriculture and later to the Board of Agriculture of Sweden. They specialized in grasses and agricultural plants, but Thomas Gibbs also, in 1818-28, experimented both at Ampthill and at his small Brompton nursery with sports of the common cowslip in many varieties.

Rather surprisingly, East Anglia seems to have been late in establishing large trade nurseries, in spite of the very early florists in Norwich and the mention of a country supplier of plants at Creake as far back as 1637. There is no evidence of any substantial nursery at Norwich before 1773, when John Mackie (died 1797) reclaimed a large area of waste land at Lakenham, south of the city. Under Mackie's two sons and his grandson Frederick Mackie this became much the biggest concern of the kind in the region. By acquiring the collection of cacti and other succulents of Thomas Hitchen in 1833, Mackies also secured a near-monopoly in this speciality for a considerable period. George Lindley's rather later nursery at Catton, north of Norwich, has already been mentioned. Lindley in 1815 issued a substantial but unpriced catalogue of trees, plants and seeds running to 90 pages. On the margin of

1. Conceivably identical with the John Cotterell who was under-gardener to the Frenchman Laurence Coussin at Wimbledon Manor in 1643-49.

East Anglia there were nurseries at Cambridge, by far the most important being that of Richard Clarke (c. 1757-1836), a florist of Bridge Street in the parish of St. Sepulchre. Clarke married Mary Faddock in 1787 and their daughter Mary became the wife of the Revd. James Foulkes Roberts. Huntingdon had John Wood, gardener and nursery and seedsman by 1795, when he held a freehold. The firm became John Wood & Son and was continued by his son James Wood (1792-1830), who was educated at the grammar schools of Kimbolton and Biggleswade before taking over the business from his father. James experimented in raising varieties of *Dodecatheon meadia*. The nursery survived his early death and was one of the principal provincial nurseries when listed by Mangles in 1839. By 1798 there had been a nursery at Long Melford, Suffolk, run by Timothy Constable, and that of James Crick at Rochford, Essex.

To the south of London there were nurseries at Chichester. The first to be recorded was that of Moses Small (died 1798), who in 1767 was sufficiently established to take John Wood as an apprentice, and bought an extra acre of ground in 1784. The business was carried on and further enlarged by Small's grandson Henry Silverlock, son of Nevill Silverlock who had married Small's daughter Elizabeth. Henry Silverlock, who in 1822-1839 was reckoned to run the principal nursery in Sussex, was also 'distinguished as the inventor of a hollow wall which promises to be of real utility both in gardening and cottage-building', as Loudon wrote. The main rival at Chichester was the firm of Newman, founded by William Newman, who had a shop as a mealman and seedsman in 1784, but who had also ground in the parish of St. Bartholomew known by 1787 as Newman's Nursery. He died in 1789, leaving 'all my Stock in Trade Shrubs Plants and Utensils' to his son William Newman, and 'my Watch' to his grandson of the same name. The business went on as Newman & Son under one or the other William Newman until after 1830 and then became James Newman & Co.

The early Southampton nursery of George Irwin has already been mentioned. The next on record is Isaac Keen, who in 1780 married Elizabeth Candey in All Saints Church and in that same year was sending large numbers of trees to Winchester College for the Fellows' garden there. Of these some great London Planes (which, as large trees in 1780, cost 1s. each) are still living. Keen had part of the Lower Garden at the bottom of Southampton town south of East Street in 1781 and by 1803 also a part of Tolsbury Field nearby; all this was still occupied by him in 1818. Too late to be discussed in detail here, Southampton got two other nurseries of long continued fame: in 1812 that started or re-founded by William Rogers with the help of his father, John Rogers (1752-1842) who had worked in the Royal Gardens at Richmond and Kew, and in his old age wrote *The Fruit Cultivator* (1834) and *The Vegetable Cultivator* (1839). The firm, after various moves and transfers, is still in business as W. H. Rogers Ltd. of Chandlers Ford. The other Southampton nursery was launched in 1815 by William Bridgewater Page, who had trained at the Hammersmith Nursery and married Amelia Emily the daughter of John Kennedy (1759-1842). Kennedy was probably the main author of the valuable catalogue published only two years later under the title of *Page's Prodromus; or a general nomenclature of all the plants indigenous and exotic cultivated by him in the Southampton Botanic Gardens...* As was to be expected in a nursery so closely allied to the Hammersmith centre, this was very active in introductions: in August 1838 Page first flowered the blue *Salvia patens* grown by him from seed sent by John Parkinson, the British Consul at Mexico. In the next year Mangles listed Page as celebrated for New Holland (i.e. Australian) plants, and among the principal provincial firms. By 1861 the company was Page & Toogood, and as Toogoods it survived as a famous seedsman until 1965.

A less prominent but earlier Hampshire nursery was at North Warnborough near Odiham, whence John Armstrong sent to Winchester College on 4 March 1782: 12 Green Holleys (3s.), 12 Evergreen Oaks small (3s.) and another 12 Green Holleys (3s.) on 13 March. Armstrong was something of a specialist, for in 1796 he raised *Geranium* (i.e. *Pelargonium*) *quinquevulnerum* from seeds sent from the Cape of Good Hope (Plate 15). This was recorded almost at the time by Henry Andrews in the *Botanist's Repository,* volume II of 1799, so that it is difficult to understand the date of '1807' given for this introduction in modern sources. In the 1830's the North Warnborough Nursery was in the hands of John Shilling, a noted raiser of hybrid forms of *Delphinium* based on *D. chinense* (*grandiflorum*) and *Tropaeolum*. Mangles included him among the chief provincial nurserymen of England.

The county town of Berkshire, Reading, was a centre of the garden trade well before the founding of the agricultural seed shop of John Sutton (1777-1863) in 1806. About 1775 James Swallow was first rated for 'land late Brasseys' in Pangbourn Lane (Oxford Road), St. Mary's parish; by 1810-12 Messrs. Swallow & Son had Nursery Farm there, assessed at a rental value of £102, besides £72 of meadow rented off the Caversham Road. Mr. Swallow senior was separately rated at £21, increased from £16, in Newbury Road, but by 1832 it was his widow of Russell Street who paid rates on a reduced value of £12 for a nursery and £10 for buildings. Between 1767 and 1786 eight children of James and Ann Swallow were baptized at St. Laurence, Reading, including John Swallow born in 1779 and described as of Henley when he married Sarah Dredge at St. Giles, Reading on 17 July 1808. This suggests that his father, besides keeping the nursery at Reading, was the James Swallow who in 1795 was a gardener and baker at Henley-on-Thames. One of James Swallow's sons already had a nursery at Maidenhead by 1792, when the father, described as nursery and seedsman, Broad Street, Reading, advertised 'fine large Battersea Asparagus Plants as usual, viz. one years 2s., two years 2s. 6d. per hundred', which want 'no other recommendation than the proof his friends have already had' of the goodness of his own and his son's plants. By 1798 Reading also had the nursery of Henry Poole.

Between 1766 and 1771 Lord Bruce of Tottenham (Earl of Ailesbury in 1776) was getting plants and fruit trees for the Savernake estate in Wiltshire from a Berkshire nursery at Woolhampton, kept by William Pendar. A surprisingly wide range could be supplied as is shown by a letter of 2

December 1766 (see Appendix IX). Pendar also issued a sheet catalogue of his Fruit Trees, printed by C. Micklewright and Comp. in the Market Place, Reading. There were 44 varieties of peaches, 17 nectarines, 10 apricots, 44 pears, 32 plums, 18 cherries and 50 apples; 'Also Apples upon Paradise Stocks, Vines, Figs, Goosberries. Currants, Raspberries, Quinces, Medlars and Mulberries, with Variety of Flowering Shrubs, Ever-Greens, and Forest-Trees. . . . Bass-Mats, and Seeds of most Sorts'.

Pendar had probably taken over a much older nursery, for the diary of Thomas Smith of Shaw in Melksham, Wilts., on 23 August 1721 has the entry: 'At 7 this morning we left our Quarters and called at Woolhampton to see a Nursery Garden, where Mr [Daniel] Webb [of Monkton Farleigh] bought many trees and plants to a great value, which detained us till near three . . .' It is clear that even quite remote places might have an important plant centre with distinguished patrons over a radius of 20 miles or more. To the subject of specialized fruit nurseries we shall return in dealing with Wigan (p.116).

Salisbury was an exceptionally early centre of nurseries, as we know from Anthony Lawrence's statement of 1677 (p.70). It is surprisingly difficult to get any connected picture of the men responsible for the 'goodly Nurseries' mentioned. From 1710 to 1760 the registers of Wiltshire Apprenticeships have been printed, and over a dozen gardeners are named; but the same name never occurs twice. The Milford Nursery was certainly the most influential at a later date, and so we may suspect that one of the growers of 1677 was the John Totty of Milford, gardener, who died in 1681. Totty was the grand-father of John Totty Baker, gardener of Milford, who on 12 January 1722/3 took as apprentice George Ham for a premium of £6. By 1783 Andrew Chapman Geary (died 1792) and William Geary were nursery and seedsmen of Salisbury, and when A. C. Geary made his will in 1791 he was of Milford and of Idmiston. In directories of 1791-1798 the firm appears as J. & P. Geary, seedsmen, then from 1805 to 1830 as Geary & Moody. They were said by J. C. Loudon to 'grow the best crocuses in England, of which they send large quantities annually to London, and other parts'. In 1841 Thomas Moody was nurseryman, seedsman and gardener of Castle Street, Salisbury, and four years later he was leasing a substantial holding in Milford from the trustees of Wadham Wyndham esq.

In 1782 Thomas Biggs, florist at 'Fishburton', presumably Fisherton, by Salisbury, put out a catalogue of 251 named varieties of auricula, of which one hundred cost 10 guineas each, the rest 4 guineas. He may have moved to Andover, Hants., where a gardener Thomas Biggs was in the directory of 1793. Another specialist in the district was one Dodds of Salisbury who, in 1836, supplied 27 bulbs of hybrid Amaryllis for £1. 2s. 0d., for the gardens at Nynehead near Wellington, Somerset; and in the following year pineapples: 6 Providence Pine plants, 6 Black Jamaica ditto, and 3 Enville ditto, at 5s. each, with hamper and package £3. 16s. 6d. (see also Appendix XI.C). He was very likely William Dodds (c. 1808-1900), who as gardener to Colonel Baker was winning prizes for camellias at a meeting of the Wiltshire Horticultural

Society in 1833. Rather mysteriously, the only firms mentioned by Mangles
in 1839 are R. W. Squibb of Salisbury, and a Robert Coe of Milford, which
may be the place in Wiltshire.

Moving on to the West, the suburbs of Bristol had several nurseries before
1800, but none of them appears to have been founded in 1785. Peter Lauder
had a nursery at Lawrence Hill by 1792 and within the next few years issued
quite an impressive though unpriced catalogue of Fruit and Forest Trees,
Flowering Shrubs, and Perennial and Biennial Flower Roots; in 1814 this
business was taken over by William Spiring of the Upper Easton Nursery. This
had begun about 1793 under Edward Spiring senior, in 1795 was Spiring,
Mortimore & Co., and from 1801 was kept by William Spiring. In 1814 he
was able to supply Edward Jones Esq. of Llandovery, Carmarthenshire, with
6000 Scotch Firs one year old and 3000 Larch of one year, sent by ship 'The
New Comet'. Also at Upper Easton, in 1803-1805, was a nursery run by Peter
Lauder junior. John Maddock or Maddocks had a nursery at Lampblack Hill
from 1795 to 1816, and then moved to a site near Stokes Croft where he was
still in business in 1834. Though not founded until 1815, the firm of William
Maule & Co. in Stapleton Road rapidly achieved fame. William was the son of
James Maule, who came of a family of factors and gardeners to the Earls of
Dalhousie at Brechin Castle, Forfarshire. About 1769 James Maule moved to
England to become gardener to the Coddrington family at Dodington near
Chipping Sodbury. By 1839 Mangles recorded that the firm was celebrated
for American Bog plants, but the heyday of the business came under
William's son Alexander James Maule (1820-1884), a kind and whimsical
personality and a great expert on the culture of Orchids. He is mainly
remembered for the introduction and propagation, in 1869-74, of
Chaenomeles japonica (*Pyrus* or *Cydonia Maulei*).

The most influential of all the Bristol nurseries was that founded in 1786 at
St. Michael's Hill, but better known as the Durdham Down (Clifton) Nursery
after a move in 1791-92. The name kept changing, but the succession seems to
have been: from 1786 to 1808, Miller & Sweet; 1809-1824, Sweets & Miller;
1824-1837, John Miller, who went bankrupt. The business was taken over as a
going concern by James Garaway, and continued as Garaway, Mayes & Co. after
1845, later James Garaway & Co., until it became absorbed into Brown & Sons
Seeds Ltd. Garaway was working for Miller, probably as foreman of the nursery,
in 1828. It is not clear whether the John Miller who was sole proprietor from
1824 was identical with the founder of the firm, but the chief plantsman
concerned at the start seems to have been James Sweet, elder half-brother of the
more famous Robert Sweet (1783-1835). They were sons of William Sweet of
Cockington near Torquay in South Devon. James was gardener to Richard
Bright Esq. of Ham Green near Bristol; according to Loudon at the time Robert
was in his 16th year (about 1798), but this is hard to reconcile with the
statement that James was 'afterwards the founder of the extensive nursery' at
Bristol. In 1795 a bill for trees sent to William Blathwayt Esq. of Dyrham Park
was receipted for Miller & Sweet by John Sweet; John and James were
presumably the Sweets of the succeeding phase of the partnership.

An unusual range of catalogues issued by the firm from 1808 to 1838 has survived, and it would be possible to work out in some detail the development of their stock. By 1822 they were reckoned by Loudon 'the most extensive garden-tradesmen in the west of England'. So far as bills have survived, it would seem that the firm began in a traditional way with fruit and forest trees, but the catalogue of 1808 includes long lists of bulbous and herbaceous, greenhouse and hothouse plants. Entries in the *Floricultural Cabinet* and in Paxton's *Magazine of Botany* show that between 1833 and 1837 John Miller was extremely active in raising new plants and in experimental work. A letter of 5 November 1833 to the former journal described a visit to their grounds: 'one portion of their garden was laid out in small compartments, each allotted to a particular plant, such as the *Anagallis monelli, Verbena melindris,* &c., &c. . . . the *Thunbergia alata* attracted my attention . . . it covered the whole bed', grown as a trailer slightly above the surface, not as a climber. Miller had in 1824 planted a 'new Experimental Garden' with his own kinds of peach and nectarine, and he kept up the tradition of personal visits to his customers. In all this it is evident that Miller disastrously over-extended his resources.

James Wheeler of Gloucester has already been mentioned. It is probable that Loudon left out a generation in stating that the nursery founded by him before 1763 was carried on by his two daughters, and in 1822 by one of them. In 1795 the Universal British Directory lists both Wheeler & Son, marked as 'County Freeholder' and Edward Wheeler as nurserymen at Gloucester; in 1802 there were W. Wheeler and E. Wheeler (? Edward or Elizabeth), called seedsmen, Hare Lane; in 1814-20 Elizabeth Wheeler, 'nursery and seedswoman', Northgate Street. Probably Edward was son of James, and Elizabeth, the lady mentioned by Loudon, daughter of Edward and granddaughter of James Wheeler. The Hare Lane firm appears in 1820-1844 as that of James Daniel Wheeler; but the more noted business was that carried on at 99 Northgate Street by James Cheslin Wheeler (died 1860) and as J. C. Wheeler & Son by his son Alfred Cummins Wheeler. In his time an enterprising policy of issuing catalogues got up as attractive 'Little Books' of Seeds, Grasses, etc. was pursued. Worcester in 1798 had the two nurseries of James Biggs and of Thomas Hammond.

Taunton had two nurseries in the early 19th century, but only one went back before 1800. In 1782-83 John Harris senior was buying land in the tithing of Mill Lane, Taunton and in 1802 was granted a parcel of waste at North Town, Taunton. He was described as a yeoman, but by 1804 when he had left Taunton to live at Chulmleigh, Devon, as a gardener. By 1800 certainly, and probably from the 1780's he worked a small nursery, and part of this was taken on by his son John Harris junior. But in 1811 the rest was sold to James Poole (c. 1777-c. 1827), who ran the nursery with his brother William Poole. In 1827 this small garden formed part of the purchases being made by John Young (c. 1790-1862), a Quaker, who since 1825 had been a seedsman in North Street, Taunton. Young also bought much more land in North Town (about a half-mile from North Street, in the parish of St. James), and by 1840 the area amounted to 14 or 15 acres. Mangles in 1839 had listed Young as one of the principal garden firms, and Loudon visiting in 1843 greatly praised the Taunton Nursery. The other Taunton nursery was much smaller, covering only 4 acres in 1840, at South Road. Known as Hammond & Stephens, it was in fact Thomas Stephens who was the main personality. First heard of in 1835, the firm was already a principal one four years later and became noted for raising new shrubby calceolarias, as well as many kinds of trees, shrubs and flowering plants. Wells, Somerset, had the nursery of John Tucker by 1798. (see also p.xii)

At Exeter the nursery of the Lucombe family has already been discussed, but another was founded later in the eighteenth century by Joseph Ford (died 1796), who in 1779 subscribed to William Speechly's treatise on the Pine-Apple. The firm was described as nursery and seedsman at New Bridge, Exeter, until 1795; in 1805 was Ford & Please. William Ford (c. 1760-1829), seedsman, St. Thomas, Exeter, also mentioned as early as 1795, was by 1825 a nurseryman of Longbrook Street. About 1826 he introduced the Exeter Elm (*Ulmus glabra exoniensis*), but died soon afterwards, as in 1831 the nursery was run by Ann Ford, probably his widow. The nursery, on the site of Blackall Road and the railway, finally disappeared under houses in 1854. The immensely famous nursery founded by John Veitch (1752-1839) in 1808 belongs entirely to modern history.

Leaving the West Country for the Midlands, the predominance of Birmingham is very marked. Thanks to the detailed researches of Mr. Miles Hadfield, a great deal is known of one of the earliest firms, founded by Luke Pope (1740-1825) and continued by his son John Pope and grandson Alexander Pope. Luke Pope was originally of Smethwick and in 1771 had a lease of land in Ruck of Stone Lane there, and in 1796 he was one of the constables of Smethwick Manor; in 1802 bailiff of the Manor. Though his first nursery was in Smethwick, it seems to have been the purchase of land at Gib Heath in Handsworth in 1790 that led to the rise and fame of what was long called the Handsworth Nursery (to be carefully distinguished from the one in Yorkshire at Handsworth near Sheffield; see below, p.118). The other early nursery in the area has an extremely complex history, not yet entirely clarified. It was founded some time before 1777 by John Brunton (c. 1721-1803), very likely the gardener at Trentham in 1758-9, whom we have already met. In 1777 a catalogue came out, listing 'Plants, botanically arranged according to the system of Linnaeus, most of which are cultivated and sold by John Brunton & Co.'. There was a shop at 83 High Street, Birmingham, and a nursery at Perry Hill, apparently at Quinton in the ancient parish of Halesowen, Worcestershire (and formerly a detached part of Shropshire). In 1782 a priced catalogue appeared, but this was almost a verbatim reprint of that of 1776 issued by Perfects of Pontefract, with a few added items from the list of Telford of York, and some prices changed. There could be no clearer evidence of the Yorkshire origin of the great innovation in trade practices.

The firm in 1782 was Brunton & Forbes, but Brunton, Forbes, Forbes & Hunter by 1787 when another priced catalogue came out; this shows new introductions added from the London lists, as against the purely Yorkshire scope of five years before. By 1792 the address was 25 High Street, but by 1797 it was Brunton, Hunter & Co.; later the address changed to 18 High Street. In 1799 the firm was Brunton & Co., but in 1798 Hunter dissolved partnership and appeared as a separate business. Brunton must have retired aged about 78, some four years before his death. James Augustus Hunter had taken one of the Forbes into partnership by 1805 and was back in 18 High Street; but by 1821 he had gone into bankruptcy. John Forbes was running a separate business in 1805 and in 1808 was in New Street; at 13 New Street were Forbes & Son in 1830. It is not clear whether this was a continuation of Alexander Forbes & Co., which about 1792 took over the old Brunton shop at 83 High Street, and soon afterwards announced that their nursery was at Small Heath, Warwickshire, about a mile away. Nor is there any evidence yet available as to any relationship to the great gardener Alexander Forbes, who took over at Levens Hall in Westmorland in 1810 and re-stocked the old garden there in the next few years. In 1794 the Birmingham firm was Forbes & Blakesley; from 1795 to 1801 the junior partner John Blakesley was apparently trading on his own account and buying trees from the Knutsford Nursery in Cheshire.

There is little sign of any serious competition with the Birmingham nurseries within a radius of 20 to 30 miles in the West Midlands, but further to the east several were founded in Northamptonshire, Rutland and the south-east of Leicestershire, precisely the region for which the Hanbury Trustees at Church Langton purported to cater. This is a curious fact and one so far without explanation. The Trust's income at Hanbury's death in 1778 was £190 a year, and had risen to £900 in 1864 when the gardens were closed, so that it must have carried on a substantial trade by the standards of the time. The profits of the Knutsford Nursery from 1803 to 1815 varied from about £45 to £200; in 1832-1850 from £60 to £500, but commonly about £250. Church Langton is only some five miles from Market Harborough, where William Hubbard (died 1787) already had a flourishing nursery in the year of Hanbury's death, 1778. In that year Hubbard sold to Sir Justinian Isham of Lamport Hall, Northants., for £82. 18s. 9d. an order comprising Firs, Pines, Cypress, Cedars, Laurustinus, Phillyreas, Evergreen Oaks, Swedish Junipers, Sweet-scented Chinese Arbor Vitae, Common ditto, Portugal Laurels, Hollys, Bays, Laurels and Box.

Some twenty miles to the south, at Daventry, there was already a nursery and seedsman, Samuel King, in 1784, and between 1812 and 1825 Robert Turnbull of Daventry was sending out large orders of trees, shrubs and seeds. Less than twenty miles to the east of Church Langton was Tinwell, Rutland, where a nursery was started or taken over about 1796 by William Murray. Murray had been gardener to the Earl of Exeter at Burghley House, nearby, from 1780 or earlier, and in 1790 had subscribed to Speechly's treatise on the Vine. Between 1797 and 1808 he sold over £140 worth of trees and seeds to Normanton Hall alone. Murray's successor at Burghley, William Maddock, had only held that post about five years when, on 6 November 1801, he advertised in the *Lincoln, Rutland & Stamford Mercury* that he would lay out and take care of gentlemen's Pleasure and Kitchen gardens, plant, prune and train Fruit Trees 'on the newest Plan', and that he 'intends opening a Seed Shop near the Bull Gate, Stamford, where he purposes laying in a Stock of the best Garden and other Seeds, Green House Plants, &c.'. As if this were not enough, Thomas Haynes, nurseryman of Oundle, Northants., by 1802 also had a shop in Stamford, and issued a large sheet catalogue, fully priced. Besides a long list of Roses at prices from 2d. for a Single Sweet Briar up to 4s. for the Unique or White Provence, Haynes offered not only all the usual trees and shrubs and fruit trees, but a selection of over 350 kinds of Herbaceous Plants, as well as bulbs. As has already been mentioned Haynes commenced author in 1811 and has several treatises to his credit.

In the next chapter the story of the great explosion of country nurseries will be carried to the North Midlands and the North to culmination in the firm of William Falla & Co. just before the opening of the Victorian era. Here is a convenient place for comment on the great revolution in transport which in the second half of the 18th century made this development possible. It was the improvement of inland navigation on rivers, and the cutting of canals, that changed the whole picture of cost in regard to planting on a large scale. Whereas York, Leeds, Pontefract, and Newark had for centuries enjoyed convenient river transport, as did Oxford down the Thames Valley to London; it will be noticed that most sites of early nurseries of importance were on or near the sea: Gateshead, Colchester, Southampton, Exeter. The spread of nurseries through southern, eastern and midland England after 1760 went more or less hand in hand with the opening of canals. Before the completion of the first links in the mesh of main-line railways about 1840, the whole of England as far as south Yorkshire had been given an inter-communicating system of water transport by which bulky and heavy consignments could be sent with relative cheapness, safety and ease. It was this that tipped the balance, over a great part of the country, in favour of planting as a profitable as well as pleasurable pursuit.

VII

CULMINATION AND CONCLUSION

IT WAS, WE SAW, in the North of England that the move towards mass production of plants began. For reasons of social and economic history there was there a general demand on a grand scale that did not exist elsewhere. It was a demand necessarily linked to reasonable prices, and from 1775 onwards prices were given adequate publicity through the catalogues. Land in the North was plentiful and cheap, and the soil and climate were suitable for the production of really tough hardy stock. There was also, beside the general demand, a special demand in this period, roughly 1760-1840, for enormous numbers of forest trees for improvement. Thousands of acres of waste land on the bleak fells, seldom cropped and until then regarded as barren and unprofitable, were put under trees which, in a generation or so, yielded large profits from their timber. In these circumstances it is not surprising that, outside the metropolitan area, the greatest concentration of major nurseries should have been in the North.

To find an acceptable definition of 'the North' is not easy. Many would limit the term to the six northern counties; but this fails to take into account the close community of interest between Cheshire and south Lancashire; between North Staffordshire and both eastern Cheshire and Derbyshire; between Derbyshire and the Sheffield region; between Nottinghamshire and the Northern Province to which it belonged; between north Lincolnshire and the East Riding. At least some of these debatable counties needs must be regarded as northern in character. On the other hand, some would think that there is a grain or two of truth among the chaff that considers there is a 'Black Pudding Curtain' hung just north of Potters Bar. On the whole, the most acceptable line of division is the one implied in the phrase 'north of Trent'. This is here interpreted to mean all those counties any part of which lies on the north side of the Trent — thus including Lincolnshire and Staffordshire as well as Nottinghamshire and Derbyshire; and Cheshire regarded by analogy as a southern extension of Lancashire. It is this whole region, stretching from the Border down to the northern suburbs of Birmingham on the west, and to Stamford on the east, that must now be considered.

Birmingham has already been dealt with, along with its technically northern outliers in ancient Staffordshire, and so has the area immediately around Stamford, since Tinwell, Burghley Park and Oundle in any case lie to the south of the line. Here we shall begin at the south-west, in Staffordshire, moving north-eastwards towards the Tyne. At Rugeley, twenty miles or so north of Birmingham, there was a nursery by about 1780 kept by Henry Hammond. Not much is known of Hammond beyond what can be gleaned from his general catalogue of 26 pages, printed in 1791 by M. Morgan at Lichfield. The list is based firmly on the Yorkshire type, but the prices for many lines are higher, reflecting the fact that Hammond must for the less common trees and shrubs have been acting as a middleman rather than growing his own stock. Children born to him and his wife Mary were baptized between 1781 and 1793, including his successor in business, Henry Hammond junior, on 20 October 1790. William Caldwell of Knutsford was a main supplier of plants to Hammond from 1798 to 1811, and from 1812 onwards to Henry Hammond & Son. The Staffordshire Directory for 1818 shows Henry Hammond & Son as gardener and seedsman, Horse Fair, Rugeley, and Mrs. Mary Hammond conducting a seminary for young ladies. When the son succeeded he seems to have abandoned the garden trade by degrees: in 1834 he was a grocer, tea dealer and seedsman in Stafford Road, but next year in Market Street he was no longer called seedsman. By 1850 the name had disappeared from the town.

At Cheadle in 1784 there was a gardener and nurseryman, William Heap, still there in 1793. By 1820 his place had been taken by Joseph Plant, nurseryman and florist, who contributed articles to the *Floricultural Cabinet:* on the culture of *Oxalis Deppeii* in 1836, and then on *Erythrolena conspicua.* He was one of many contemporary florists to specialize in the calceolaria. Not far from Cheadle, at Checkley, was Thomas Welton, who in 1827 was offering terms for contract planting of trees by the acre, either insured for three years or not insured; with a separate set of prices per thousand merely for supplying the trees. He could be recommended by John Philips Esq. of Heath House and by James Blair Esq. of Uttoxeter, who had employed him. Burslem had Daniel Haywood, buying fruit trees from the Knutsford Nursery in 1796, and in 1811-12 supplying trees to the Marquess of Stafford for Trentham. John Haywood, probably a relative, had a nursery at Leek, and in 1794 was buying from Nickson & Carr at Knutsford a dozen Moss Roses and also 200 Pear stocks, the latter being set off against two dozen striped hollies sent from Haywood to the Knutsford Nursery. These were no doubt quite small grounds, but at Burton-upon-Trent was the more important business of William Smith, a subscriber in 1790 to Speechly's treatise on the Vine, as a nurseryman, in 1793 described as gardener and seedsman, then as nursery and seedsman from 1818 to 1844.

The rather nebulous beginnings of the firm of Wilson at Derby have been mentioned. In the north of the county, at Bolsover, Joseph Outram was a gardener and seedsman in 1793; while at Bolsover Hill, described as 'near Sheffield' were the nurserymen Fox & Oldham who in the same year were dealing with Nickson & Carr at Knutsford. Crossing over into Nottinghamshire, several quite early nurseries have been dealt with. In Nottingham itself John Rayner in the High Street flourished by 1795, issued a broadsheet catalogue shortly before 1800, and was still there in 1805. But the great firm of the district was that founded in 1782 at Chilwell by John Pearson. This was carried on by a son and grandson of the same name, the latter born in 1819 and dying in 1876. Later still the partners were James Royston Pearson and Alfred Pearson, and as J. R. Pearson & Co. the business continued until 1932 or later. The founder, who died in 1825, 'stood high as a breeder of Tulips for a short time' and was held to deserve first place among raisers of carnations. 'He may be truly styled the Father of the Fancy in this neighbourhood . . . He was indeed a kind-hearted enthusiastic florist. . . . It was no matter to him how coarsely dressed his visitor might be.' Between 1805 and 1812 the Chilwell firm was doing business with Caldwell at Knutsford, on a part exchange basis, but the trade balance was in Pearsons' favour. In 1807 they were first called John Pearson & Son, and in that same year John Pearson junior, nurseryman of Chilwell, subscribed to the *Flora of Nottinghamshire* of Thomas Ordoyno. A catalogue of the second John Pearson, of about 1832, has survived, and shows attention to new varieties of azaleas, rhododendrons and camellias, a list of over 20 Roses and mention of 'about 100 distinct varieties and all good new sorts added' at prices from 6d. to 2s. At this time Pearson had the Fountain Head Seed Warehouse in Exchange Row, Nottingham, open only on Wednesdays, Saturdays and principal fair days.

Newark-upon-Trent, which had had the early nursery of Francis and Michael Noble (see p.68) became a considerable gardening centre. What may have been Nobles' old nursery was before 1776 run by the brothers Garrett Ordoyno (c. 1723-1795) and Jacob Ordoyno (c. 1734-1812). In 1776 Jacob subscribed to John Kennedy's *Treatise upon Planting,* and the firm appears in Bailey's Directory as nursery and seedsmen, along with Simon Holt & Son. Garrett's son, Garrett Ordoyno junior, was left his father's share in the nursery but seems to have sold it at once, as in 1796 the business was named as Ordoyno & Withers, by 1800 Withers & Co. From 1802 Withers was in partnership with William Speechley, who died on 7 June 1804; he was perhaps a son of the great gardener William Speechly (c. 1734-1819). The firm still survived, at Market Place and Millgate, Newark in 1832 as George & Thomas Withers. Old Jacob Ordoyno had retired to live at Coddington as a gentleman and when he died, a lifelong bachelor, in 1812, he left substantial estates to his nephews Garret, Thomas and Charles. It was Thomas Ordoyno who also had 'all my Botanical Books and Books on Gardening' as well as all Book Debts due 'during the time I was in business as a Nurseryman, Gardener and Seedsman at Newark'.

Thomas Ordoyno, who on 19 June 1792 married Ann Brown at Newark, was the serious botanist of the family, publishing the county flora already mentioned, a book subscribed to by Lord Byron. It was perhaps his influence that gave to the catalogue of J. & G. Ordoyno issued in or shortly before 1795 a scientific new look in the sections on Herbaceous, Greenhouse and Stove plants. This was an important innovation in a priced catalogue otherwise of Northern style. But whereas these new lists had Latin and English names in parallel column, those of Forest Trees and of Flowering Shrubs were still basically identical with those of Telford and Perfect. An appended list of Seeds, vegetable and flower, is also antiquated and not even in alphabetical order. There was a Thomas Ordoyno who, on 17 January

1810, was paid £3. 18s. 0d. as his 'Wages to this day' by Samuel Harrison, the Brompton nurseryman; this was possibly a son of the botanist.

Other Newark nurseries were those of Thomas Palethorpe, in Appletongate between 1793 and 1807 and succeeded by Joseph Palethorpe, of Chain Lane in 1832; and George Clark(e) of Strawberry Hall, Lincoln Road, who flourished from 1807 to 1832, and was succeeded by William Clark & Co., in the Market Place in 1835. Both Thomas Palethorpe and George Clark were subscribers in 1807 to Thomas Ordoyno's comital flora. Another man of enterprise in the Newark garden trade was Philip Saxe, who about 1790 put out a trade card stating that he had been gardener to Robert Wilson-Cracroft Esq. at Newark and 'Having taken the Gardens, Hot-Houses, and all belonging thereunto, will be glad to serve any Ladies or Gentlemen with Pine-Apples, or Pine-Plants, and any other Fruits or Vegetables in Season'. In 1794 he advertised his invention of a covering made of osiers for protecting 'fruit trees whilst in Blossom, against frosts, Beating Rain, and Hail'. This could be had 'three feet wide at 7d. per Yard, four feet wide at 9d. per Yard, and other Breadths in Proportion'.

The Lincoln Nursery was founded in 1780 on land at Gowts Bridge, and greatly expanded after 1825 under Richard Pennell (died 1869) and his son Charles Pennell (c. 1821-1896), who took over in 1856 after wide experience in France and Germany. His father in the 1840's had been able to supply estates in the county with very large orders of forest trees of many sorts, but the firm later specialized in Roses. It continues as Pennell & Sons Ltd. with a wide basis but specializing particularly in Clematis. Messrs. Pennell have preserved many of their business archives and have taken the generous step of depositing many of them in the Lincolnshire Archives Office. Another old nursery in the county was that at Grantham kept by William Wood in 1784, by William and John Wood in 1795, by John until 1811 or later, in 1826 by another William Wood and in 1842 by Henry Wood. The firm was supplying trees and shrubs to Normanton Hall, Rutland, on a large scale in 1804-06 under John Wood, and in 1807 he also sold stock for £2. 2s. 6d. to Samuel Harrison of Brompton on Harrison's northern tour. In regard to the migrations of gardeners it is of interest that Messrs. W. Crowder & Sons, still in business at Horncastle, derive in direct descent from William Crowder (died 1836) who came from Bawtry, Yorks. about 1800 to set up a walled nursery garden at Cagthorpe in Horncastle, carried on by his son Anderson Crowder (1792-1873). Presumably the founder derived from the horticultural family of Doncaster. The little town of Waltham near Grimsby in 1798 supported the business of Robert Fountain, gardener, seedsman and nurseryman.

In spite of the continuous existence through the Middle Ages and early modern times of the orchard and garden in Chester Castle, there is no definite record of plant nurseries in Cheshire, or in Lancashire and Flintshire which have always preserved social links, until after the middle of the 18th century. It is quite likely that there was horticultural continuity over a long term in the Nuns' Gardens at Chester, but this cannot be proved until 1781 when they were run by George Rogers (died 1799) who also kept the Sun tavern in

St. Peter's churchyard. Rogers was called gardener, seedsman and nurseryman at various dates and the little that is known of his activities suggests that he was a local middleman getting a good deal from other larger gardens. Thus he bought 12 pear trees and a Trumpet Honeysuckle in 1795 from William Caldwell of the Knowsley Nursery near Liverpool, and in the same and the following year numbers of Larch and Scotch Firs, Birch and flowering shrubs from Nickson & Carr of Knutsford. Rogers died in 1799 and his will (see Appendix VI) shows that in addition to the Nuns' Gardens he had leasehold gardens in Handbridge and Flookersbrook. He left the reversion of his interests, after the death of his wife Sarah, to her Son John Gorton, but it looks as though Gorton used his stepfather's surname, for a nursery at Handbridge and a shop at 104 Upper Bridge Street belonged to John Rogers in 1818-20 and in 1828-1840 to Mary Rogers, presumably his widow. John Rogers, possibly the nurseryman listed at Nantwich in 1781, is mentioned in 1789 at the Nuns' Gardens, Chester, as well as George; and John Rogers was in Castle Street in 1814-15. This career suggests a single personality and identity with George's stepson John Gorton.

Around 1800 and later the other nurseries around Chester were very small and it was not until 1820 that the important business of Francis Dickson (1793-1866) was founded. Though really outside our period, this firm must be mentioned for its rapid rise to a distinguished position. In early days from 1820 onwards Francis and James Dickson bought a good deal of stock from William Caldwell & Co. of Knutsford. By 1828 they were issuing a lengthy seed list which referred to their extensive nurseries at Bache Pool and Piper's Ash, with 'a great Stock of Forest and Fruit Trees, Flowering and Evergreen Shrubs, Greenhouse Herbaceous and Alpine Plants'. The mention of Alpine plants at this date is noteworthy. By 1835 the *Floricultural Cabinet* printed a list of evergreen shrubs which could be procured 'from any respectable nurseryman; Messrs. Dickson, at Chester, are as good as any'. In 1839 Mangles regarded them as among the principal nurserymen in the country; in that year they were settled in what became their famous Newton Nursery, and flowered a *Rhododendron campanulatum* planted in 1832. Dickson, apparently Francis, was cited in 1850 by Knight & Perry in their manual of *Coniferous Plants* as authority for the name of *Abies alba nana*, so he must have had a botanical reputation in the trade.

In 1822 Loudon wrote of Cheshire that there were 'good nurseries at Nantwich and at Knutsford'. The latter, probably better documented at an early period than any other in the country, will shortly be dealt with; but whose was the garden at Nantwich? It can only have been that which in 1791 was in the occupation of Isaac Mullock, at Houghton Moss near Nantwich. By 1800, and on to 1824, the nurseryman was Peter Mullock, trading in both directions with Caldwells of Knutsford. He must have died soon afterwards, as the directories of 1828 and 1834 show Catharine Mullock as nurseryman and seedsman, Nursery Grounds, High Street, Nantwich. Also carrying on a two-way business with Knutsford was Moses Reid, who flourished from 1793 to 1833 at Pepper Street, Middlewich. Possibly his relative, Thomas Reid of

Doddington was a seed grower, supplying Knutsford with cabbage seed and, in 1799, with 3 lb. of Mignonette seed for which Caldwells paid one guinea. Another small nursery was that of Andrew Plant at Stockport, evidenced in 1791-1800, and dealing with both the Knowsley and the Knutsford nurseries. At this point may be mentioned one of the very few nurserymen in Wales, Thomas Vickers who was gardener, nursery and seedsman at Holywell, Flintshire, in 1795. He, or possibly a son, was probably the authority quoted by Benjamin Maund in *The Fruitist* in 1846. The Cambrian Plum, said Maund, is 'cultivated extensively by Mr. Vickars . . . He has informed us that the original tree is now growing at Denbigh, about forty years old'.

The border areas along the Mersey valley in north Cheshire and south Lancashire have long been famous for fruit. As far back as the reign of Henry VIII, John Leland in his itinerary of 1535-45 singled out for mention the gardens at Morley near Leigh in Lancashire, saying that there was there 'as much pleasur of orchardes of great varite of frute and fair made walkes and gardines as ther is in any place of Lancastreshire'. Though it is not possible to trace a connected history of nurseries in the region from late mediaeval times, it can be regarded as certain that this regional interest in fruit, and most especially in small fruit − notably the gooseberry − has a deeply rooted tradition. Loudon, writing in 1822, referred to the almost universal cultivation of gooseberries in every cottage garden in Lancashire and adjacent parts, and to the 136 meetings for the award of prizes recorded in the *Manchester Gooseberry-Book* for 1819. 'The present lists of London nurserymen contain from 80 to 100 names; but those of some of the Lancashire growers above 300.' In fact, as far back as 1780 Richard Weston had printed the price-list of 320 named varieties of Gooseberry Trees raised from seed in Lancashire, and sold by James Maddox (Maddock), florist, at Walworth, London.

Within this region the earliest specific records of nurseries relate to those at Knutsford. Whether newly founded or not, these were in the hands of John Nickson by 1759 when his son Joseph was baptized on 27 September. John Nickson (died 1809) was then and later described as of Over Knutsford, in 1784 as botanist, gardener and seedsman; in 1793-4, when he served as one of the High Constables for the Hundred of Bucklow, and afterwards, he was termed gentleman. It is probable though not certain that he was the son of Joseph Nixon, gardener of Over Knutsford, who was buried on 21 June 1755 and his wife Sarah, buried on 25 September 1759. When he made his will on 12 February 1809 John Nickson was living in a freehold house in Nether Knutsford, and this he left to his wife Margaret (died 1823) for life. He had retired from the firm in 1796 but as late as 1803 rented a part of the ground for £8. 8s. a year. It is uncertain when he took John Carr (died c.1803) into partnership, but it was probably by 1780, when William Caldwell (1766-1844) became his apprentice. In 1793, J. Nickson & Carr, nurserymen, Knutsford, were subscribers to Richard Steele, *An Essay upon Gardening,* published at York by George Peacock. Caldwell, who in 1788 married Sarah Bradbury (1763-1825), daughter of John Bradbury of Higher Town Farm, Knutsford, took over about that time the Radshaw Nook Nursery at

Knowsley in Lancashire. He sold his stock to Thomas Caldwell for £100 in 1796, when he joined John Carr as junior partner at Knutsford on Nickson's retirement.

The Knutsford Nursery was and has ever since remained one of regional importance, though in that part of the early 19th century for which its balances survive, the profits fluctuated violently (see above, p.105). In 1802 Carr & Caldwell had a balance of £230. 1s. 10d. to divide; in 1816 the nursery was valued at £980. 15s. 9d. We have seen that the nursery did business over a wide area of Midland and Northern England, not only with the public but also in buying and selling plants from and to other nurseries. From the Knutsford books which, like those of William Caldwell's earlier nursery at Knowsley, survive from 1789, a picture emerges of a very wide stock held and well cultivated, with a large body of satisfied regular customers. Caldwell, like his old master Nickson, was evidently a botanist in the then accepted sense of the term. He studied land surveying as a manuscript book including geometrical problems of survey solved by him still survives, as well as his copy of William Davis, *A Complete Treatise on Land Surveying* . . . (1805). He was also something of a musician.

The only early catalogue of the Knutsford Nursery so far known is a priced list of forest trees for 1824, but catalogues were printed before this, since on 27 September 1814 there occurs the cash book entry of £5 paid to 'J. Wilson for printing Catalogues'. On 24 April 1799 'Advertising the Raspberry in Manchester Paper' cost 16s. 6d. On 7 September that year there was £1. 3s. spent on 'Subscription & Expence to Lathom Goosberry Meeting'. It is impossible to deal here with the details of the business, but a few general conclusions must be given. The geographical scope, so far as private clients was concerned, covered the whole of the eastern half of Cheshire and the southern fringe of Lancashire as far as Liverpool and Manchester. The range of trade contacts was very much wider and, apart from dealings with the great London firms of nurserymen and seedsmen, extended from Keswick and Hawick in the north to Birmingham and Coventry in the south; from Chester and Liverpool in the west to Pickhill, York, Cottingham, Newark and Chilwell on the east. It is instructive to compare this with the much more local range of the Knowsley Nursery in 1789-96, covering private clients mainly between Liverpool and Wigan, and from Ormskirk to Runcorn, and trade contacts with Pickhill, Cottingham and Birmingham, but little else.

Liverpool was the centre around which the nurseries of the region gravitated, rather than Manchester. Caldwell's partner of the early 1830's, Joseph Picken (c. 1806-1835), was a Liverpool nurseryman. Dying in his 30th year on 16 October 1835, Picken was described by J. C. Loudon as 'a good man, of business habits, and a scientific practical botanist'. It was natural that Caldwell should turn to the great Merseyside port, for in his period of business at Knowsley he had been in some kind of partnership with a Liverpool seedsman, William Kirke, referred to in the books in 1789-91. Kirke & Caldwell, nurserymen at Liverpool, subscribed in 1790 to William Speechly's treatise on the Vine. Another nursery in the Caldwell family was that at Wavertree, run by James Caldwell (died 1795) and after his death by Thomas Caldwell until 1800. The Knutsford branch of the family has continued there to the present day in the fifth and sixth generations from the founder, beginning with his son William Caldwell (1789-1852) and grandson William George Caldwell (1824-1873).

At this point something must be said of the overall picture of the costs of running a nursery at the opening of the 19th century. In general, most nursery land was on lease, and the rents were substantial. At Knutsford the rent paid in 1800 was £83. 10s., and by 1835, for a larger area of ground, this had gone up to £130. Taking the year 1805, for which fully detailed records survive, we can make up the cost of seeds, bulbs and plants bought *from* the great London firms as, in round figures:

(1) *Seed and Bulb firms*	£
John Beck & Co.	56
Blair & Co.	50
John Mason	17
Minier, Minier & Nash	46
Warner & Seaman	34
	£ 203

(2) *Nurseries*	£
John Allport (Shoreditch)	11
Gordon (Mile End)	26
Gray, Wear & Gray (Brompton Park)	10
William Malcolm & Co. (Kensington)	14
Malcolm & Doughty (Stockwell)	34
Whitley & Brames (Old Brompton)	25
	£ 120

To this total of about £323 for seeds, bulbs and plants from London we have also to add orders placed with several provincial firms:

Telford (York)	10
Thos. Rigg & Son (York)	4
James Weare (Coventry)	5
John Pearson (Chilwell)	16
William Thompson (Pickhill)	8
	£ 43

There is therefore a grand total of at least £366 in outgoings on stock, besides many small local purchases from suppliers of seeds, tree mast and other items found close to Knutsford. No wonder William Caldwell's profit for 1805 was only £51. 4s. 0d.

There were in Liverpool, besides the Knowsley and Wavertree nurseries run by the Caldwells, two major firms of standing. One was founded by George

Plate 9: *Three South African plants introduced to the Brompton Park Nursery and drawn by Henrietta London, daughter of George London, c.1705. For identifications see p. xiii; the plant on the right is* Nemesia strumosa, *parent of the popular half-hardy annuals and usually stated to have been first introduced to Britain only in 1892. From Badminton MS. D.4.11, by kind permission of His Grace the Duke of Beaufort.*

Plate 10: Banksia serrata, *the first Australian plant raised in Britain, by James Lee at the Vineyard Nursery, Hammersmith, in 1788. From a coloured engraving of 1807.*

Plate 11: Vaccinium amoenum, *introduced in 1765 from North America by John Cree of the Addlestone Nursery. From* The Botanist's Repository, *vol II, plate 138.*

Plate 12: Erica ampullacea, *grown in 1780 from seed from South Africa by Richard Williams of the Turnham Green Nursery, and first flowered in June 1784.* Botanical Magazine, *vol. IX, plate 303.*

Plate 13: Narcissus tenuior, *grown by James Maddock at the Walworth Nursery*
before 1794. Botanical Magazine, *vol. XI, plate 379.*

Plate 14: Chrysanthemum indicum, *parent of* the *chrysanthemum, first flow-ered in Britain in November 1795 at the Chelsea Nursery of James Colvill.* Botanical Magazine, *vol. X, plate 327.*

Plate 15: Geranium *(now* Pelargonium*)* quinquevulnerum, *introduced in 1796 from South Africa by John Armstrong of the North Warnborough Nursery.* The Botanist's Repository, *vol. II, plate 114.*

Plate 16: Azalea pontica *(now* Rhododendron luteum*), first flowered in Britain in 1798 at the Islington Nursery by Thomas Watson, from whose plant the plate was drawn by Sydenham Edwards.* Botanical Magazine, *vol. XIII, plate 433.*

Cunningham the elder, who may have been the man of that name at West Derby who in 1794-96 was dealing with William Caldwell at Knowsley. The firm was certainly Cunningham & Johnson of 71 Paradise Street and Wavertree in 1811-1824 and George Cunningham & Son, at 75 Paradise Street, in 1834 and later, and their manager for 40 years from 1855 was George Watson, a Methodist and well known local character. Most of what is recorded of the firm comes from the Notes on Local History compiled by James Hoult, who about 1900 had access to some of the old books of the business. Hoult states that the founder played a great part in introducing the Brown Beech from America (? *Fagus grandifolia* or *ferruginea,* introduced in 1766) and was the propagator of the original stock of the Irish or Florence Court Yew in 1780. Cunningham, on one of his tours to Irish estates, was told by Lord Enniskillen of Florence Court, Co. Fermanagh, that one of his tenants, Mr. T. Willis, had found two unknown trees growing on a mountain side. Cunningham was allowed to take one of the trees, from which he successfully propagated *Taxus baccata fastigiata*; the other, left in Irish soil, died. Cunningham's son, George Cunningham junior, carried on the Old Swan Nursery and 'imported the scarlet Dahlia, then the only kind known'.

The other great Liverpool plant business was that of Thomas Whalley, who began before 1783 as a grocer and seedsman in Castle Street. By 1814 the firm was Thomas Whalley & Son of 24 Castle Street and Maghull Nurseries near Ormskirk. In that year they issued a catalogue of 112 pages, covering every aspect of the trade in Trees, Shrubs, Plants, Bulbs and Seeds. Of outstanding interest are the sections on Herbaceous and Alpine Plants (pp. 27-63) and Hardy American or Bog Plants (pp. 75-81). Though the greater part of the catalogue is unpriced, prices are given for the year's bulbs: Hyacinths, Narcissus, Tulips, Ranunculus, and for Anemones and Auriculas (pp. 3-12). After 1815 the firm seems to have disappeared, though the business of John & Joseph Whalley of South Crescent, Lord Street flourished from 1811 until 1834 or later. In addition to the Maghull nurseries of Thomas Whalley there had been an earlier Ormskirk nursery kept in 1784 by James Blundell (died 1798), and from 1790 by a partnership with James Hankin. Blundell was primarily a grocer, and the real plantsman seems to have been Hankin, for William Caldwell from Knowsley made a valuation of 'Hankin's Nursery' at Ormskirk in 1796. Hankin was still in charge as late as 1821.

There was a small nursery at Barton-upon-Irwell near Manchester kept by Thomas Wilkinson between 1791 and 1815, and he got a good deal of stock from Caldwell at Knowsley and from Knutsford, both in the days of Nickson & Carr and later. In the Manchester area there were a great many small nurseries, mostly founded after 1800, but few seem to have been of any significance. The larger businesses were those of seedsmen, such as the William Middlewood of Market Street Lane, whose catalogue of seeds and plants of 1776 survives; or of florists, such as Taylor & Withington, later Taylor, Weston & Co., and Taylor & Smith, of 39 Deansgate, in business from before 1795 until after 1822. In 1783 Hulme & Raffald were nurserymen and gardeners at Salford, and the junior partner probably belonged to the Stockport family of gardeners. John Raffald, gardener of Stockport (died 1790) made his will in 1787 leaving his residuary estate to his son George Raffald, gardener of Stockport, who died in 1805. A much more important firm was that of Peter McNiven (died 1818) and Charles McNiven (died 1815), brothers, who were both surveyors and nurserymen at Alport Lane, Manchester in 1783, and between 1791 and 1803 were buying plants from the Knowsley and Knutsford nurseries. The business must have prospered, for the personal estate of Charles McNiven was sworn 'under £35,000', administration being granted to his son Charles because his mother Margaret, the widow, was a lunatic then living with her brother Mr. James Broad at Selkirk in Scotland. Messrs. McNiven communicated to William Forsyth (1737-1804), for his *Treatise on the Culture and Management of Fruit-trees* (1802), the list of the largest new sorts of gooseberries shown in Lancashire in 1800, and this has been reprinted by Mr. Ronald Webber in *The Early Horticulturists.*

One other nursery in Lancashire deserves mention as having been undoubtedly one of the greatest orchard nurseries on record. It was kept in, of all unlikely places, Wigan by William Pinkerton who also appears disguised as 'Penkett' and 'Penkington' in the directories. Pinkerton's catalogue of 1782, well printed by William Eyres of Warrington, is a classified list of varieties filling 16 pages. The totals are so remarkable that it may be worth while to consider how this early list compares with later and modern collections of fruit. By including also the numbers of sorts given by Rea in 1665 it is possible to see some recession (in plums and quinces) as well as advance. The other lists used are those of Peter Lauder of Bristol, c. 1795; William Falla & Son, Hebburn Quay, 1797; William Falla & Co., Gateshead, (1827); and George Bunyard & Sons, Maidstone, 1938 — this last taken from the quotation by Mr. Miles Hadfield in *A History of British Gardening.*

Fruits   *Numbers of Varieties offered*

	Rea 1665	Pinkerton 1782	Lauder c. 1795	Falla 1797	Falla c. 1827	Bunyard 1938
Apples	20	121	132	67	149	128
Apricots	6	14	8	8	11	9
Cherries	24	24	20	15	29	37
Nectarines	1	23	18	13	15	14
Peaches	35	48	43	25	40	26
Pears	20	68	68	45	60	74
Plums	44	38	34	31	53	53
Quinces	5	2	1	1	1	4
Vines	9	30	30	28	57	25
Total	164	368	354	233	415	370

The Wigan Nursery was therefore in the top bracket, both by the standards of its own period and by those of the 20th century. Pinkerton was also a general nurseryman and seedsman and got some stock from Knutsford and from Knowsley between 1789 and 1796; he was still in business in 1798.

In 1795 Lancaster had J. Richmond, nursery and seedsman, in Penny Street, but nothing more can at present be said of him. There were several small firms at Kendal, including A. Henderson, who was a gardener and seedsman able to supply normal orders of flower and vegetable seeds, and sundries, to local residents; he is evidenced from 1782 to 1795. William Furnass, gardener and nurseryman, likewise supplied seeds and plants, with a few fruit and ornamental trees, in 1786-1800, but he also carried out jobbing gardening. Henry Hoggarth and Robert Petrie are also styled nurserymen in their entries in the directory of 1795. At the same time Thomas Brockbank was called nurseryman and gardener at Hawkshead.

Cumberland had several nurseries of standing before 1800, and as we have seen, Carlisle had a seed trade even in 1621. Henry & T. Dennison were the principal nurserymen there in 1792-1811, with an address in English Street. The same establishment may have been continued by William & Thomas Hutton, who were in English Street in 1829 and 1834, and by Little & Ballantyne, there in 1858 with a nursery in London Road. A much more important centre of the trade was Keswick. John Sander about 1790 originated the Keswick Codlin Apple, and in 1794 undertook to plant 14 acres with oaks at £5 an acre for John Christian Curwen of Workington Hall. Sander still appears as a nurseryman in 1811. What seems to have been the principal nursery had been founded by Thomas Clark before 1787, when he planted 84,500 larches at Wansfell, Ambleside, for the Bishop of Llandaff, Richard Watson. The firm was Clark & Stevenson in 1795, Clark & (Caleb) Atkinson in 1798, when they sent plants to Mrs. Morland at Kendal: 4 dwarf apples (2s. 6d.), 1 Virgin's Bower (1s. 6d.), 1 Pyracantha (4d.), 1 Hypericum (1s.), 1 Oxalis versicolor (1s. 6d.). A covering letter remarked: 'I can think of nothing better for the front of your room window than a Virgin's Bower, and a Pyracantha if you give them large Pots may answer the purpose as a shade. Shd. the Oxalis top be broak will not be of any consequence as the roots is bulbous'. The business was carried on after 1805 as Thomas Clark & Co., with the partners William Clark and James Hanks, both of Keighley, Yorkshire, where they had other grounds. What appears to have been the same firm, as gardeners, nurserymen and seedsmen in Keswick, was Gray & Clark in 1829. On the coast to the west of Keswick, at Workington, there was one nursery of standing, that of John Greener. Greener in 1776 offered to plant 21 acres with trees spaced 4 feet apart for J. C. Curwen of Workington Hall at £4 an acre, and to 'uphold' the trees for 3 years; in 1807 and 1808 he was a subscriber to the Workington Agricultural Society at 7s. a year. Doubtless the same business was that in the hands of Peter Greener, gardener, nursery and seedsman, of Back Guards, Workington, in 1829 and 1834.

Although Cumberland had this fair sprinkling of nurseries, none of them was of outstanding importance, and the reason is to be found in the existence across the Border of one of the most significant in the whole of Britain. This was the firm founded by Robert Dickson in 1728 at Hassendeanburn near

Hawick, only some 45 miles to the north of Carlisle. The business was continued by Archibald Dickson, who in 1776 advertised in the *Cumberland Pacquet* that he could supply 2-year-old transplanted Scotch Firs at 10s. per thousand ('six score to the hundred given') or one-year trees at 7s. 6d. per thousand; 2-year spruce or Norway Firs were 25s. a thousand. The first of these prices represented a big undercutting of the Yorkshire current price of 15s. per thousand for 2-year transplanted Scotch Firs, even apart from the advantage given by the Scottish long hundred. Both Archibald Dickson, and Archibald Dickson junior, were subscribers to the Workington Agricultural Society at 10s. 6d. a year in 1807 and 1808, and it is evident that the Hassendeanburn Nursery had secured a big foothold south of the Border. In 1795 Nicholas Ashton Esq., of Woolton Hall near Liverpool, received a Gold Medal of the Society of Arts for having planted 133 acres of enclosed land with forest trees. He had employed Messrs. Dickson of Hassendeanburn, who in November and December 1795 planted 487,040 trees on this land in Weaverham near Northwich, Cheshire.

We saw that the Keswick firm of Thomas Clark & Co. operated also at Keighley in the West Riding. One of the partners, James Hanks, had been a foreman or senior assistant to Messrs. Perfect of Pontefract in 1798, and he married Sarah daughter of Richard Dunhill, one of the great Pontefract liquorice growers. His later career was divided between the two places. In 1802-1809 he was a nurseryman of Pontefract, on his own or as James Hanks & Co., dealing with Caldwell of Knutsford. Then, under the same company's name, but at Keighley, he issued a list of forest and ornamental trees in 1810. Then in 1811 he disposed of the Keighley property and formed a new firm at Carlton near Pontefract as Hanks & Dunhill. In 1812 the firm issued a priced list of trees, and in the following year they were paid £124. 4s. 0d. for planting at Sandall Beat near Doncaster, an area of 20 acres 2 roods 32 perches at £6 an acre. By 1822 James Hanks alone is named as nursery and seedsman at Carlton, Pontefract; in 1834 Hanks & Co. were in the Beast Fair, Pontefract; and in 1837 Hanks & Muscroft were in the Corn Market, as well as at their Nursery. Also in Beast Fair, Pontefract, from 1809 or earlier until 1822 was the firm of Thomas Oxley & Scholey.

In the extreme south of Yorkshire one other important nursery had been founded before 1779 by John Littlewood. This was at Handsworth near Sheffield, to be distinguished from the Handsworth in Staffordshire on the northern outskirts of Birmingham (see p.104). Littlewood subscribed to both the treatises of William Speechly, on the Pine-Apple in 1779 and on the Vine in 1790. In 1822 he was described as nurseryman and seedsman, Handsworth, and in that year he made his will, two of the witnesses being Robert Michael Hirst, of Handsworth, nurseryman, and Charles Fisher of the same, nurseryman. Littlewood died on 13 May 1825. He had undertaken planting on the grand scale, and records survive of his work in that line for Doncaster Corporation. In 1807-8 his bill for plants was £191. 5s. 6d.; in 1811 he had £100 on account of planting at Sandal Beat; in 1812 he had £211. 12s. 6d. for planting 30 acres and 37 perches there at £7 an acre. As we have seen, he was undercut in 1813 by Hanks & Dunhill, who did the work for £6 an acre. The trees ordered to be planted in Sandal Beat in 1810, probably obtained from Littlewood, were to be 20,000 oaks, 10,000 ashes, 60,000 larches, 5,000 Dutch Elms, 500 grafted elms, 3,000 beeches, 2,000 sycamores, 500 Scotch firs, 5,000 chestnuts and 500 limes.

The Handsworth Nursery after Littlewood's death was taken over by Fisher, Holmes & Co. Charles Fisher, George Fisher and James Foster were among the partners in the next 20 years. In 1831 they received *Fuchsia elegans* from Port Antonio; turned them into the open border in 1832 and in 1833 had 200 plants ready for sale — 'they have not the slightest doubt of the plant being perfectly hardy'. This was apparently what is now regarded as *Fuchsia magellanica (macrostemma) globosa.* In 1835 the firm was winning prizes at the Sheffield Horticultural Society's show for greenhouse plants, geraniums, mimulus etc., and in 1839 Mangles not only listed them among the principal nurserymen but remarked that they were 'celebrated for a fine collection of Rhododendrons'. By 1859 they had a shop at 98 Market Place, Sheffield, and ten years later had spacious grounds of over 100 acres skirting the south side of Handsworth village. The nurseries 'are celebrated more particularly for the cultivation of shrubs. Many of the cemeteries of America are planted with trees supplied from these nurseries'.

The earliest nurserymen recorded at Beverley have already been named, but there and at Cottingham, on the way to Hull, were several different firms around 1800. What Loudon in 1822 described as the large nursery at Cottingham was that founded in 1788 by Abraham Martin. The firm lasted until 1885, eventually as Martin & Son, with a shop in Market Place, Hull, as well as premises in Northgate, Cottingham. In 1818 Abraham Martin inserted a notice in the *Hull Advertiser* of 28 November that he 'has a very good stock of Fruit as well as of Forest Trees, particularly Larch ... a large Collection of Evergreens, Flowering Shrubs, Perennial Flower Roots, etc'. Another nursery at Cottingham, with a second garden at Beverley, was that of Robert Scales who in 1793 subscribed to *An Essay upon Gardening,* by Richard Steele. As Philipson & Scales the firm dealt with the Knutsford Nursery, both under Nickson & Carr and later in the time of Caldwell. In 1795 they seem to have obtained early seed potatoes from Knutsford, for 2 bushels were sent on 7 November charged at £5. 4s. 0d., with 6s. for 2 hogsheads, 2s. 6d. for cooperage, but less 8s. 6d. for carriage to Manchester. The original senior partner was John Philipson, living on his freehold at Cottingham in 1807; but by 1811 it was Henry Philipson who went bankrupt. A great sale of stock was announced on 31 August 1811, and the final days of sale were held on 19 and 20 March 1812 at Cottingham, and on 21 March at the Beverley nursery. Philipson survived, and in 1823 was listed in the directory as a gardener of Jackson Street, Neptune Street, Hull.

The great nursery of Beverley was not founded until after 1800, but is too important to be passed over in silence. George Tindall took up the freedom of Beverley in 1806, as gardener, nurseryman and seedsman, and between that date and 1820 was acquiring properties mostly by lease from private landowners or from Beverley Corporation. In 1823 George & William Tindall were nurserymen of Eastgate, Beverley, and had a shop at 25, Market Place, Hull. The years 1825-1827 saw them carrying out planting at Warter Hall for Lord Muncaster. By 1828 they had four nurseries, two off Lairgate, both owned by James Walker Esq., one on the east side of Eastgate; and The Trinities on the east side of Trinity Lane, owned by the Corporation. This last, which had become their principal ground, was where the railway station stands. In 1829 the nurseries comprised 130 acres, entirely cultivated by the spade. They then formed 'the most extensive speculation which is carried on at Beverly in the way of trade. . . . Fifty persons are usually employed on at Beverley in the way of trade. . . . Fifty persons are usually employed on the town: 'The inner and a considerable portion of the outer Trinities at present comprise a part of the extensive gardens and nurseries of Messrs. George and William Tindall, which, with the adjoining grounds, form an amusing promenade to the respectable inhabitants of the town, who are privileged to walk there by special permission. The magnitude of these nurseries, as far as concerns spade cultivation, is perhaps not exceeded by any in the kingdom; and for neatness, management, and produce cannot easily be surpassed'. George Tindall subscribed in 1829 to a large paper copy of George Oliver, *The History and Antiquities of the Town and Minster of Beverley*, from which the above extracts are taken; and in the same year G. and W. Tindall were subscribers to two copies of the rival book *Beverlac*, by George Poulson, which also mentions their nurseries. The railway came and its station, built on the site of the main nursery, was opened in 1846. Next year William Tindall, doubtless well compensated, is mentioned as 'Gentleman'.

James Innis, nurseryman and seedsman of Bridlington in 1793 is no more at present than a name in a directory. Further north at Scarborough, William Bean (died c.1801), was less a nurseryman than a fruiterer, florist and high-class greengrocer, but he was a seedsman and in a prosperous way. He founded the Scarborough Vauxhall Gardens and was the father of William Bean (1787-1866) the geologist and conchologist. Hitherto no evidence has come to light regarding early nurseries in the Tees valley, whether on the North Riding or the Durham side. Though this may at first seem surprising, it is probably due to the accident that by about the middle of the 18th century the district was served, from either side, by three powerful firms: that of the Thompsons at Pickhill, and at Gateshead or near it those of Joyce and Dale, later of Falla. Before returning to the Gateshead nurseries we have to consider a few lesser gardens in Durham and Northumberland. Though perhaps not a nursery, the garden of the Friary (former Grey Friars) at Hartlepool, was about 1816 producing 'the best reputed Ribston Pippins in the country'.

At Houghton-le-Spring in Co. Durham there was a nursery of local scope combined with the seedsman's business of James Clarke. Nothing would be known of him, had not a copy of his catalogue of 1779 come into the hands of the late William Roberts. The list itself has regrettably disappeared, but Roberts devoted a substantial article to its contents. It was a surprisingly large booklet of 52 pages, listing seeds and plants and giving 'their season of

Sowing etc. Chiefly adapted to the Northern Climates', and also a list of prices for Fruit Trees. These prices, either the same or rather cheaper than those of Telford of York in 1775, suggest that the trees were locally grown by Clarke's own efforts. At Hexham, Thomas Garland was listed as a seedsman and gardener in 1784 but then disappears. Newcastle-upon-Tyne could boast of the elusive florist James Thompson, said to have published in 1757 a tract on the Auricula,[1] and in the next year a translation of *The Dutch Florist.* These works, in the form specified by the early bibliographers who list them, have not been rediscovered in modern times. The earliest nursery firm of standing seems to have been that at The Orange Tree in Middle Street, supplying vegetable seeds and fruit trees to Lord Delaval in 1794-95. The proprietors were Michael Callender and William R. Callender, probably relatives of the partner in Thomas Barnes' contemporary business at Leeds.

Something has already been said of the nursery which William Joyce had launched at Gateshead by 1754. As he made his will as early as 1760 and died in 1767 it is quite possible that he was the Mr. William Joyce who in 1730 subscribed to Furber's *Twelve Months of Flowers;* this may suggest, but is far from proving, that Joyce came from the London area. Joyce's will shows him to have been prosperous, and to have had a half-share in the nursery, the other half being apparently already transferred to his son Stanley Joyce before 1757. William's share was to be equally divided among his grand-children, the children of Stanley and of his sister Sarah Elerton. Stanley's son John Joyce was to have £20 'to put him Apprentice to some Trade which he may Chuse, a Gardner Excepted' and he was to have a capital sum of £150 when 21 and £5 a year 'dureing the Continuation of the Nursery and Trade which we now carry on to be paid out of my half share'. A sum of £30 a year was allowed 'for a Gardner of Judgment and Fedelity to be hired to assist in Trade and see Justice done' as between the various family interests. Mr. Richard Stephenson at Gibside was to inspect the Books twice a year; James Duncan was to account in place of the testator. One of those who made an affidavit as to the handwriting of the will was William Falla of Gateshead, gardener, who knew Joyce and had frequently seen him subscribe his name.

The firm of Joyce was enterprising, and in 1766 sent into Scotland a hand-ruled list of 25 kinds of forest trees available for the planting of forfeited estates, one of the great opportunities for improvement on the largest scale. Stanley Joyce in 1770 took as apprentice John Joyce, presumably his son in spite of the curious provision in William Joyce's will. Stanley in 1778 subscribed to William Boutcher, *A Treatise on Forest Trees,* the only English nurseryman to do so apart from Messrs. Williamson and Company, London (i.e. of Kensington). Ten Scottish nurserymen and seedsmen, and three Scottish gardeners were the other trade subscribers who declared their conditions. By 1793 John Joyce was running the firm, in 1827 it was John & William Joyce of 87 High Street, Gateshead, and in 1834 William Joyce of

---

1. Also (?) attributed to James Douglas.

109 High Street, probably the great-grandson of the founder. By that time the Joyce nursery, promising and profitable as it had been, was thrown quite in the shade by its giant neighbour, William Falla & Co.

It is a puzzling question, just why the district around Gateshead should have become a centre for early nurseries. The founding of one might be due to the merest accident, but it is hard to explain away the arrival of two major nurseries and some smaller ones, within the half-century after 1730. At least part of the explanation must lie in the preponderant commercial standing of Newcastle at that period. It had become a place of immense economic importance in the far north of England, nearly 300 miles from London, a great port in its own right and activated by the trade in coal. Newcastle itself and its suburbs already spread over much of the north bank, and it is said too that the climate of the southern side of the Tyne estuary is more propitious to gardening than the northern. The probability is that, to an intelligent nurseryman with capital, seeking an opportunity for expansion, the site would appeal as having excellent transport and an ideal position as beach-head from which to exploit the hinterland. Estates in Northumberland and Co. Durham had to get much of their stock sent from London by long sea, and these shipping costs could be eliminated. At the time the Pickhill Nursery in the North Riding had almost certainly not been founded; the rather awkward routes for water transport from York or Pontefract, and the costly alternative by wagon or coach, were not greatly to be feared as providing really economic competition.

We already know that, up to 1733, Gateshead Park was dependent upon London for its main supplies of trees and shrubs for the new planting (see p. 82 and Appendix VII). From a schedule of garden implements handed over we also know that Henry Ellison, after dismissing Thomas Woolley, had appointed James Deel or Dale to be his new head gardener, by 18 December 1733. The surname, though not very common, is well known in the region on either side of the Tyne, and several other gardeners named Dale are found in the course of the 18th century. Most of these were certainly relatives of George Dale, the nurseryman, and it seems quite likely that James Dale may have been his brother or cousin. It is at any rate a plausible hypothesis that some repercussions of the affair of Stephen Switzer, Thomas Woolley and Henry Woodman may have been a decisive factor in causing George Dale to launch out on a new enterprise. Already a gardener of Hebburn Quay in the parish of Jarrow, about three miles east of Gateshead and with immediate water transport, he took a lease of a considerable property there in 1734. His original term was for 21 years, entered upon on 15 October, at a rent of £18. 10s.

The terms of Dale's lease, which was from Cuthbert Ellison Esq. of Hebburn, throw a good deal of light on the practices of the period in regard to this specialized form of agriculture. The property was a burgage with a stable etc. and a garden adjoining the house on the south and another garden near the south-east corner with a Garden House to be built thereon, also a close of land called Damis Close and a lane called Damis Lane. The landlord would repair the house and stable, but Dale was bound to scour and dress the hedges, ditches and fences and to keep the doors, gates and 'styles' in good repair. Dale was to lay and spread on Damis Close and Lane all the manure compost or dung produced from the hay growing there, subject to the penalty for every load of hay taken off that he should lay on four 'futhers' (fodders or 'tons') of good rotten manure. He was not to cut trees, timber wood or underwood, but was to manure, cultivate, dress and keep the gardens 'in good order and according to the usuall and accustomed course of gardening'. There were, standing and growing in the garden near the south-east corner of the house, 99 Pear trees and 9 Apple trees, which Dale was to keep and prune in the best manner — a clause which may indicate that the garden had already been in use as a fruit nursery. Dale might otherwise take away all 'Barron Trees Fruitt Trees, Gooseberry & Curran Bushes and all other Trees and Bushes' except these and the trees in the hedgerows. The only taxes for which Dale would be responsible were 'the Poor Sess, Window Sess and the Tax for the Reparation of the Highways'. There was a right of renewal and George Dale continued as tenant for over 46 years to his death in 1781.

George Dale probably married about the same time that he took the lease at Hebburn Quay. One of his daughters married in 1764 and a George Dale, gardener of Ovingham, Northumberland, half way to Hexham, aged 24 in May 1762, was very likely a son. His son Joseph Dale, who worked with him and gave a receipt on his behalf on 29 September 1780, died shortly afterwards, before his father made his will on 8 May 1781. Joseph Dale had left six children, all under 21, and there were four other grandchildren; all ten were to have £100 each. George Dale left £1,000 to his daughter Isabella, and the interest secured from another £1,000 to his 'dear wife Ann' for her life. One guinea was left to George Dale, gardener, of Heaton, Northumberland. The trustees of the will were Joseph Ramsey of Cowpen, Northumberland, farmer; John Clennell of Newcastle, hatter and hosier; James Dale of Halnaby, Yorks. (5 miles south of Darlington), gardener; and William Hallgarth of South Shields, Salt Officer. George Dale was in partnership with Ramsey in the farm at Cowpen and left to Ramsey 'my old favourite Brown Saddle Mare and my best Saddle and Bridle'.

When, at Michaelmas 1781, William Falla entered upon the land formerly of George Dale, together with the whole of the stock, he was taking over a going concern. The nursery held a wide variety of different kinds of trees and plants, and for several years past between six and seven acres had been devoted to propagating fruit trees of the best varieties. Some idea of the effective value of the nursery can be obtained from the statement of William Falla (c.1739-1804) that a capital sum of £500 plus an annuity of £20 for life was equivalent to a share of one-quarter of the Hebburn Quay and Gateshead Nurseries. By the time that a good deal more land had been taken in, therefore, the whole of the business was regarded as worth £2,000 plus £80 a year. Another of William Falla's calculations put the value of the whole of the goodwill of the nursery and seed business in 1800 at about £1,900 after allowing for all debts; and the value of the stock-in-trade of the two nurseries including seeds and garden tools, at a low valuation, at £1,600, making a total of not less than £3,500 together. William Falla also had a three-quarter interest, purchased for £1,200 in 1799, in a freehold estate at Cramar Dykes in Gateshead. Apart from his real estate and other equities, he died in 1804 with personalty valued at 'under £5,000'. All this put together amounts to less than half the fortune of £20,000 amassed by John Russell at Lewisham in the same period; but it was enough to enable the second William Falla (1761-1830) to build the business into the largest nursery ever known in Britain.

Before carrying the story of the nursery further, we must look into the origins of William Falla. Born probably in 1739, since he died on 20 May 1804 aged 65, he was married to Isabella Bolam at Heworth Church, Co. Durham, on 21 October 1760. We have seen that in 1767 he was a gardener at Gateshead and very well acquainted with William Joyce and had often seen him sign his name: implying that he was probably employed on the Joyce nursery. In 1770 he was still described as 'of Gateshead, gardener' when he was a witness to two marriages, of Charles Adams of Hartburn, gardener, on 26 March; and of Robert Mackey, of Alnwick, Northumberland, gardener, on 14 April. But we know that when he took over Dale's nursery in the autumn of 1781 he had been foreman and bookkeeper to Christopher Thompson at the Pickhill Nursery for 'upwards of ten years', therefore since 1771 at latest. This was confirmed by his description as 'late of Pickhill near Bidall (Bedale), Co. York' when, on 1 July 1782, he took a lease from Henry Ellison Esq. of the house, stables etc. and two nurseries at Hebburn for 21 years at £46 a year. In 1800 his brother Thomas Falla and sisters Mary and Isabel were all living near Berwick-upon-Tweed. A Thomas Falla, very probably the same, died at Belford in 1811 aged 75. Mr. Trevor Falla, the historian of the family, has so far been unable to prove their precise origins further back, but finds a close concentration of the name, from 1695 onwards, in the extreme north of Northumberland between the Tweed, Belford and Wooler. Mr. Falla also finds abundant proof that the name appears indiscriminately as Falla and Fallow. The family of the nurserymen seems always to have been Nonconformist, at first Congregational, later Unitarian.

To follow out in detail the history of the firm would require a substantial book in itself, so numerous are the detailed bills and other records concerning their trade. All that can be done here is to indicate the outline of what they did in the course of less than 60 years to transform the nursery gardening of the North. At this point it is convenient to set out the dates of the various partnerships and the personal careers involved. The firm, founded by George Dale and carried on by him continuously from 1734 to 1781, was taken over by the first William Falla but very soon became William Falla & Son with his eldest son William Falla (1761-1830) as partner. The first William died on 20 May 1804 and by 12 June the business was already being called William Falla & Co., the title under which trade was carried on until 1840. After reconstruction the nursery was continued by Charles I'Anson and Samuel

Finney, trading as I'Anson & Finney; this later became Samuel Finney & Co. Ltd. and Finneys Seeds after the nursery had been abandoned. To revert to the Fallas: the second William married Rebecca Stor(e)y at Jarrow on 4 February 1795, and their eldest son William Falla, (III) was born on 28 December 1799. William Falla II (Plate 8) was married a second time in 1811 at St. Andrew's, Newcastle, to Elizabeth Rutherford. He died on 4 August 1830, and his widow followed on 22 October 1831. In the meantime the third William had married Eleanor Coates on 16 January 1831.

In 1790 William Falla & Son took out a subscription to Speechly's treatise on the Vine, and in 1793 John Falla, William's second son, subscribed to Richard Steele's *Essay on Gardening*. John was then a nurseryman of Hebburn Quay, but by 1800 was living at Brentford, Middlesex, married with three daughters; a son Myler Falla, born c. 1808, died in 1881 at Richmond, Surrey. Since John Falla had left Gateshead his father provided for him the financial equivalent of a quarter-share in the business but left all the stock of trees, seeds etc. in both the nurseries, 'as likewise every article in the Warehouses at Gateshead, Newcastle and Hebburn Quay', with the freehold estate at Cramar Dyke, Cows, Horses etc. to William Falla his son, the second. It was in his time, 1804-1830, that the nursery became the largest in Britain.

When the first William Falla took over the Hebburn Quay nursery, an advertisement was inserted in the *Newcastle Chronicle* by the executors of George Dale, recommending him, and stating that 'he will attend at the Robin Hood (Mr. Rayne's) in Pilgrim Street every Saturday; and will, on the shortest notice, wait on any Gentleman who may think proper to employ him in laying out new gardens, pleasure grounds, or surveying land'. Later a shop was taken at 20 Dean Street, Newcastle, but in May 1793 it was advertised that this would be given up, an office being taken instead at Mr. Eblet's, the sign of the Spread Eagle in the Groat Market. The earliest catalogues found are of 1795 and 1797 and cover bulbs, seeds, and general nursery stock, the last a book of 35 pages. Reference is made to a separate Botanical Catalogue of Greenhouse Plants, but this does not seem to have survived. The general catalogue does, however, give full lists of varieties of Fruit Trees, as does the later 64-page catalogue of 1827 or 1828. After 1800 the fashion for improvement led to the issue every year of priced lists of forest trees, and copies of those sent out by Fallas in 1811 and 1816 are in existence.

From the prices charged, in comparison with those of other competing nurserymen, it can be seen that in the time of the first William Falla there was already emphasis on large-scale production leading to slashed prices. This had been the method of Dickson of Hassendeanburn as far back as 1776, and the Scottish system — whether by deliberate imitation or not — was found to be equally applicable in the Northumbrian region, with its vast areas of cheap land suitable for nurseries. The second William Falla developed this policy to such a tune that, when the Crown began planting Chopwell Woods, Co. Durham, in 1813, he obtained the contract, and was said to have nurseries of his own extending to 500 acres. Some of Falla's surviving letters show that he was an advocate of new machinery, including an iron plough and a 'Roller

& Miner' with which he worked his nurseries. The iron ploughs were made at Uddingston near Hamilton in Scotland and the cost of two in 1818 was £10. 10s. 0d., with carriage by land to Newcastle £1. 6s. 3d. and the maker's letter 10½d. postage. 'The Carrier says he charges 7s. for a Plough to Leith & he thinks if sent by Sea from Leith to Newcastle would come to more than charged by the Waggon.' Shortly before 1816 Falla had bought part of the Felling Hall estate, south of Gateshead, and this may have provided some of the great area for his tree nurseries.

The cult of forest trees did not interfere with the other sides of the giant business, and in 1810-1813 the firm provided all the plants required for re-stocking the gardens at Levens in Westmorland, after they had been taken over by Alexander Forbes, a gardener evidently an old friend of Falla's. Ten years later, when Forbes brought out his book *Short Hints on Ornamental Gardening* (1820), Falla subscribed for two copies. In 1824 Falla leased from Cuthbert Ellison Esq. further ground east of Gateshead Front Street amounting to about 26½ acres including the Old Chapel Gardens; and in 1826 William Falla was rated, in Gateshead parish alone, on 63 acres of land and 8 of grassland, 6 Greenhouses, and a house, coach-house, granary, stable, four sheds, 2-stalled byre, and dwelling-house with front shop and a warehouse. At Falla's death in 1830 his personalty was put at 'under £16,000', but his freeholds and other real estate were of immense value. The third William Falla was to have all the stock in trade but the freehold land was to be leased to him for 21 years at £900 a year, to provide for the heavy annuities and other interests left to Elizabeth Falla his stepmother, and others of the family.

William Falla II might well be distinguished as 'the spade husbandman'. Soon after his death he was said to have been 'no less distinguished for knowledge and enterprise than for liberality of sentiment and benevolence of mind. His well-directed attempts to introduce the system of spade-husbandry attracted much notice, and still occupy the attention of some of our most enlightened statesmen'. His nurseries, said to be largely at Carr's Hill, and evidently excluding an immense area of forest tree nurseries, occupied 'above 130 acres and are considered the most extensive concern of the kind in England'. Falla had thus realized his father's and his own ambition, and reached a peak in history which is also the culmination of the story sketched in this book. His portrait shows a man of bright and cheerful temperament, and this is borne out by his letters and by what is known of his part in public life. In spite of his nonconformity he seems to have been a convivial personality and his end came when, after attending a public dinner he died of apoplexy, aged 69, at 1 a.m. on 4 August 1830.

His son too must have had great charm. Helping to arrange a dinner to the Earl of Durham at the Black Bull Inn in Gateshead on 23 October 1833 he wrote from Gateshead Nursery Office: (I send) '3 Melons, some Green Peas, Jerusalem artichokes, Parsley of the finest kind I ever had, & a Cart load of Flowers and Evergreens − . . . I have sent my Greenhouse foreman who is really clever to superintend the Arrangement of the Flowers &c.'. Some months later he lent specimens of armour from his private collection to decorate a dinner of the Literary and Philosophical Society of Newcastle-upon-Tyne. Expensive tastes as a collector may have contributed to financial difficulties, but the burden of finding the gigantic rent of £900 a year became too much. The third and last William Falla disappeared on 2 April 1836, and when his body was found in May in Ravensworth Woods near Lamesley, it was discovered that he had committed suicide. His personal estate was sworn under £600 and the nurseries taken over for the benefit of his many creditors.

EPILOGUE

FROM THE VERY slight indications of a nursery trade in the Middle Ages, a by-product of more generalized gardening, the story of English nurseries has been brought down to the tragic failure, a year before Queen Victoria's accession, of the largest nursery known in this country. From a total list of perhaps 200 cultivated plants the numbers had grown, mainly after 1540, to the 18,000 species listed by Loudon as cultivated in Britain by 1839. No nursery ever attempted to grow all of these, indeed many of them were mere weeds, or plants of no economic or horticultural interest. Yet by the opening of the 19th century there were several nurseries, most of them near London, which were making a serious effort to supply everything worth while in all categories. The greater provincial nurseries, even though they would have to obtain the latest exotics from metropolitan sources, were by that time able to meet most of the regional demand for trees, for the principal hardy shrubs, and for herbaceous plants. The seeds of vegetables and of annual flowers for the most part have always had to be bought from the great firms of seedsmen and importers, and the bulb trade has been chiefly based in Holland.

What has been said is very far from being the complete tale, even within the limits of date deliberately set. The London firms have been dealt with only as the merest outline, and to 1760 at that. Because of the outstanding importance of several businesses which started in the last 40 years of the 18th century, a brief recapitulation must here be given of these London nurseries, most of which contributed substantially to the early stages of the boom in exotics. Their contributions were not merely recorded by William Aiton (1731-1793) in the *Hortus Kewensis,* continued by his son William Townsend Aiton (1766-1849), but provided the models for most of the coloured plates issued in a flood of publications. The trade nurseries were ancillary to Kew Gardens, superintended by the two Aitons from 1759, and by their growing competition greatly improved the practical knowledge of plants and the standards of cultivation.

The two great nurseries at Mile End and Hammersmith, which had begun in the 1740's, for long set the standard, and both continued in being many years into the 19th century. So too did the older centres at Brompton, Kensington Gore and Fulham, with yet more, already mentioned, continuing at Putney, at Brentford, at Barnet, Hackney, Leytonstone and Lewisham. All round London the gaps began to be filled with still more gardens, in most cases due to the enterprise of a single individual but doubtless with financial backing. This backing probably came to a considerable extent from the London seedsmen, who dominated the economic aspects of the scene. On the other hand, several quite small businesses, usually of florists, had an importance out of all proportion to the mere volume of their trade, or the acreage they had under cultivation. There was a good deal of fluctuation as regarded size, but on the whole the period was one of steady expansion. By 1800, when we have fairly accurate information on the sites and sizes of all the important London firms, they were mostly much enlarged since their foundation, though a few were already diminished by building.

Much of the significant development took place in South London, where Lambeth and Newington still provided suitable land for gardens very close to the fashionable patrons of the West End. The most notable event, which cannot so far be exactly dated, was the arrival from the North of England of James Maddock the elder (c. 1715-1786). A Quaker from Warrington, Lancashire, he had apparently lived at Cave in the East Riding (between Hull and Howden) and North Walsham in Norfolk, before coming to London. Though his garden at Walworth was well established by 1777, its period of fame came largely after the founder's death under his son James Maddock the younger (1763-1825). The son in 1788 married Mary Curtis of Alton, Hampshire, and thus entered the orbit of William Curtis the botanist (1746-1799), Mary's first cousin. We cannot here follow the fortunes of the Maddock firm, which remained for many years in the hands of members of the two families. Apart from the production of immense numbers of new varieties of florists' flowers (Plate 13), the priced lists of the Walworth Nursery, as reprinted by Richard Weston from 1777 onwards, show that it was a vital centre, and by 1788 the gardens were 'well known to the curious in flowers throughout the kingdom'.

William Curtis was himself to a limited extent a nurseryman, but it is his foundation of the _Botanical Magazine_, the first parts of which appeared in 1786, that brings him into prominence as historian and commentator upon the trade. During the 15 years to 1800 Curtis published drawings of flowers from 15 different London nurserymen and florists. Among these were the old firms of Gordon, Grimwood (of the Kensington Nursery), Lee, Loddiges, and Malcolm of Kennington and Stockwell; and the more recent establishments of Maddock and of Richard Williams at Turnham Green, whose catalogue of Heaths Curtis reprinted in 1794 at plate 303 (Plate 12). There were also the florists James Dickson (1738-1822) of Covent Garden and Franklin of Lambeth Marsh, Curtis's close neighbour. At this point, though not represented in the _Botanical Magazine_, Thomas Davey (c. 1758-1833) must be mentioned. He and his father before him (the father lived to over ninety) had a small garden at Camberwell, but in 1798 it was moved to Chelsea, and it was after this move that Davey rose to great fame as a breeder of carnations, pinks and tulips.

Among those figuring substantially in Curtis's journal and in the history of introductions was William Watson (died c.1792) of Islington. By 1769 he had been able to supply rarities to Kew and in 1771 was one of the only three nurserymen, with Gordon and Lee, to take part in the 'great interchange of exotic plants' with the Apothecaries' Garden at Chelsea. In 1776 the firm was William & James Watson, and they were succeeded by Thomas Watson from 1792 to 1821. The three Watsons were brothers. It was Thomas Watson who in 1798 was the first to flower the Pontic Azalea in Britain, and his plant was immortalized as plate 433 in volume 13 of the *Botanical Magazine* (Plate 16). The first of a new wave of distinguished nurseries, coinciding with the end of the War of American Independence, was founded at Chelsea in 1783 by James Colvill the elder (c. 1746-1822). For some years after 1790 he had as partner one Buchanan, almost certainly James Buchanan who in 1795 set up the Camberwell nursery. In November 1795 Colvill displayed the first garden Chrysanthemums (Plate 14). He later took into partnership his son the younger James Colvill (c. 1778-1832), famous for hybridizations which were probably the work of his foreman, the great botanist Robert Sweet (1783-1835), who worked for Colvills from 1819 to 1826.

Another nursery was added to those already in Brompton by Frank Thoburn in 1784 and this was soon to become famous under his partner and successor Reginald Whitley (c.1754-1835). In Chelsea again, at the corner of Sloane Square, the great plant collector John Fraser (1750-1811) established his own nursery about 1786. One year later still it was the turn of Islington, where Robert Mackie started the Kingsland Nursery, taken over in 1800 by Thomas Bassington and after 1825 by George Hockley Bunney, one of the hybridizers of the Fuchsia. Very near to the Kingsland Nursery, the Northampton Nursery was founded by Thomas Barr in 1791. At first only about two acres in area, this had grown to 11 acres in 1806. Samuel Brookes became a partner in 1819 and for ten years or more the nursery was famous for sending out collectors to different countries and importing many new plants. Lastly, begun about 1800, we must mention the small but select nursery of William Rollison (c. 1765-1842) at Upper Tooting, noted for Heaths and Orchids; and that in Vauxhall started by Napier but distinguished after 1805 by the hybridization of camellias carried on by the junior partner Alfred Chandler the elder, later succeeded by his son Alfred Chandler (1804-1896).

Several other nurseries in the London area, though less famous for new introductions, were either very large, or had a fashionable business. Of the latter type, patronized by the nobility and consulted over the appointment of gardeners, was the firm of James Hairs of St. James's Street, with nurseries near Ranelagh, Chelsea, and Ham Common in Surrey. Hairs was already well established by 1777, when Thomas Blaikie was getting from him most of the plants he did not obtain of Lee at Hammersmith. The firm continued as Hairs, Hairs & Smith, and later as James and Ivie Hairs. Larger nurseries, possibly commercial enterprises linked with market gardening in the first place, were those of William Coleman (c.1743-1808) at Tottenham, and of Crombie & Cormack at New Cross. The Tottenham Nursery comprised 60 acres, made up of various parcels of leasehold, copyhold and freehold land, and was reckoned one of the principal firms in London. So too was the New Cross Nursery, which had about 40 acres and later, as Cormack, Son & Sinclair, took part in the new Conservatories at Covent Garden in 1830.

To disentangle the respective shares of all these firms in new introduction of exotics, in successful plantsmanship, in hybridization, will require a long period of research. Future workers will, one may hope, follow the example of Miss E. J. Willson in her admirable study of James Lee and his associates in the Vineyard Nursery at Hammersmith. Not the least important aspect of this monograph is the appendix of plants introduced or first cultivated by the Hammersmith Nursery in Lee's lifetime, year by year (Plate 10). Comparable studies of Gordon's nursery at Mile End, of Brompton Park and the Kensington Nursery, of Loddiges and of Colvill, will have to be made before even the main strands can be seen clearly. For the true details of the experiments in hybridization carried on from the time of Fairchild to the accession of Queen Victoria we may have to wait even longer, though the science of chromosome counts comes to the aid of defective historical record.

Whereas the first introductions of plants from distant lands were due only in part to nurserymen and their collectors, and even in that measure almost exclusively to London firms, it will be found that the later development of hybrids has been due very largely to the efforts of many individual florists and plantsmen scattered over the whole country. Private strains, not only of the famous florists' flowers shown to the societies, but of a wide spectrum of flowering plants, distinguished many quite small firms. Admittedly most of these developments came after the period dealt with in this book, but their roots went deep. In Yorkshire alone there were three small nurseries with an importance out of all proportion to their economic standing. At York, Thomas Rigg (c.1746-1835) took up the freedom in 1777 and started a suburban garden in the old precinct of St. Andrew's Priory by Fishergate which soon achieved national fame as the source of the best seed of Early York Cabbage. The garden grew to some 30 acres and Rigg was joined successively by his sons, Thomas Rigg junior (c. 1774-1811) and John Rigg (1777-1833). Tragedy dogged the family: the younger Thomas died of palpitation of the heart at 37; in 1830 six of John's family were drowned in the Ouse, and he died aged only 57 three years later. His father, aided by John's widow Ann, managed to carry on until old Thomas Rigg died at 89, and the ground was sold to T. & J. Backhouse, who were shortly to transfer their main nursery to Fishergate from the Friar's Gardens when the railway came.

Wakefield had from 1796 the small business of John Barratt (c.1770-1829), who combined market gardening with a seedsman's shop and branched out into forest and fruit trees and greenhouse plants in pots. This became too much for his resources, and in 1803 he went bankrupt. Luckier than some others in the like position, Barratt made a recovery and by 1807 again had a shop, next to the Strafford Arms. Under his son William Barratt, the business refounded by John took an upward turn. In 1833 William opened the Subscription Botanic Gardens in St. John's, Wakefield, and had a seed warehouse opposite. Only two years later he had 'by far the best collection of Fuchsias in the trade' and was carrying on the raising of Pansies (170 varieties) and Calceolarias. He obtained seeds from Brazil, and in 1834 was reporting on his experiment of growing *Erythrina crista-galli* in the open since 1831. Among his many successes was the form of Flowering Currant

(*Ribes sanguineum*) known as '*R. coccinea*', the first notable improvement upon the type. His firm was regarded as a principal one by Mangles in his list of 1839.

Finally we must consider an odd-man-out, the working master blacksmith Benjamin Ely (1779-1843). The son of Matthew Eli or Ely of Rothwell in the West Riding, and his wife Sarah (née Bilsbrough), Benjamin was born on 12 January 1779 and married Elizabeth Turton at Rothwell on 5 February 1799. From then on he kept a smithy at Carlton in Rothwell for 30 years, but from 1803 began to grow Carnations as a hobby. In 1811 he first bloomed a few of his own seedlings, and he devoted more and more attention to improved strains until, in 1826, he decided to launch out, buying ground at Rothwell Haigh and building a house and florist's shop. Three years later he finally ceased to work as a blacksmith, moved to Rothwell Haigh, and spent the rest of his life as a florist. His fame in the North was very great, and culminated in 1838 when he raised the 'Dr. Horner' picotee, selling in 1839 at 7s. 6d. a pair. He was joined by his seventh son, the second Benjamin Ely, born in 1810 and apprenticed to him as a smith in 1824. The son too became a florist, and after his father's death continued the firm as Benjamin Ely & Son.

In the great majority of cases, the nurseries described belonged to the same family through several generations. The hereditary nature of the work is evidently based on an actual inherited aptitude. This must, in turn, raise the question of other relationships as yet merely suspected, or quite unsuspected. We have seen that there is a possible link between the great John Parkinson who died in 1650 and his namesake at Lambeth who died in 1719; between the Hoxton nurseryman John Noble of the first half of the 17th century, and Francis Noble of Newark a century later. The gardening families of Lucombe, Ford and Pince at Exeter were all inter-related. One of the daughters of Henry Marsh of Hammersmith, Sarah, married the younger Thomas Greening (died 1757), gardener to King George II; their son Henry Thomas Greening was later better known as Sir Henry Thomas Gott. There were complex relationships between the Quaker families of Maddock, Curtis, Goring and Wright. The third John Telford of York (1744-1830) married in 1811 as his second wife Elizabeth, sister of Samuel Hailstone (1768-1851) the botanist; his first wife Elizabeth had been the daughter of Christopher and Elizabeth Fisher of Knaresbrough and was probably closely related to William Fisher (died 1743), the great gardener of Studley Royal. Many questions are raised to which answers will only be given after an immense aggregate of genealogical research.

Another series of problems concerns the gardeners who were certainly foreign immigrants to England. It is unlikely that very much will ever be discovered as to their ancestry in the countries where they were born, though some of the Huguenots are well documented. But it would be of considerable interest to discover how many of these men, such as Pierre Collin at Hatfield, Laurence de Coussin at Wimbledon, André Mollet, left descendants in Britain. The name Bonnor seems English enough; yet in 1618 John Bonnor the Queen's Gardener, lodging at Bartholomew Daniells, a tyler, in the Minori

Street, Portsoken Ward, London, was a Frenchman born at 'Mountilly in Province of France'. Was the Quaker explorer and plant-collector John Bartram (1699-1777) a descendant of the gardener Peter Barteram, who in 1568 'goeth to the Parish Church (of St. James, Clerkenwell, London) but is a French person.' Was the surname Furber a corruption of a Dutch or Flemish name, comparable to that of Jan Verbadhome who, in 1642, sent 280 trees for Queen Henrietta Maria's gardens at Wimbledon Manor House? In all this there is room for patient bringing together of the botanical and horticultural factors on one side, and those of history, biography and genealogy on the other.

Very occasionally, through the pattern of hard facts, glimpses are seized of human personality and of the realities of social history. The subordinates who carried out much of the work in the nurseries are usually, at best, mere names on wage lists. At times the nursery foreman was a man of distinction, as Leonard Meager at Brompton Park or Robert Sweet working for Colvills at Chelsea. The records of apprenticeships tell us of men who later had their own gardens but whose training began humbly enough. But in spite of the total of documentation this is a trade which, on the whole, has suffered from being passed over in silence. Few serious writers, that is of works other than the strictly horticultural, have written of nurseries or have been nurserymen. (A rare exception was R. D. Blackmore, author of *Lorna Doone,* and the horticultural *Kit and Kitty*). At the very end of our period, however, we succeed in getting a look at a nursery − a most unusual one − from the inside. For the last 11 years of his life William Cobbett (1762-1835), who had been almost everything in his time, kept a nursery at Kensington, mainly devoted to the raising of large numbers of American Trees. The nursery was not a mere amusement and Loudon, who visited 'the veteran writer' there in 1828, gives a serious account of it. It is, however, from Cobbett's preface to his catalogue of 1827 that we get a more immediate notion of his aims and methods,

'I am this day (4 December 1827) taking up not much short of a million of trees by the hands of sixteen Englishmen, boarded and lodged in my farm-house, and about thirty Englishmen, Irishmen and Scotchmen promiscuously, who, in these short days, give me their labour in exchange for 2 lbs. of bread, such as every one of my family eats, and such as the ladies and gentlemen of two gentlemen's families, have requested the favour to be supplied with. It is, indeed, the very best bread I ever tasted, made from flour ground by my own men ... from wheat for which I gave at the barn door seven shilling and sixpence a bushel, while the average price of wheat is less than six shillings. Besides ... I give (them) ... half a pound of good sound Cheshire cheese, and 2 lbs. of mutton or pork ...

'I, myself, must be present with them, and also my foreman. Our time, and especially mine, is precious; and therefore I have done, in one day, by forty men, what another would have done in twenty days by two men. I bring the whole body together at their work, so as to have every man under my eye at one and the same time. I take notice of their different capacities: and in about an hour after they begin, all having begun with the spade to take up trees, the distribution of the labour is made; some taking up trees; some sorting them, the large from the small; some counting them into hundreds and thousands; some laying them by the heels in little rows, after they are counted; . . . I began yesterday morning, and by this day week I shall not be far from being done. Then, when an order is received (if the weather be open), it can be executed instantly, as there will be some men at Kensington, constantly packing up trees, from this time to the middle of April.'

Cobbett was inspired by a sense of moral purpose: it was a right and proper thing that the useful and beautiful products of nature should be multiplied and sold at the lowest possible price. Of his catalpa trees, at 4s. for 100, he wrote: 'I should suppose that while I offer these plants for less than a halfpenny apiece, . . . no nurseryman can or ought to sell them under *a shilling apiece, if for so little;* my object is to make the thing general; and to make it general, it must be sold at a cheap price'. The Althea Frutex (*Hibiscus syriacus*) were sold at the same price . . . 'less than a halfpenny apiece for a shrub, the leaves of which have not, even to this day, dropped off . . . and which I saw in full bloom, within this month, at Mr. Malcomb's nursery at Kensington. The beauty of the shrub may be easily guessed by his having selected a patch of it to plant just by the side of the Turnpike road, to attract the attention of the lovers of shrubs. . . . I would recommend to purchasers to put my seedlings into a nursery for a year, and then plant them out. In clumps of low shrubs this surpasses almost any thing I know of. It removes well, it grows fast, and is, in every respect, a most beautiful shrub'. Hard times in the 1820's; but there were compensations.

APPENDIX I

THE CULTURE OF ROSEMARY IN ENGLAND

ROSEMARY, though mentioned as an important drug in early herbal literature, does not seem to have been introduced to Britain as a living plant until the 14th century. Even then it was not common, for it does not appear (though lavender does) among the drawings of plants in the Arderne MS. (British Museum, Add. MS. 29301) of the early 15th century, and in John Bray's detailed list of plant names it is clearly only the dried flowers that are meant by the entries: 'Ros marinus: antos deutrolibanus' and 'Antos: ys the flowre of the rose marine'. This was compiled some time before Bray's death in 1381. On the other hand, the plant had reached Paris and the north of France before 1393, but 'gardeners say that the seed of rosemary groweth never in French soil,' i.e. in the region of the ancient *Francia,* northern France. The Goodman of Paris, who recorded this, described the method used to wrap up cuttings of rosemary to send 'wheresoever you will'. As this is by way of exception to his other hints on gardening, it seems to show that rosemary was the first instance in northern Europe of a somewhat tender plant for which special horticultural provision had to be made. As a garden plant in England it was listed by or for Thomas Fromond of Carshalton and Cheam in Surrey, who died on 21 March 1542/3 as a herb necessary for a garden, and particularly as a herb for the cup (see J. Harvey, *Early Gardening Catalogues,* 1972, 58-64). By the early 16th century it was already well known, not only in the king's gardens, but elsewhere, as in that of Sir Thomas More at Chelsea.

By More's time the plant had in fact been in the country for almost two centuries. Its many real or supposed medicinal virtues had caused it to be sent or given to Queen Philippa of Hainault by her mother in 1338. The problems set by rosemary to English gardeners were evidently new in kind, and thus produced in many versions and copies one of the earliest of specific horticultural treatises. In spite of variations the text is essentially a unity and implies serious experiments which had led to successful culture before 1400. The manuscripts have been discussed elsewhere (see *Garden History,* I, no. 1, September 1972, 14-21). What follows here is the strictly cultural section of the treatise, modernized in spelling.

This foresaid tree and herb rosemary may thrive with every weather and with every time of the year, out taken four weathers, that is to say: the northern wind; the worst of all winds, that is the wind between the north and the east; and the eastern wind; and black frost — these four weathers are death to him in the wintertide. Snow and white frost are cooling and freshing and nourishing to him, annoys him not but if it be of burden of his branches.

It longeth (grows longer) twice in a year and bloometh twice in a year, in April and in September, and he seedeth but once. His first flowers are of most virtue (i.e. in medicine). And of all that is in him his flowers be more of virtue than are his leaves, than his tree (trunk), than his root and than his rind (bark).

His wife or else the female to him is Lavender, but lavender is less, lower and whiter in rind and leaves than is rosemary; mickle like in shape and length and quantity and hardihood, save whiter green, and flowers small as hyssop, fair blooms and of him whitest; and she is of less effect than he . . .

And it is a manner of brushel (brushwood) in many other countries and lands it groweth by his own, and one of other, and is not dained (i.e. is disdained) because of plenty, and virtue unknown, and is trodden under feet and burnt among other brushel. And in some countries (e.g. England) unneth (scarcely) it groweth but with mickle travail of main and with mickle watering in two the first years, but principally in the first year.

It is an holy tree and with folk that been rightful and just gladly it groweth and thriveth. In growing it passeth not commonly in height the height of our Lord Jesu Christ while he walked as man on earth ('that is man's height and half as man is now'); nor, after it is 33 year old ('at the age of Christ'), it groweth not in height but waxeth in breadth and that but little. It never seareth (scorches) all but if some of the foresaid four weathers make it.

His leaves are evermore green, and never falleth in every month; and in every time of the year and in every weather, out taken the four foresaid weathers, though it be in white frost or in snow. And in every time of the year that it is set it groweth and thriveth, save in the foresaid points.

If it be once transplanted after it is perfectly rooted and great waxed, unneth thriveth it. Then if it shall be transplanted or taken up the root, all to set, abide not long ere it be set, nor lay it not in water nor in ground but it be a little while, nor let not the sun nor air take the root. And it must be set with mickle water, and make the earth as nesh (soft) as pap be nigh (i.e. nearly as soft as pap). And you cram in and thrust well and harden the earth about (the plant), that the sun nor the air smite not to his root, nor that his root sag not, nor stir not in the ground. And make a grip (groove) about him that the water may stand and ooze. And when you shall water him, water him not in the hot sun but well afterward in the cool; and pour the water above on his crop that it may run down all about him and stand in grip.

And if it be set after mid-May till the great heat of summer be done, it will have a shadowing from the sun from mid-morn till mid-overnoon (afternoon) while the great heat of the day lasts. And as long as great winds and black frosts last, a screen must be between him and the wind ('If it have reflection of wall or of wood it is the better').

In hot weather and in dry weather every other day when it raineth not, it will be watered well above in the top, and that as soon after the heat of the sun be gone; and if you will, also a little or the heat come. On this wise it will be served till it be three year old.

If it shall be set rootless (i.e. by cuttings), cut off with a sharp edge knife his little branch that is most able (suitable), fast by the body of the tree or of the bough as razor doth the hair from the head, that you make no gall (sore) nor no sliver. When it beginneth to show out his crops of his boughs (i.e. to make new growth), then is most secure of setting of him, and that in May and in September. And then shave off the small twists (twigs) with a sharp edged knife to the midst, or else be past (i.e. half way up the cutting or more); and writhe (twist) the nether end a little, a good inch at the most; that it may gather root thereof; and set it well over the wrying (i.e. above the twisted part), and water him as it is aforesaid. If you serve him thus you there not reckon in what ground you set him (i.e. need not be particular as to soil), so it be not new dunged; nor never dung, nor meynt (mix) nigh (to it) none such (manure). It is tree and herb holy and clean kindly (by nature), and kindly it loveth not but clean.

If it shall be taken to (for) medicine or to set, cut every other little twist and every other second branch, or else every third, with a sharp edge knife fast by the body of the tree, for (fear of) hurting of the bark as it is said before, and evermore cut upward, for (fear of) galling and for slivering. Pull him not, nor sliver him not, nor strip him not, and save his principal crops shred (clip) them not; nor make him not over poor of his boughs and branches and twists, but as it is said. And if you nourish him thus you shall have rosemary enough and great help and comfort thereby, with the grace of Almighty God of Heaven.

APPENDIX II

GARDEN PLANTS OF THE FOURTEENTH CENTURY

THE ONE IMPORTANT source for the contents of the English garden in the 14th century is The Feate of Gardening by Mayster Jon Gardener, but it cannot be regarded as a complete list of all plants in cultivation. On the other hand, a few of its entries are unidentifiable or at least uncertain. Trees are not included, apart from the apple and pear, and incidental mentions of the ash, hawthorn and hazel. Although we do not know to what extent native forest trees were really in cultivation, it is certain that some were deliberately sown and planted in parks and hedgerows. The many trees mentioned by Chaucer, with the purposes for which many of them were used, have to be regarded as a cultivated rather than a genuinely wild flora. The attempt has been made, in the four following lists, to show as far as possible what forest trees, fruit trees, vegetables and herbs were certainly being grown. Each list is arranged alphabetically, with the modern names of Jon Gardener's plants shown in capitals, and scientific identifications given, using the nomenclature of the *Dictionary of Gardening* of the Royal Horticultural Society (1956/1965 edition).

Most of the additions come from Chaucer's list of trees, often overlapping, in the Romaunt of the Rose (lines 1373-85), the Parlement of Foules (ll. 176-82) and the Knightes Tale (ll. 2921-23); and from his short list of purgative herbs in the Nonne Preestes Tale (ll. 4153-56). Apart from these, medicinal herbs listed elsewhere have not been added, for they may have been gathered in the wild rather than grown in gardens. The result is a list of 136 species, apart from kinds of corn but including broad beans and peas which, like corn, were field rather than garden crops. Among the vegetables it is noticeable that the roots already grown in Paris before 1400 were absent: beet, carrot, parsnip and turnip; though the parsnip was certainly known in England as a medicinal herb, as was the skirret. The pumpkin too, used in France, seems not to have reached England. With the problem of the spinach we have to deal in considering dubious identifications. The (black) mulberry was being grown in York in a walled garden called Mulberihawe in 1361 (York Minster Library, Chapter Wills, Reg. 1, f. 33v).

Emphasis must be placed on the doubtfulness of several of the identifications proposed. In most cases the genus at least is certain, but there may be latitude in regard to the species normally grown. Some plants, however, present serious difficulties because of the contradictory equations for names found in the literature of the period. The most serious puzzles are two plants named by John Gardener and not hitherto found elsewhere: 'Carsyndyllys' and 'Redenay'. The suggestion, made long ago by Amherst, that the latter is

'Red Ray' (Grass), *Lolium perenne*, seems hardly admissible. A far more likely candidate occurs in Gerard's *Herball* of 1597, in his supplement of names taken from ancient sources and oral tradition: 'Red knees is *Hydropiper*'. This is *Polygonum hydropiper*, Water Pepper, Arsesmart, or Smartweed, a herb found in other lists and in garden cultivation from early times and included in the 'Fromond' list of c.1500. Besides use as a medicine it was a yellow dye for woollen cloth.

There does not seem to be any explanation for 'Carsyndyllys' as it stands. Amherst's 'cress and lilies?' was a counsel of despair, and though 'cress and dill' might be acceptable, the fact that cress, as 'tuncarse' appears elsewhere in the list seems to rule this out also. The curious 'Cutberdole and Cutbertill' is given by Gerard as an ancient name for Branke ursine, *Acanthus mollis*, but the verbal resemblance is insufficient to make this at all probable as an identification. We are left with the possibility of a major textual corruption, and if the word could stand for some form of *caryophyllum*, the clove or gilliflower (carnation and pink), this would explain the surprising absence of one of the famous flowers of the Middle Ages, certainly grown in Paris at the time. Another plant, which Amherst admitted she could not identify, was the mysterious Herb Walter. But in this case the field can be narrowed down with certainty to an umbelliferous plant. 'Herbe Walter, his leves be lyke parselye but whytier and thykker and fatt and tender, he wyll ease wounds, but he stynkethe.' This is very suggestive of *Apium graveolens*, Wild Celery, and this is supported by the drawing in the Arderne manuscript. There is a difficulty in regard to the possible duplication in the list by 'Merge' or March, but this point will be discussed further below.

There are in fact doubts about a dozen of the remaining herbs, though the degrees of uncertainty differ greatly. Adder's Tongue certainly should be the curious fern *Ophioglossum vulgatum*, but both *Arum maculatum* and *Dracunculus vulgaris* are within the bounds of possibility. Centaury in the Arderne manuscript is clearly drawn as *Centaurium umbellatum (erythraea)*, and that is presumably what is meant. 'Tuncarse' undoubtedly means cress, probably but not quite certainly *Lepidium sativum*. In theory dittander is also a cress, *Lepidium latifolium*, but early usage equated the word with dittany, and it is *Origanum dictamnus* that is likely to be right here. Hollyhock presents a much more difficult problem, for while the genus *Althaea* is not doubtful, the old English name shifted from one species to another in course of time. An oriental species of mallow was brought back by returning crusaders, which accounts for the attribute of 'holy', and was probably *A. cretica*, but by the 16th century if not earlier had been supplanted by *A. rosea* from China. This may, however, have been cultivated in Persia and other lands of the Middle East at the time of the Crusades, and cannot absolutely be excluded. All the same, there is a suspicion that the name was sometimes applied to the common native Marsh Mallow, *Althaea officinalis*. All these were known in Arabic as *Khatmia*, the Ketmia of the botanists of the 17th and 18th centuries.*

*then applied especially to the Althea Frutex (*Hisbiscus syriacus*)

The French equivalent of bugloss, 'langue de boeuf' or langdebefe, may be another instance of ambiguity, but identity with *Picris echioides* is perhaps rather more likely than with *Echium vulgare* or any of the other boraginaceous plants usually known as bugloss. With the plant called by Master John 'merege', that is march, we return to one of the more tantalizing puzzles. The now obsolete word 'ache' (pronounced as the letter H) covered a group of umbellifers related to celery, and John Bray in his vocabulary of plant names made an attempt to disentangle them. Under *Apium* he stated 'ther beth .v. spices (species) of hem: apium domesticum, apium ranarum, apium risus, apium emoroidarum, ache, merche and smalache'. This apparently yields seven sorts rather than five, and it is by no means clear whether Bray thought of ache, march (i.e. more or greater ache) and smallage (small ache) as three varieties of a single species, or as English equivalents of some of his Latin names. Gerard states that chervil was called 'though untruly', *Apium risus;* Parkinson remarks of *Apium graveolens* that 'his evil taste and savour doth cause it not to be accepted in meates as Parsley'. This sounds suspiciously like the mediaeval statement regarding Herb Walter, quoted above, and it must be supposed that that was at any rate another member of this group.

It is commonly suggested that pimpernel, in medieval sources, stood for the salad burnet, *Poterium sanguisorba,* but this is another case where the drawing in the Arderne manuscript explicitly proves that 'pimpernole' was used for the scarlet pimpernel, *Anagallis arvensis.* In yet another instance, that of scabious, the drawing shows the Devil's bit, *Scabiosa succisa,* though other species were probably in cultivation too. Spinach cannot be solved so simply. Amherst regarded it as *Spinacia oleracea,* and there is no doubt that a plant nominally identical with spinach was widely eaten in the 14th century. Yet the Arderne manuscript depicts a plant unlike spinach as 'spinoke' and Bray refers to a 'spynnache the wiche bereth an ynde blew flore', that is an indigo blue flower, as identical with 'linoyse'. The most probable identity for this, and the Arderne drawing, is a *Linaria,* possibly *L. repens.* Wallwort is another highly ambiguous name, being sometimes used for pellitory of the wall, *Parietaria officinalis,* which here almost certainly corresponds to 'pelyter'. Bray in one passage specifies 'walwort' as one of the sorts of spurge ('titumallus'), but elsewhere gives it as an equivalent for 'Ebulus', the dwarf elder, *Sambucus ebulus.* Gerard agrees that 'Walwort is *Ebulus*'. Finally we may wonder whether the water lily was *Nymphaea alba* or a *Nuphar,* though the former is much more likely on account of its pure white colour suggesting the madonna lily.

In the list which follows, plants mentioned by John Gardener are in capitals; the rest are taken mainly from Chaucer, with a few added from record sources. Identifications are certain or at least highly probable except for those discussed above, which are marked with a query.

PLANTS CULTIVATED IN ENGLAND IN THE PERIOD ABOUT 1375-1400.

(I)   FOREST TREES

Alder	*Alnus glutinosa*
ASH	*Fraxinus excelsior*
Aspen — see Poplar	
Beech	*Fagus sylvatica*
Birch	*Betula* sp.
Box	*Buxus sempervirens*
Buckthorn	*Rhamnus catharticus*
Chestnut	*Castanea sativa*
Cornel (Wippeltree)	*Cornus sanguinea*
Elm	*Ulmus* sp.
Fir	? *Picea abies*
Holly	*Ilex aquifolium*
Laurel (Laurer, Lorer)	*Laurus nobilis*
Lime (Lind)	*Tilia* sp.
Maple	*Acer* sp.
Oak	*Quercus petraea; Q. robur*
Pine (Pyn)	*Pinus sylvestris*
Plane	*Platanus orientalis*
Poplar	*Populus* sp.
——— Aspen	*Populus tremula*
THORN	*Crataegus* sp.
Willow	*Salix* sp.
Yew	*Taxus baccata*

(II)   FRUIT TREES

APPLE	*Malus pumila* vars.
Bullace — see Plum	
Cherry	*Prunus cerasus*
Gooseberry	*Ribes grossularia*
GRAPEVINE	*Vitis vinifera*
HAZEL (Nut)	*Corylus avellana*
Medlar	*Mespilus germanica*
Mulberry (grown in York before 1361)	*Morus nigra*
Peach	*Prunus persica*
PEAR	*Pyrus communis* vars.
Plum	*Prunus domestica* vars.
——— Bullace (Bolas)	*Prunus insititia*
Quince	*Cydonia oblonga*
Service (Aleys)	*Sorbus domestica*
Walnut (grown in Essex by 1403)	*Juglans regia*

(III)   VEGETABLES

Broad Bean	*Vicia faba*

COLEWORT, Kale etc. (Worts)	*Brassica oleracea* vars.
GARLIC	*Allium sativum*
LEEK	*Allium ampeloprasum porrum*
ONION	*Allium cepa*
Pea	*Pisum sativum*
Scallion, Shallot	*Allium ascalonicum*

(IV)   SALADS, HERBS and FLOWERS

ADDER'S TONGUE (Adderstong)	? *Ophioglossum vulgatum*
AGRIMONY (Egrimoyne)	*Agrimonia eupatoria*
ALEXANDERS (Elysauwder)	*Smyrnium olusatrum*
AVENS (Auans)	*Geum urbanum*
BETONY	*Stachys officinalis*
BIGOLD (Bygull)	*Chrysanthemum segetum*
BORAGE	*Borago officinalis*
Brisewort — see DAISY	
BUGLE (Bugull)	*Ajuga reptans*
CALAMINT (Calamynte)	*Calamintha ascendens*
CAMOMILE (Camemyl)	*Anthemis nobilis*
CAMPION (RED) (Flos Campi)	*Melandrium rubrum (dioicum)*
'CARSYNDYLLYS'	? *Dianthus caryophyllus*
CENTAURY (Centory)	*Centaurium umbellatum*
CLARY (Clarey)	*Salvia sclarea*
CLARY, WILD (Oculus Christi)	*Salvia verbenaca*
COMFREY (Comfery)	*Symphytum officinale*
CORIANDER (Coryawnder)	*Coriandrum sativum*
COWSLIP (Cowslyppe)	*Primula veris*
CRESS (Tuncarse)	? *Lepidium sativum*
DAFFODIL (Affodyll)	*Narcissus pseudonarcissus*
DAISY (Brisewort)	*Bellis perennis*
DITTANY? (Dytawnder)	? *Origanum dictamnus*
ELECAMPANE (Horsel)	*Inula helenium*
FELWORT (Feldewort)	*Gentiana ? amarella*
FENNEL (Fynel)	*Foeniculum vulgare*
FOXGLOVE	*Digitalis purpurea*
Fumitory	*Fumaria officinalis*
GLADWIN (Gladyn)	*Iris ? pseudacorus*
GROMWELL (Gromel)	*Lithospernum officinale*
GROUNDSEL (Growdyswyly)	*Senecio vulgaris*
HART'S TONGUE (Hertystonge)	*Phyllitis scolopendrium*
Hellebore	? *Helleborus viridis*
HENBANE	*Hyoscyamus niger*
Herb Yve — see Wart Cress	
Herb John — see St John's Wort	
HERB ROBERT	*Geranium robertianum*
HERB WALTER (Herb Water)	? *Apium graveolens*

HINDHEAL (Hyndesall)	*Teucrium scorodonia*
HOLLYHOCK (Holyhocke)	*Althaea* sp.
HONEYSUCKLE (Honysoke)	*Lonicera periclymenum*
HOREHOUND	*Marrubium vulgare*
HYSSOP (Ysope)	*Hyssopus officinalis*
LANGDEBEFE (Langebefe)	*? Picris echioides*
LAVENDER (Lauyndull)	*Lavandula spica*
LETTUCE (Letows)	*Lactuca sativa*
LILY (Lyly)	*Lilium candidum*
LIVERWORT (Lyuerworte)	*Hepatica triloba*
MARCH (Merege)	*? Apium* sp.
MINT (Myntys)	*Mentha spicata* etc.
MOTHERWORT (Moderwort)	*Artemisia vulgaris*
MOUSE-EAR (Mouseer)	*Hieracium pilosella*
MUSTARD (Seneuy)	*? Brassica nigra*
NEPP (Nepte)	*Nepeta cataria*
ORACH (Orage)	*Atriplex hortensis*
ORPINE (Orpyn)	*Sedum telephium*
PARSLEY (Percell)	*Petroselinum crispum*
PELLITORY (Pelyter)	*Parietaria officinalis*
PEONY (Pyony)	*Paeonia ? officinalis*
PERIWINKLE (Peruynke)	*Vinca major; V. minor*
PIMPERNEL (Pympernould)	*Anagallis arvensis*
POLYPODY	*Polypodium vulgare*
PRIMROSE (Primerole)	*Primula vulgaris*
RADISH (Radysche)	*Raphanus sativus*
'REDENAY'	*? Polygonum hydropiper*
RIBWORT (Rybwart)	*Plantago lanceolata*
ROSE, RED (Rose ryde)	*Rosa gallica*
ROSE, WHITE (Rose whyghte)	*Rosa x alba*
Rosemary (introduced 1338)	*Rosmarinus officinalis*
RUE (Rewe)	*Ruta graveolens*
SAFFRON (Saferowne)	*Crocus sativus*
SAGE	*Salvia officinalis*
ST JOHN'S WORT (Herb Ion)	*Hypericum perforatum*
SANICLE (Sanycle)	*Sanicula europaea*
SAVORY (Sauerey)	*Satureia ? montana*
SCABIOUS (Scabyas)	*Scabiosa ? succisa*
SOUTHERNWOOD (Sowthrynwode)	*Artemisia abrotanum*
SPEARWORT (Sperewort)	*Ranunculus ? flammula*
SPINACH (Spynage)	*? Spinacia oleracea*
Spurge (Catapuce)	*Euphorbia ? lathyrus*
Spurge Laurel (Lauriol)	*Daphne laureola*
STITCHWORT (Stychewort)	*Stellaria holostea*
STRAWBERRY (Strowberys)	*Fragaria vesca*
TANSY (Tansay)	*Tanacetum vulgare*

TEASEL, WILD (Wyldtesyl)	*Dipsacus ? sylvestris*
THYME (Tyme)	*Thymus ? serpyllum*
TUTSAN (Totesayne)	*Hypericum androsaemum*
VALERIAN (Valeryan)	*Valeriana officinalis*
VERVAIN (Verueyn)	*Verbena officinalis*
VIOLET	*Viola odorata*
WALLWORT (Walwort)	*? Sambucus ebulus*
Wart Cress (Erbe Yve)	*Coronopus squamatus*
WATER LILY (Waterlyly)	*? Nymphaea alba*
WAYBREAD (Webrede)	*Plantago major*
WOODRUFF (Woderofe)	*Asperula odorata*
WOOD SORREL (Wodesour)	*Oxalis acetosella*
WORMWOOD (Warmot)	*Artemisia absinthium*
YARROW ('Parrow')	*Achillea millefolium*

THE CATALOGUE OF GEORGE RICKETS, 1688

IN THE COURSE of time, lists of plants have been compiled for various reasons, utilitarian or scientific. It is not always possible to draw a hard and fast distinction between the two main categories of purpose. In England the first list which may have in it something of the nurseryman's catalogue is that compiled by John Gerard in 1596 of the contents of his garden in Holborn (see *Early Gardening Catalogues*, 5-6, 16-17). Reissued in 1599 with English as well as Latin names, this probably was aimed to some extent at potential customers and not purely at botanists and students. Gerard's list was reprinted with identifications by B. D. Jackson in 1876. Two later lists of rather the same character, of primarily botanical interest, were made of the plants in the Lambeth garden of John Tradescant senior (died 1638) and his son John Tradescant junior (1608-1662) in 1634 and 1656. These lists have been reprinted in modern times (see M. Allan, *The Tradescants*, 1964). Although all these lists had an element of potential trade in them, none of them could be called a nurseryman's catalogue in the strict sense of the words. The first trade lists to have survived date from after the Restoration of 1660, and both the earliest priced list and the earliest general catalogue of a plant nursery come from the famous George Rickets (died 1706) of Hoxton, established before 1665.

The priced list, sent to Sir Thomas Hanmer in 1667, included named varieties of fruit trees: nectarines (3s. each), peaches (2s.), pears (1s.), apples and cherries (8d.), as well as 23 sorts of carnations at 1s. 6d. a root. Hanmer noted in 1670 the prices of other flowers from Rickets, including anemones and auriculas. The main interest of these lists, now that the named varieties are long forgotten and mostly unrecorded, lies in the fact that the combination of fruit trees and florists' flowers as specialities of a single nursery seems to have been an innovation. By 1677-79 the first surviving list of a London seedsman, William Lucas, had appeared (see *Early Gardening Catalogues*, 65-74, for reprint with identifications), but the plants in this were evidently offered by Lucas as a middleman. It was once more to George Rickets that John Woolridge turned when, in issuing the third edition of his *Systema Horti-culturae* or *The Art of Gardening* in 1688, he wished to include a complete up-to-date catalogue of nursery stock.

This catalogue is here reprinted, with identifications according to the nomenclature used in the *Dictionary of Gardening* (R. H. S., 1956/1965). It is not always possible to be precise as to the species intended, and a few names are doubtful. In one case there is a serious difficulty: 'Pardus (or Pardalianches) Theophrasti' listed among flower-bearing trees. The classical

Greek name *pardalianches* or leopard-strangler was supposed to be a form of aconite, but in Renaissance times was applied to the Doronicum (still called Leopard's Bane); *D. pardalianches* or Great Leopard's Bane remains a herbaceous border plant in general cultivation, but it is not a tree.

A CATALOGUE

of such Housed-Greens, Winter-Greens, Flowering-Shrubs, Flowering-Trees, Flowers, and other curious Plants, as well Exotick as English, that are to be Sold by Mr. George Rickets, Gardener, at the Hand in Hogsden without Bishopsgate, London, the great Collector and Improver of the Beauties of a Garden.

Greens that are Housed in the Winter

Oranges and Lemons	*Citrus sinensis; C. limonia*
Myrtles of various sorts	*Myrtus communis* vars.
The white and red Oleander	*Nerium oleander*
The yellow Indian Jasmine	*Jasminum odoratissimum*
The Spanish Jasmine	*Jasminum grandiflorum*
The Indian Jucca	*Yucca gloriosa*
Colutea odorata	? *Coronilla valentina*
Tree Housleek	*Aeonium arboreum*
Cytisus lunatus	*Medicago arborea*
Jacobea Marina, or Sea-Ragwort	*Senecio cineraria*
Gilded or strip'd Phyllyrea	*Rhamnus alaternus variegata*
Lentiscus	*Pistacia lentiscus*
Indian Figg	*Opuntia vulgaris*
Marum Syriacum	*Origanum maru*
Amomum Plinii	*Solanum pseudocapsicum*

Flower-bearing Trees.

Castanea Equina, or the Horse-Chestnut	*Aesculus hippocastanum*
Oleaster	*Elaeagnus angustifolia*
Pardus (or Pardalianches) Theophrasti	?
Laburnum Major	*Laburnum anagyroides*
Laburnum Minor	*Laburnum alpinum*
Sena-Tree	*Colutea arborescens*
Sumach	*Rhus* spp.
Cassia [probably Acacia]	? *Robinia pseudacacia*
Lilac, blew, white, and purple	*Syringa vulgaris* vars.
Pomegranate-flowers, double and single	*Punica granatum*
Jasmines, White,	*Jasminum officinale*

and Virginian	*Gelsemium sempervirens*
Periploca	*Periploca graeca*
Double Virgins-bower	*Clematis viticella flore pleno*
Virginian Climer	*Parthenocissus* sp.
Tree Passion-flower	*Passiflora incarnata*
Paliurus, or Christs-thorn	*Paliurus spina-Christi*
Hungarian Clematis	*Clematis integrifolia*
Orobus Venetus	*Lathyrus vernus*
Gelder-Rose	*Viburnum opulus*
Double blossom'd Cherry	*Prunus cerasus flore pleno*
Mezerions, Red, Purple, White	*Daphne mezereum* vars.
Dwarf-Almond	*Prunus communis?*
Hypericum frutex	*Spiraea hypericifolia*
Spirea frutex	*Spiraea salicifolia*
Cytisus Secundus Clusii	*Cytisus sessilifolius*
Althea frutex, Red, White	*Hibiscus syriacus* vars.
Syringa, White, Purple	*Philadelphus coronarius;?*
Persian Jasmine	*Syringa persica*
Woodbine, or Honisuckle, White	*Lonicera caprifolium alba*
Italian, Red, Scarlet	*Lonicera* sp.
Scorpion Sena	*Coronilla emerus*
Amigdala flore Africano	*Prunus ? tenella*

Winter Greens

Alaternus	*Rhamnus alaternus*
Pyracantha	*Pyracantha coccinea*
Ilex	*? Quercus ilex*
Laurus tinus Major } Laurus tinus Minor }	*Viburnum tinus* vars.
Spanish Broom	*Spartium junceum*
Upright Savin	*Juniperus sabina*
Laurels	*Prunus laurocerasus* etc.
Phyllirea augustifolia (*sic*)	*Phillyrea angustifolia*
Bay-tree	*Laurus nobilis*
Cypress	*Cupressus sempervirens*
Norway Firr	*Picea abies*
Scotch Firr	*Pinus sylvestris*
Silver, or flat Firr	*Abies alba*
Mountain Pine	*Pinus ? pinea*
Pinaster	*Pinus pinaster*
Cedar of Libanus	*Cedrus libani*
Winter Jasmine	*Jasminum sambac*

Other Ornamental Trees

Cornelian Cherry	*Cornus mas*
Oriental, and Occidental Platanus	*Platanus orientalis;*
	P. occidentalis
Abele	*Populus alba* or *P. nigra*
Lime-Tree	*Tilia x europea*

The Black Poplar was commonly, though incorrectly, identified with the Abele in nurserymen's catalogues in the 18th century.

Flowers and choice Plants

Cardinal's Flower, Scarlet, Blew	*Lobelia cardinalis; L. syphilitica*
Steeple Bellflower	*Campanula pyramidalis*
Scarlet Gnaphalion	? *Helichrysum sanguineum*
Double Scarlet Lychins (*sic*)	*Lychnis chalcedonica rubra plena*
White Rocket	*Hesperis matronalis*
Purple Rocket	*H. matronalis purpurea*
Auricula's double of several sorts,	
Auricula's strip'd, great varieties	*Primula auricula* vars.
Auricula's plain Colours	
Hepatica's Double, Blew, and	
Peach-colour	*Hepatica triloba* vars.
Fraxinella, White, Red	*Dictamnus albus* etc.
Peonyes, Double, White, Blush, and	
Purple	*Paeonia officinalis* vars.
Asphodil, Yellow, Red	*Asphodeline lutea;*
	? *Asphodelus fistulosus*
Geranium nocte Olens	*Pelargonium triste*
Martagons of several kinds	*Lilium martagon* etc.
Lillies of several kinds	*Lilium* spp.
Iris bulbous	*Iris xiphioides* etc.
Great varieties	
Iris tuberosus	*Hermodactylus tuberosus* etc.
Hyacinthus tuberosus	*Hyacinthus orientalis*
Jacinths many sorts	*Scilla* spp.; *Muscari* spp.
Tulips great varieties	*Tulipa* spp.
Double and single Anemones	
many sorts	*Anemone coronaria* vars.
Ranuncula's great varieties	*Ranunculus asiaticus* vars.
Carnations and Gilliflowers very	
many sorts	*Dianthus caryophyllus* vars.
Double Colchicums	*Colchicum autumnale flore pleno*

Fritillaries	*Fritillaria* spp.
Ornithogalon's	*Ornithogalum* spp.
Leucoiums	*Leucojum vernum; L. aestivum;*
	L. autumnale
Narcissus, great varieties double	
and single	*Narcissus pseudonarcissus* etc.
Globe-Flower	*Trollius europaeus*
Crocus's many varieties	*Crocus* spp.
Primroses many colours and sorts	*Primula vulgaris* vars.
Oxslips several colours and sorts	*Primula x variabilis*
Polyanthos	*Primula x variabilis*
Gentianella	? *Gentiana acaulis* or *G. Verna*
Junquils	*Narcissus jonquilla*
Campanula's or Bellflowers with	
many others	

The same Mr. Rickets can furnish you with all the best sorts of Apples, Pears, Cherries, Plumbs, Apricocks, Peaches, Nectorines, Vines, Currants, Gooseberries, and all other Fruits, Standards, or for the Wall: Of all which he hath great variety.

(From J. Woolridge [or Worlidge], *Systema Horti-culturae, or, The Art of Gardening,* 3rd edition, 1688, 268-270.)

APPENDIX IV

THOMAS FAIRCHILD'S PLANTS IN FLOWER, 1722-23

Most lists of plants, whether botanical or commercial, are concerned with the mere existence of the plant. If they go further into description, they may state the season of flowering, and for the last three centuries gardener's calendars have been printed which usually show not only the works but the rewards of each season. These are, however, ideal or hypothetical statements, and it is unusual to find specific records of the plants actually flowering from month to month in a single garden. This rarity gives a special value to the three letters sent by Thomas Fairchild (1667-1729) to Richard Bradley's *Monthly Register*. The letters list the plants actually in flower in Fairchild's Hoxton nursery from April 1722 to March 1723 inclusive. There are, of course, many repetitions from one month to the next, though only a single list is given for August and September together. There is, however, a separate list of the kinds of grapes ripening with Fairchild in the same two months.

The lists are remarkable in several ways. Firstly they witness to Fairchild's enterprise in growing the widest possible range: trees, shrubs, herbaceous plants and bulbs of all kinds. Secondly they show, as might be expected of the author of *The City Gardener* (published the same year), that Fairchild could get blossom in spite of the fumes of sea coal burning in London hearths. Thirdly, they mark an extraordinary advance upon the 'ideal' monthly list drawn up by Henry Wise. That had started with February and ended with September; too few plants were in flower in the four winter months from October to January to be worth listing in c.1700. (For Wise's list see D. Green, *Gardener to Queen Anne*, plate 52). Apart from the twenty years or so which separate the two lists, there was another factor which is the key to the difference between them. Wise was the head of an enormous business, mainly concerned with garden design and with the supply of forest trees and fruit trees in immense quantity. Though Brompton Park did indeed grow everything, it did not specialize in flowers. Thomas Fairchild, on the contrary, was a truly great plantsman and one of the greatest florists of all time, but without being merely that.

The lists are here reprinted just as they stand: April and May set out line by line; the later months run on in solid paragraphs to accommodate the vast multitude of summer blooms. It would be repetitious to attempt identifications of most of the plants, misleading in other cases where doubt exists as to what Fairchild meant by his terminology. Comments will here be limited to a few cases where positive or probable identities can be given. Anemone Spermos (October) was *Arctotis aspera*, introduced in 1710; Atamasco Lilly (May) is *Zephyranthes atamasco*; Spanish Broom, White and Yellow, were

Genista monosperma and *Spartium junceum*. 'Candytuft Tree' was probably the sub-shrub *Iberis semperflorens*, and 'Chrysanthemum Tree' (Oct.) possibly *C. frutescens*. 'French Willow' was the common Rose Bay (*Epilobium angustifolium*). Coma Aurea (Aug.-Sep.), meaning Goldilocks, presumably indicates *Helichrysum orientale*, while the Scarlet flower'd Horse Chestnut of Virginia is *Aesculus pavia*, introduced only in 1711. Since the first trees were grown from seeds it is a remarkable tribute to Fairchild's skill that he had them in flower at ten years old. Aizoid Tythimals means literally evergreen spurges, but this leaves a wide room for conjecture. 'Scarlet flow'ring Viaburnum' almost certainly means a variety of *Lantana camara*, which had reached England in 1691. 'Nettle-leav'd Jessamine' was possibly *Lantana aculeata*, and the Ilex-leav'd was *Oftia (Spielmannia) africana*, originally called a Lantana.

Fairchild's 'Passetout' (January) must be the 'Blew Hyacinth Passtoute' of Furber's 1730 plate for February; the Petasites (March) is perhaps *P. albus*, introduced c.1683; Tree-Milkwort with blue and white flowers may be *Polygala chamaebuxus purpurea*. Bird's-Eye (April) should be *Primula farinosa*, but this is made doubtful by coupling it with Yorkshire Sedum, possibly *Sedum rhodiola* or conceivably *Saxifraga umbrosa*. Two sorts of Limoniums may well be *L. sinuatum* (1629) and *L. minutum* (1658), and 'Linconium' is probably a continuation of one of these, for the South African Linconias were not introduced until after 1800. 'Tenerum' Baeticum is a misprint for Teucrium, i.e. *T. fruticans;* 'Radix cava' is now *Corydalis cava*, and 'Mr. Catesby's new Virginian Starwort' is *Aster grandiflorus* of 1720, and in flower after two years. Pearl Bugloss (April) might be *Symphytum tuberosum*, and a more remote possibility is that the 'Blue-flower'd Genista' (June) could stand for *Psoralea pinnata*, which had reached England by 1690. It is difficult to make serious suggestions as to the identity of the 'Dwarf Bell-flower'd Tree' (June), the 'French Bean-Tree' (June and July), and the 'Thorn Dasie scarlet and blue' of August and September. If the 'Chrisanthemum Tree from Carolina' (October) was *Helenium autumnale*, the date of introduction must be put back.

Fairchild's letters were printed by Richard Bradley, F.R.S., in *The Monthly Register of Experiments and Observations in Husbandry and Gardening*, vol. II part i, 81-7; ii, 76-80; iii, 181-8. The journal had in fact been issued each month from April 1721 to March 1722; then each of the two first parts of the second volume covered two months; and a final part brought the project to a close (see W. Roberts, 'R. Bradley, Pioneer Garden Journalist' in *Journal R.H.S.*, LXIV, 1939, 164-74). In the first covering letter Fairchild calls his contribution 'the List of those Plants which flower every Month in my Garden'; in the second, 'an Account of what extraordinary Flowers blow in my Garden . . .'; and in the third, 'a Catalogue of such curious Flowers as blow . . . .'.

PLANTS flowering in April.
Stock-Gillyflowers, single and double, white and red.

Wall Flowers, white and yellow, double and single.
Plantain leav'd Ranunculus.
Tulips of several Sorts, single and double.
Yorkshire Sedum, and the Bird's Eye.
Anemonies of various Kinds, the best Sorts.
Collection of Ranuncula's.
Collection of Dasies.
Candytuft-Tree, plain and variegated.
Laurustinus of several Sorts.
Nettle-leav'd Jessamine, Spanish Jessamine, and the Indian yellow Jessamine.
Collection of Polyanthos, and Primrose, double and single. Black Helebore
with a green Flower, Fenel-leav'd Helebore. Collection of Auricula's, and the
Burrage-flower'd Bears-Ear.
Crown-Imperials, ten Sorts.
Collection of Narcissus.
Star of Naples.
Simblaria.
Muscaria.
Dens caninus.
Hypericum frutex.
Violets double and single, white and blue.
The single red Violet.
Hearts Ease of several Sorts.
Dwarf Flagg-Iris.
Virginian Colombine.
Wood Anemonies double and single.
Dwarf Almond.
Dwarf Hungarian Honeysuckle.
Frittilaries, thirty Sorts.
Perwinkle double and single blue, and single white.
Radix Cava.
Dwarf Medlars, two Sorts. Purple and Ash-colour'd Pulsitilla.
Bulbous Violet.
Double Pilewort.
Lady's Mantle.
Double Lady's-Smock.
Purple and yellow Mountain Avens.
Aloe-leav'd and Onion-leav'd Asphodil.
Gentianella.
Ornithogalum.
Male Mandrake.
German Catchfly.
Tree Scabious.
Bladder-Nut.
White flower'd Male Cystus.
Starr Hyacinth.

Pearl Bugloss.
Italian Camomile.
Calcidonian Iris.
Doronicum.
Double Saxafrage.
Double flower'd creeping Crowfoot.
Meleanthus.
Venetian Vetch.
Sea Daffodil.
Globe Flower.
Scorpion Senna.
Great blue flower'd Perwinkle.
Bird-Cherry.
Double white Mountain Ranunculus.
Sage-leav'd Cystus with a purple Flower.
Sweet Molly of Virginia.
The Tree-Milkwort with blue and white Flowers.
Scarlet flower'd Horse-Chesnut of Virginia.
White flower'd Horse-Chesnut.
Persian Lilly.
Double flower'd Solomon's Seal.
Geraniums, several Sorts.
French Marygolds.
Oranges.
And the Aloe, call'd, by Dr. Comelin, *Aloe Africana humilis foliis ex albo & Viridi Variegatis.*
Collection of Hyacinths.

Flowers Blowing in MAY, besides those which continu'd Blossoming, that were mention'd in the foregoing Month.

Oranges.
Lemons of several Sorts.
Pinks of various Kinds.
Collection of Tulips.
Lilly of the Valley.
Two Sorts of London Pride.
Ranunculus of the Persian Kind.
Double white Narcissus.
Sea Narcissus.
Fox Gloves.
Sweet William.
The Mule between the Sweet William and Carnation.
Colombines.
Several Kinds of Thalictrums.
Double purple Perwinkle.

The Pasque Flower purple and ash Colour.
Arbor Judae.
King's Spear.
Aloe-leav'd Asphodel.
White-flower'd Tree Scabious.
Blue flower'd Tree Scabious.
Rosemary-leav'd Buckthorn.
Citissus Lunatus.
Four Sorts of Corn Flags.
Cistus several Sorts.
Camomile.
Flagg Iris, several Sorts.
Thrift or Sea Pink, several Sorts.
Rockets.
Persian Jessamine.
Lylacs three Sorts.
Peach-leav'd Bell Flower.
Hungarian Iris.
Laburnums, two Sorts.
Yellow Martagon.
Geranium, several Sorts, among which the sweet Night smelling Kind.
Double white Mountain Ranunculus.
English Hyacinths, white, blue, and Peach-colour'd.
The double blue Harebell.
Male Peony.
Hyacinth of Peru, blue and white.
Bleu Grape Hyacinth.
Atamasco Lilly.
Tradescant's Spiderwort.
The Savoy Spiderwort.
Fraxinella, white and red.
Blue feather'd Hyacinth.
Guilder Rose.
Yellow Jessamine.
Bleu Monk's-Hood.
Double white and red Batchelors-Buttons.
Germander-leav'd Chickweed.
Greek Valerian, white and blue.
Virginian Astragulus.
Bulbose Iris.
Roman and fiery Lilly.
Meum.
Syringa.
Widowwale.
Honysuckles.
Tree Cinquefoil.

Day Lilly.
Sweet Lilly-Asphodel.
French Honeysuckles.
Nastertium Indicum.
French Marygold.
Lyssimachia.
Lichnoides.
Valerian.
Double Featherfew.
Ficoides of two or three Kinds.

The End of the Month of MAY.

Flowers for the Month of JUNE.

Great Apocinum of Virginia; White Wall-Flowers, and several other un-
common Kinds; the Turkey and Sweet Scabious, various Kinds; Ash colour &
White-Flower'd-Tree Scabious; several Kinds of Fox-Gloves; Mules Two Sorts;
Candy-Tuft-Tree; Sweet Williams; All the Sorts of Lillies of the Valley, Sweet
Lilly Asphodils, Day-Lilly, The Roman and Flaming Lilly, The White Lilly
striped with Scarlet; Sedums several Sorts; great Variety of Daisies; Fine
Ranunculas; Double-Creeping Crow-Foot; Sea Daffodil; various Kinds of
Columbines; Ladies Mantle; Tree Spurge; Onion-leav'd Asphodil; Aloe-leav'd
Asphodil; Rosemary-leav'd Buck-Thorn; Geraniums several Sorts; Palma
Christi; Scorpion Senna, and Bladder Senna; Convolvulus; Scrophularia;
Blue-flower'd Genista; Holy-oaks; some Carnations; Oranges and Lemons;
Roses; Four Sorts of Corn Flags; Small White-flower'd Female Cystus, and
Large Gum Cystus, Dwarf Yellow-flower'd Cystus; Globe-flower'd Rockets,
Double and Single; White and Purple Iris; Ten Sorts of Flag Iris, Collection of
Boulbous Iris; Peach leav'd Bell-Flower; White and Blue Canterbury Bells;
Dwarf Bellflower'd-Tree; Milkwort; Nettle-leav'd Jessamine; Valerian White
and Red, Greek Valerian; White and Blue Sea Pink; Yellow Moly, Sweet
scented Moly, Indian Serpents, and Homer's Moly; several Sorts of Heart's-
Ease; great Blue-Bottle, Savoy and Tradescants Spiderworts; Fraxinella
White and Red; Blue Monks-Hood; Blue-Feather'd Hyacinth; Double White
and Red Batchelors Buttons; Germander, and Germander-leav'd Chickweed;
Italian Honysuckle; French Honysuckles; Virginian Astragalus; Syringa;
French Willow; Turkey Lichness, Tree Lichness; Early White and Red
Honysuckles; Tree Cinquefoil; Dwarf Broom; Moon-trefoil; Lotus Tree;
Spanish Broom; Yellow, White and Red Yerrow; Pomegranates; Yellow,
White, Common and Imperial Martagons; Double White Mountain Ranun-
culus; Calaminth; Goats Rue White and Blue; Double and Single Scarlet
Lichness; Larks Spurs; Horned Poppies, Ever-Living, Black, and other
Poppies; Sweet and Everlasting Pease; White Jessamine; Yellow Indian and
Spanish Single and Double Jessamine, Yellow and Virginia Jessamine;

Mastick-Tree; Three Sorts of Thrift; French Sage; Single and Double Virgins
Bower; French Bean-Tree; Spirea Frutex, and Currant-leav'd Spirea; Double
and Single Feather'd Campion; Two Sorts of Ornithogalum; Golden Rod; Sir
George Wheeler's Tutson; Mountain Scabious; Deptford Pink; Two Sorts of
Limoniums; Dwarf Mountain-Milkwort; several Sorts of Ficoides; Four Sorts
of Tongue-leav'd Aloes; Lichnoides; Virginian Purple Sun Flower; Fennel
Flower; Double and Single White and Blue Throatworts.

Flowers for the Month of JULY.

Oranges and Lemons; Annual Stocks; Ash-colour and White Tree Scabious,
Sweet-scented and Mountain Scabious; Collection of Carnations; Two Sorts
of Mules; Sweet Williams; Roman, Orange and Day-Lilly; Sedums several
Sorts; Rosemary-leav'd Buck-Thorn; several Sorts of Roses; Peach-leav'd Bell
Flower Two Sorts, and Dwarf and Steeple Bell Flowers; Double Creeping
Crowfoot; Valerian White and Red, Greek Valerian White and Blue; Four
Sorts of Hearts Ease; Great Blue Bottle; Tradescants Spiderwort; Double
White and Red Batchelors Buttons; Virginian Astragalus; French Hony-
suckles; French Willow; Annual Lichness, Tree Lichness, Double and Single
Scarlet Lichness; Lichnoides; Lisynachia; Tree Milkwort, small Mountain
Milkwort; Dutch, Late, Red, and Ever-Green Honysuckle; Tree Cinquefoil;
Yellow and Red Yerrow; Spanish Broom White and Yellow; White, Imperial,
Scarlet Lichness; Lichnoides; Lisymachia; Tree Milkwort, small Mountain
and Blue Goats-Rue; Horned, Ever-living, Black and Common Poppies; Sweet
Pease Scarlet and Common; Yellow, White, Blue and Scarlet Lupines; Colutea
of Aethipoia and Canada; White Jessamine; Virginian Yellow, Common
Yellow, Spanish Double and Single Jessamine; Common Spirea, and Currant-
leav'd Spirea; Feather'd Campion, Double and Single Rose Campion; Double
and Single Virgins Bower; Everlasting Pease; Starworts; Golden Rod of several
Sorts; Spiked Speedwell; Two Sorts of Limoniums; Ficoides several sorts;
Winter Cherry; White flower'd Nightshade-Tree; Capsicums; Love Apples;
French Bean-Tree; Myrtles; African and French Marigolds; Amaranthus and
Balsamines; Four Sorts of Sun-Flowers; White Helebore, with a Black Flower;
Oliander leav'd Tree Apocinum; Four Sorts of Gnaphaliums; Four Sorts of
Olianders; Scarlet and Blue Cardinal Flowers; White and Yellow Mullen; Red
and White Orpin, and the small Ever-Green Sort; Fritilaria Crassa, small and
great; Two Sorts of Passion Flowers.

END of the Months of June and July.

[Curious Flowers in August and September.]

Stock Gilly-Flowers, double and single, white and red, purple and white, Tree
Scabius, Musk Scabius, Turky Scabius, Fairchild's Mule, Valerian white and
red, six Sorts of Viola Tricolor, Spanish Broom, Virginia Martagon, two Sorts

of Goat Rue, horned Poppy, Spanish Jessamine single and double, Brazil Jessamine, Indian Yellow Jessamine, Arabian Jessamine, Ilex-leav'd Jessamine, Virginian yellow Jessamine, Linconium, several Sorts of Ficoides, Aloes several Sorts, Corn Marigold white and yellow, two sorts of Anemone Spermos, Amomum Plinii, white flower'd Nightshade, double and single Virgin's Bower, double and single flower'd Myrtle, five Sorts of Sun-Flowers, four Sorts of Gnaphaliums, Holyoaks, four Sorts of Apocinums, Campanula two Sorts, Oleanders four Sorts, Thorn Dasie scarlet and blue, Cardinal Flowers, Orpine white and red, Fritilaria-crassa two Sorts, Passion Flowers four Sorts, Colchicums several Sorts, Cyclamens two Sorts, Trumpet Flower, Sopewort, Leonorus two Sorts, Arbutus, Guernsey Lilly, Bella Donna, Starworts several Sorts, Geraniums several Sorts, Cotiledons several sorts, Autumn Crocus, Autumn Daisie, Tree Milkwort, Aloe-leav'd Asphodel, true Saffron, Onion-leav'd Asphodel, Viburnum, Golden Rods two Sorts, Shrub Mallows four Sorts, double Pinks several Sorts, Laurus Tinus, Tamarisk, Jalop, Moon Trefoil, Stacus Two Sorts, Colutea, Roses, Carnations several Sorts, yellow Colchicum, Candytuft Tree, Grounsel Tree, Dutch Honysuckle, Barba Jovis, Tenerum Baeticum, Tradescants double Spiderwort, Coma Aurea two Sorts, Platanus-leav'd Chrisanthemum, Roman Wall-Flower, Antirrhimum, Rose Campion single and double, Throatwort double white and blue, Tree Love-Apple two Sorts, Sampiere, Polyanthus, Auricula's, the monthly Grape, several new Sorts of Annals.

The following Grapes ripen with me in August and September.
The Sweet-water Grape black and white, the Muscadine white, the Royal Muscadine, the black Muscadine, the white Chasselass, the black Chasselass, the black Cluster Grape, the black Curran Grape, the Zant Curran, the Narbois, Chianti, the Burgundy, the Melier, the Munier, the black Morillion, white Morillion, the white Malvoisie, black Malvoisie, variegated Grape, Parsley Grape, Bourdeaux Claret Grape, white Frontigniac, blue Frontigniac, red Frontigniac, grizle Frontigniac, Muscadelle, Greek Grape, Fox Grape, St. Peter's Grape, Hesperion, white Raisin, red Raisin, blue Raisin, Bourlac, Lombardie, red Hamborow, blue Hamborow, white Grizleine, Matchless Grape.

Curious Flowers in October.

Ash-colour and white Tree Scabius, Horn'd Poppy, double Stock Gilly-flowers, Spanish Jessamin double and single, Brazil Jessamine, Arabian Jessamine, Nettle-leav'd Jessamine, yellow Indian Jessamine, several Sorts of Ficoides, Onion-leav'd Asphodel, Aloe-leav'd Asphodel, two Sorts of Anemone Spermos, Tree Chrisanthemum, Myrtles, several Sorts, ten Sorts of Colchicums, four Sorts of Cyclamens, two Sorts of Leonurus, true Saffron, Arbutus, Guernsey Lilly, Bella Donna, Autumn Crocus, Tree Milkwort, scarlet flow'ring Geranium, with several other Sorts, Chrisanthemum Tree from Carolina, Mr. Catesby's new Virginian Starwort, Pelitory of Spain, scarlet flow'ring Viaburnum, black flow'ring Lotus, Coma Aurea, Tree Lychnes, purple flow'ring everlasting Kidney-Bean, old Man's Head Pinks, new Sort of Barba Jovis, Limonium, Laurus-tinus several Sorts, Colutea, Aizoid Tythimals, Roses, Moon-trefoile, scarlet flow'ring Cotildon, Passion Flower, Carnations, Fennel-leav'd Tree Scabius.

Curious Flowers in November.

Spanish Jessamine double and single, yellow Indian Jessamine, Azores Jessamine, double Stock Gilliflowers of several Colours, Nettle-leav'd Jessamine, Aloes of several Sorts, Ficoides of several Sorts, Sedums of several Sorts, Aloe-leav'd Asphodil, Onion-leav'd Asphodil, Chrisanthemum Creticum white and yellow, Leonurus two Sorts, scarlet flower'd Geranium, with several other Sorts, Venetian Vetch, Mr. Catesby's fine blue Starwort, Colutea, Tree Milkwort, Coma Aurea, everlasting Kidney-Bean, black flow'ring Lotus, Pelitory of Spain, Scabius of several Sorts, Passion Tree in Fruit, Carnations, Sensitive Plant in Flower, Polyanthus.

Curious Flowers in December

Double Stock Gilliflowers of various Kinds, Sensitive Plants in Flower, Carnations, Tulips, Polianthus, Hyacinths, Spanish Jessamine, Indian Jessamine, Cyclamens, Azores Jessamine, Nettle-leav'd Jessamine, Geraniums several Sorts, Ficoides of several Sorts, Aloes of several Sorts, new sort of Barba Jovis, old Man's Head Pink, Venetian Vetch, sweet scented Cyclamen, Laurus-tinus several Sorts, Candy-tuft Tree, Mr. Catesby's fine blue Starwort, Glastonbury Thorn.

Curious Flowers in January

Black Helebore with white Flowers, Helebore with green Flowers, Winter Aconite, Mezereon, Snow Drops double and single, Candy-tuft Tree, Laurustinus several Sorts, blue Star Hyacinth, Passetout, Spring Cyclamen, sweet scented Cyclamen, Canary Campanula, Polyanthus, Wall Flowers, Tulips, Anemonies, Glastenbury Thorn, new Sort of Barba Jovis, Venetian Vetch, Auricula's, Carnations, Kidney-Bean Tree.

Curious Flowers in February

Spurge Laurel, Mezereon, Snow Drops double and single, double Stocks of several Colours, black Helebore with a white Flower, Helebore with a green

Flower, Tulips, Hyacinths, Radix Cava, double and single white and yellow Wall-Flowers, Polyanthus, Misleto, Canary Campanula, Spring Colchicum, sweet scented and Spring Cyclamens, Narcissus of Constantinople, Narcissus of Naples, Winter Aconite, 20 Sorts of Crocus, Collection of Hyacinths, Auricula's, Polyanthus, Carnations, white and red Mezereons, Persian Iris, double Primrose, Venetian Vetch, Cornelian Cherry, Dens Caninus, Yorkshire Sedum, Muscary Hyacinth Ash Colour and white, Periwinkle white and blue, forty Sorts of Narcissus, Hepaticas, Dwarf Almond, Fritilaries, Oranges, Anana's or Pine-Apple Fruit begins to appear.

Curious Flowers in March.

Stock Gilliflowers double of several Kinds, Wall-Flowers double white and red, 30 Sorts of early Tulips, Laurustinus, Oranges, Candy-tuft Tree, York-shire Sedum, black Helebore with a white Flower, black Helebore with a green Flower, Polyanthus, double Primroses, 20 Sorts of Crocus, single white Hepatica, double and single blue and Peach-colour Hepatica, Hyacinths, Spring Colchicum, four Sorts of Spring Cyclamen, four Sorts of Narcissus, Cornelian Cherry, Star of Naples, Ranunculus, Dens caninus, Fumetory, Violets single and double white and blue, Fenel-leav'd Helebore, Radix cava, Periwinkle white and blue and double purple, Dwarf Hungary Honysuckle, Assarabacca of Virginia, Petasites, Male Mandrake, Dwarf Medlar, Dwarf Flag Iris, Venetian Vetch, Nettle-leav'd Jessamine, 30 Sorts of Fritilaries, Dwarf Almond, Fruit bearing Almond, Simblaria, Misleto, bulbose Iris, double blosson Peach, Anemonies, monthly Rose, Jonquils, double blossom Pear, double blossom Cherry, double blossom Almond, Arbor Judae, with several other Sorts of Plants, whose Time of flow'ring is uncertain.

LISTS OF PLANTS in gardens were made fairly often, but they very rarely stated the numbers of each kind stocked. Stock books were sometimes compiled by nurserymen, though probably more often of amounts of seeds than of living plants. In any case hardly any records of firms in the trade appear to survive from before the 19th century, and the few that are accessible do not include any early material of this type. The gap is to some slight extent filled by inventories taken for probate and by catalogues of sales of nursery stock, usually at a bankruptcy. In view of the amount of time required to count the many thousands of plants in a large nursery, it is not surprising that the probate authorities should have relaxed the rules at a time when detailed inventories of other goods were generally demanded. We have to be thankful for those few inventories which have so far been identified, and for some analogous catalogues of stock. (For a study of this evidence as a whole see J. H. Harvey, 'The Stocks held by Early Nurseries', in *Agricultural History Review*, XXII pt.i(1974), 18-35).

About 1705 the great nursery at Brompton Park was said to have about ten million plants in all, on an area between 50 and 100 acres. William Cox of Kew (1680-1722) had over 30,000 plants on a small nursery, run together with a farm of 11½ acres. Peter Mason of Isleworth (1680-1730), had at his death over 115,000, but there is no evidence as to the area of his nursery. The length of Mason's inventory precludes transcription in full, but a summary is given here, following the full inventory of William Leeson (died 1721/2), a gardener and nurseryman of Hodsock Woodhouse in Blyth parish in the north of Nottinghamshire and close by the border of Yorkshire. Leeson, who was very likely the gardener of that name at Worksop who, in 1716, took as apprentice George Naylor, son of William Naylor of Derbyshire, made his will (proved 20 August 1722) on 19 March 1718/19. He was able to leave an annuity of £10 to his wife Mary, and a sum of £20 to his son William Leeson. The residue including all his real and personal estate was left to his daughter Mary Leeson, who was the executrix. The son was almost certainly the chief gardener to the Duke of Leeds at Kiveton Park, about six miles west of Hodsock. He held that post by 1730, in 1731 when he subscribed to the first edition of Philip Miller's folio *Gardener's Dictionary,* and for the next twenty years or more. The second William Leeson had charge of great works on the gardens and extensive planting, and in the latter part of his career was assisted by his son, the third William Leeson.

A True and perfect Inventory of all the Goods Chattells and Credits of

William Leeson late of Hodsock Woodhouse in the parish of Blyth and County of Nottingham Gardiner deceased taken and appraised the 8th day of February 1721/2, by John Shuttleworth, Ralph Langfitt, John Gildon, George Fox, Edmund Hodgkinson.

	£.	s.	d.
Imprimis: His purse and apparell	10	0	0
Goods in the House. Range Grate Froggs Fire			
Shovell Tongs	01	10	0
Candlesticks Brass Ladles Tosting Fork Beef Fork			
Bellows with other Materialls	00	05	0
A pan in the Corner	01	10	0
3 brass Pans 2 Kettles one Saucepan	02	00	0
6 pewter Dishes 1 Plate 1 Tankard 2 Copper Potts			
2 Porringers 1 Mustard Pott	01	06	0
a Cubbard Table Safe and Forme	00	15	0
a Wanded Chair 6 other Chairs	00	08	0
a pewter Case	00	06	0
a Looking Glass a Clock	01	01	0
Earthen Ware & Books	00	07	6
Shelves 2 Kitts and a Bend Kitt	00	05	0
a Bed with furniture	01	10	0
Garden shears	00	12	0
	21	15	6

	£.	s.	d.
Goods in the Parlour. One Bed with Furniture	01	10	0
One Bedstead & hangings	00	14	0
Two Tables and Forme	00	08	0
3 Chairs	00	02	6
3 Tubbs 2 Kitts	00	16	0
a Wash Tubb	00	02	6
a Warming Pan & Reel	00	04	0
	03	17	0

	£.	s.	d.
Goods in the Passage & Dairy			
One Salting Tubb Kinmell (?)	00	11	0
4 Barrells a Serge Tems (?) & Churn	00	17	0
3 Kitts Bowls and Panchions	00	04	6
a Chees Press and 3 Chees Fatts	00	05	0
One Dozen of Glass bottles	00	02	6
1 Sack 3 Meal bags	00	02	6
2 Wood bottles	00	01	6
	02	04	0

Goods in the Chamber over the House

A Bed and Furniture	05	00	0
2 Chests 5 Boxes 1 Trunk	00	15	0
a Close press 5s Three Chairs 2:6	00	07	6
2 Shelves 1s a pair of Baggs 1:6	00	02	6
5 pair of Sheets 2 Table Cloths & one Dozen of Napkins	01	10	0
7 Cheeses	00	10	0
	08	05	0

Goods in the Chamber over the Parlour

A Bed and Bedstead	00	18	0
3 Wheels	00	06	0
Boards	00	10	0
5 Basketts and Hampers	00	03	6
a Window Cloath a peck half peck and Quartern	00	04	6
	02	02	0

Goods in the Barne

7 Spades 2 Gruls	00	18	0
6 Howes 2 Spittles 3 Rakes 2 Watering Pans	01	00	0
Garden Lines	01	00	0
3 pair of Panyiers 3 Skins	00	06	6
3 Wheel Barrows 5 Ladders	00	18	0
a Scyth Saws Chissells Wimbles	00	06	6
a parcell of Sawn Ware	01	10	0
a Table Grindstone and well Frame	00	08	0
	06	07	0

Goods in the Stable and Cowhouse

A Mare	04	00	0
a Cow	03	10	0
a Sadle and bridle	00	05	0
a Collar and a pair of Gears	00	05	0
a Pannell and Mail Pillion	00	02	0
a Shovell 6 Forks & a Dragg	00	06	0
a Spade 3 Hay Rakes	00	02	6
a Slead	00	07	0
a Hay Stack	04	10	0

Wood and other Lumber there	00	10	0
	13	17	6

Stock in the Gardens. Hill Close			
Cherries & Stocks	00	10	0
Chesnutts	03	00	0
Elms	12	15	0
Limes	12	00	0
Oaks	03	00	0
Scotch Firrs	02	10	0
Crabbs and Whiggeys	00	15	0
Apples	02	00	0
Witch Elmes	05	00	0
Walnutts	00	13	0
Small Elmes Quinces & Laurells	01	15	0
	43	18	0

In the Middle piece.			
Scotch Firrs	05	00	0
Chesnutts	06	18	0
Walnutts	05	10	0
Limes	01	00	0
Oakes	00	05	0
Elmes	41	06	0
Small Chesnutts	01	16	0
Pear Stocks Plumbs Nectarins	03	00	0
	63	15	0

Little Garden			
Elmes	09	10	0
Ewes and Box	03	00	0
Apples	05	10	0
Walnutts	03	00	0
Holleys Firrs Peaches & Nectarins	01	05	0
	22	05	0

Farr Side Dike and Narr Side

Elmes	18	10	0
Limes	08	00	0
Pears and Walnutts	04	00	0
Hollies	05	10	0
Dutch Box and Peaches	01	15	0
	37	15	0

In the Garden before the House

Hollies & Yiews	115	00	0
Hollies & Yiews in the other part of the Garden	030	00	0
Firrs	026	10	0
Mulberries and Wall fruit	000	05	0
Apples and Stocks	006	00	0
Limes & Elmes & Planes	010	00	0
Span. Chesnutts Walnutts	001	10	0
Pears Phillerayes	002	00	0
Bayes Laurelstinus	(? 000	10	0)
Lawrells with all other odd parcells	01	10	0
	193	05	0

Totall of all at Woodhouse	419	06	0
All at Blyth is	020	06	0
Totall	439	06	0

Funerall Charges & other Debts after all Bills deducted	078	00	0
True Totall of all is	361	06	0

(Nottinghamshire Record Office, Archdeaconry of Nottingham probate records transferred from York 1972)

Leeson was a provincial nurseryman in a rather small way, living in a house of five rooms. The value of his household goods was put at £58 8s. 0d. William Cox of Kew Green, who died at almost exactly the same time, was also in rather a small way, and his household goods were assessed at £50 11s. 6d. Much more prosperous was Peter Mason of Isleworth, who lived in a ten-roomed house amid belongings valued at £153 15s. 6d. The house contained a Hall, Parlour, Kitchen and Counting Room, on an upper floor a passage and the Red Room, the Green Room and the Yellow Room, with what seems to have been a top floor consisting of George's Room, the Middle Garrett and the Nursery (for children). There were also a Bakehouse, a Brewhouse, Yard and Cellar. The establishment at the time of Mason's death, aged 50, consisted of his wife Matilda or Mertilla and probably six living children ranging from fifteen down to six, three of them boys. To give an indication of their standard of living the contents of the Parlour, appraised at £15, may be cited: Three pair of Window Curtains Callico Vallence & Rods One large Peer Glass one Chimney Glass two Sconces Eight Matted Chairs One Black Card Table Tea Kettle Lamp & Stand One ovall Table four Family Pictures Nine Prints in Glass One Stove Compleate Bellows & Brush One Tea Table Eight coloured Tea Cupps Eight Saucers five Chocolate Cups One Tea Pott & Stand four Basons one Plate. In the passage upstairs were three pictures, two maps and a print; in the Green Room a picture and seven prints; in the Yellow Room thirty-six prints, besides a great deal of furniture, china and fittings. The nursery, which we know from Batty Langley's informed comments had a high reputation, must have provided the Mason family with a really comfortable living.

The inventory of Mason's stock is extremely voluminous, and only a general indication of the trees and plants can be given here. Among Fruit Trees there were 4000 apples and nearly 9000 stocks; over 5000 pears and stocks; about a thousand plums and 3000 stocks including White Pear, Mussel and Brussels stocks; about 3000 cherries and 1500 stocks; besides apricots, damsons, figs (only ten), 100 grapevines, medlars, mulberries, nectarines and peaches, and 56 quinces; with a thousand currants, 250 gooseberries and 50 raspberries. The Forest Trees comprised a wide selection, particularly strong in beech (about 3500), horse chestnut (over 4000), Spanish chestnut (1500), various elms (about 8000 English, 6000 Dutch, 1670 wych and 20 'yellow'), lime, poplar and sycamore (about 1300 of each), and over 2000 walnut. Among evergreens first place was taken by the yew with a total of more than 13,000 including standards, fan and pyramid trained. There were some 2500 hollies of different sorts, about 5000 Scotch Fir, 2700 Silver Fir, and over 5000 spruce in which Mason was then the principal specialist. Rather surprisingly there were fewer than 500 planes, 300 birch, and just over a hundred cypress. On the other hand Mason's list did include over 6000 hornbeam as against only a few hundred English oaks and about 600 evergreen oak.

ᵥ The range of evergreen and flowering shrubs stocked included almonds, althea frutex (Hibiscus syriacus), arbor vitae, barberry, baytree, five-leaved bladder-nut, box, Spanish broom, bird cherry, cornelian cherry (Cornus mas), over 1500 honeysuckles, hypericum frutex (Spiraea hypericifolia), ivy, white and yellow jasmines, juniper, common laburnum, common laurel, about 200 laurustinus, 400 lilacs, a hundred maples, a dozen small mezereons, 125 true phillyrea, 200 small privet, 20 pyracantha, 750 roses, a hundred each of bladder senna (Colutea arborescens) and scorpion senna (Coronilla emerus), service trees, spiraea frutex (S. salicifolia), sumach, syringa, and Egyptian thorn. In 1730 ornamental species were limited and the stocks held were generally not very large. It was still the age of the clipped yew, of the holly in many varieties, of avenues of elm and lime.

APPENDIX VI

SOME WILLS OF EARLY NURSERYMEN

IN COMPARISON with probate inventories, wills are relatively uninformative on the subject of the possessions, household or business, of early nurserymen. On the other hand some of the surviving wills not merely provide a great deal of information as to family and estates, but give a precious insight into the personalities of men who would otherwise be little more than names. The three wills here printed in full represent the 16th, 17th and 18th centuries. The first, of Henry Russell of Westminster, though not the earliest will of a professional gardener to survive, may be the first which can be connected with a documented business; it yields the important information that Russell was in the service of Henry VIII when he made his will, ten years before his death, in 1539. The second, of 1685, is the deathbed will of Roger Looker, senior partner and moving spirit of the great enterprise of Brompton Park. Looker had been the Queen's Gardener and also in charge of the gardens of the Earl of Clarendon at Cornbury, Oxfordshire, and Swallowfield, Berks.; of the Earl of Burlington in London and at Londesborough, Yorkshire; of the Duchess of Lauderdale at Ham in Surrey; of Viscount Cullen at Rushton, Northants.; and of the plantations of 'his honored Master' Sir Thomas Fanshaw at Kempton Park, Middlesex, and at Jenkins near Barking in Essex. The third will is of a provincial nurseryman of relatively humble station, George Rogers of Chester, who died in 1799. He is of interest to us as having leased, among other grounds, the Nuns' Gardens near Chester Castle.

In these wills the original spelling has been preserved but contractions have been expanded and the use of i and j, u and v, modernized. Latin phrases, for example in the form of probate, have been translated.

Will of Henry Russell of Westminster, made 1539, proved 1 Dec. 1549

In the name of god amen the vth daie of September in the yere of our Lord god a Thousand Fyve hundreth thirtie and nyen I Henry Russell of the Citie of Westminster gardiner and servaunte unto the Kinges majestie being hole of mynde and in perfit remembrance thanks be unto god dothe ordeine and make this my present Testamente and last Will in manner ensueng First I bequeath my soull unto allmightie god my maker Saviour and Redeamour to doo therwith as it shall please his godhid Item that my will is that Ellen Russell my Wiff pay or cause to be paid unto Thomas Cacy of London gardener iiij li. sterling and to Robert Smallwood of the said Citie of Westminster beerebruer Twentie shelings sterling Also to Thomas Chephant of Wikeham (Wycombe) in the Countie of Buckingham gentleman xl. s. and

to oon Mr. Barkley x. s. and to Thomas Rudley in Cheep vintener iij. s. iiij. d.
To Richard Gill of Westminster glover vj. s. Item I will that my Wiff see my
bodie buried honestlie according to her powre whear and in what place it
shall please god unto whom my said wiff I frelye geve all such goodes
Leasums (?) and other whatsoever it be which I have or shall leave behinde
me Also all debtes to me owing by anny personne or personnes and she to
bestowe the same as she shall thinke most best by her discression for the
dischardge of my soull which Ellen my said Wif I ordein and make my sole
executrice of this my present Testament and last Will and the said Thomas
Casy to be supervisor of the same as my desire is he shoulde take paines
therin In witnes wherof I the said Henrye Russell have herunto sett my seale
and signe manuell the daie and yere abovsaid In the presence of Richard
Babbes of the said Citie of Westminster pulter (poulterer) Henry Morrice
sporrier Richerd Gill glover John Barbour cappor and other

Proved 1 December 1549 by the executrix through the person of Hugh
Egerton first sworn etc.

(A will proved before the Vicar General of the Bishop of Westminster during
the short period, 1540-50, when Westminster Abbey was a cathedral; now
Consistory Court of London wills, register 'Wymesley', ff. 35v-36; Greater
London Record Office, DL/C/356).

Will of Roger Looker of St Martin in the Fields, Middlesex, 1685

In the name of God Amen the second day of March in the first yeare of the
raigne of our Soveraigne Lord King James the second and in the yeare of our
Lord 1684/5 I Roger Looker being sicke and weake in body but perfect
memory and knowing the uncertainty of this life on earth and being desirous
to settle things in order doe make this my last will and Testament in manner
and forme following that is to say first and principally I commend my soule
to Allmighty God my Creator assuredly beleiveing that I shall receive full
pardon and free remission of my sinns and to bee saved by the precious death
and merritts of my blessed saviour and redeemer Christ Jesus and my body to
the earth from whence it was taken to bee buried in such decent and
Christian manner as to my Executor hereafter named shall bee thought meet
and convenient and as touching such worldly estate as the Lord in mercy hath
lent mee my will and meaning is the same shall bee imployed and bestowed as
hereafter by this my will is expressed Item I give and bequeath to my beloved
sonn William Looker all my share or parte which I have now in Bromton
Parke with three other parteners in as ample manner as I my selfe now enjoy
it that is with all Advantages whatsoever dureing the terme I have in the same
Item I give and bequeath unto my dearly beloved wife my lease of my now
dwelling house and Garden with the appurtenances together with the said
house and Garden to have and to hold the same dureing her naturall life and
noe longer and my will is and I doe hereby give and bequeath my said lease

and dwelling house and Garden unto my said sonn William Looker to bee had and enjoyed unto and by him from and after the day of the death of my said deare wife dureing the remainder of the terme of yeares which shall bee then to come in the said lease Item I give and bequeath unto my said deare wife Bridgett Looker all the rest and residue of my estate both reall and personall which I shall dye possessed of my debts and funerall charges being first thereout paid and deducted Lastly I doe make and ordaine my said dear wife Bridgett Looker sole and absolute Executrix of this my last will and Testament hereby revoaking all former or other will or wills Testament or testaments by mee made or declared either by word or in writing and this to bee taken as my last will and testament and none other In wittnesse whereof I have hereunto sett my hand and seale the day and yeare first above written Roger Looker Memorandum the words videlicet: (dureing the terme I have in the same) was interlined above before thensealeing hereof and then signed sealed published and declared by the said Roger Looker in the presence of

9 March 1684/5

Which day appeared personally Emera Crosse wife of Peter Crosse of St Martins in the feilds Gent. Edward Fuller of St Mary Savoy Citizen and Joyner of London and Edward Godfrey of St Martins in the Feilds Gent. and by vertue of their severall Oaths deposed that they did on or about the date of the will hereunto annexed hear the same read over to Roger Looker of St Martins in the feilds in the County of Middlesex Gardner deceased who well liked and approved thereof and after it was soe read over to him did endeavour to write his name and Sirname to the bottome or end thereof as now appeareth but his hand did soe shake that hee could not write the same and they doe verily beleive in their conscience that hee was at all the said time of perfect mind and memory and well understood what hee sayed and did and lived till the next day signed by Emera Crosse Edward Fuller Edw: Godfrey 9 March 1684/5 the said Emera Crosse Edward Fuller and Edward Godfrey were sworn upon the truth of the premisses before me Richard Lloyd surrogate

Proved at London . . . on the ninth day of the month of March in the year of the Lord (according to the style of England) 1684 on the oath of Bridgett Looker relict of the said deceased and Executrix named in the said Testament . . .

(Prerogative Court of Canterbury, 35 Cann; Public Record Office, Prob 11/379).

Will of George Rogers of Chester, made 1798, proved 31 Aug. 1799

In The Name of God amen I Gearge Rogers of the City of Chester Gardenor being of sound and disposing mind memory and understanding do hereby make this my last Will and Testament in manner following first I commit my

Body to the Earth to be decently intered and have all my just Debts and Funeral Expenses fully Paid I give and bequeath to my Dear Wife Sarah Rogers all that I am Possessed of at my decess as ready money Book Debts or money owing to me by any Person or Persons on my account with all my Household Furniture of every kind also the lease of my House and Garden calld the Nun Garden also the lease of a Garden I hold in Handbridge also the lease of a Garden I hold at Flookersbrook with all stock that may be on the several Gardens at my decese with all Proffits that may arise from the same I give to the said Sarah Rogers so long as she shall live and at her decese to John Gorton her son by a former Husband for his sole use and I do hereby nominate constitute and appoint the said Sarah Rogers and John Gorton Executors hereof hereby revoking and utterly making void all former and other will or wills by me at any times heretofore made Ratifying and Confirming this and none other to be my last Will and Testament In Witness whereof I have hereunto set and put my hand and seal this Twentyfourth day of April in the year of our Lord one Thousand Seven Hundred and Ninety Eight. George Rogers Signed sealed Published and declared by the said Testater George Rogers as and for his last Will and Testament in the sight and Presence of us who have subscribed our names as Witness hereto Sam Jones Robert Goff

Aug. 31st 1799 Sarah Rogers widow and John Gorton the Executors within named were sworn in Common form before me Richd. Mytton surrogate (Personalty sworn at) under £300
Probate issued Dated 31st Augst. 1799

(Consistory Court of Chester, original will; Cheshire Record Office, WS 1799).

APPENDIX VII

LETTERS OF HENRY WOODMAN, NURSERYMAN,
1729-1733

ALTHOUGH a good deal of correspondence from nurserymen has survived, little of it tells a connected story or throws much light on questions of plantsmanship. A group of letters concerned with the planting of Gateshead Park for Henry Ellison Esq., early in the reign of George II, forms an exception. These letters (which form part of the Ellison Papers deposited in the Central Library, Gateshead, Co. Durham), together with interspersed lists and accounts, were addressed to Ellison himself, to his somewhat unsatisfactory gardener Thomas Woolley, or to Thomas Sisson, the agent or steward at Gateshead Park. The nurseryman was Henry Woodman of Strand-on-the-Green, Chiswick, (c.1698-1758) who established his nursery by 1727 and in the following year married Eleanor Compton of Chiswick, in St. Paul's Cathedral. Woodman's gardens included a half-acre of walled garden adjoining his house between Strand-on-the-Green and Back Lane, and six acres on the opposite or north-east side of the lane. He was a man of some education, writing a good hand, and in 1731 was a subscriber to the first edition of Philip Miller's famous *Gardener's Dictionary*. In his will made on 27 June 1755 Woodman left to his wife 'all my Stock on the Ground and in the Ground as being a Nursery Man' for her life, with reversion to his son Henry. In fact Mrs. Woodman survived until 1780, but paying rates on assessments heavily reduced in 1768 and again in 1775. The nursery does not seem to have been taken over by any later occupier.

About 1733 Woolley was dismissed, and Woodman ceased to supply plants to Gateshead. Whatever may have been the rights and wrongs of the case, the reason emerges from a letter sent by Stephen Switzer to Mr. Ellison on 16 January 1733/34. Switzer, who had by that time completely ousted Woodman, wrote scathingly: 'When I found that Woolley had prevaild Sir on you to goe to Strand in the Green I guess't at the Reason, and that by a Private Understanding between the Nurseryman and him (which he knew I would never submit to) you was in a fair (*sic*) of Being well cheated. But it was not proper for me as I tho! at that Time to intermeddle in it. I take Woolley to be as Great a Rogue (as) any in England that way, he has had the assurance to call and write often to me for a Place, But I never answer'd him. I suppose the Bill the Gentleman Brings contains the hedge Plants, fruit trees shrubbs &c. that Planted the new Garden. I Remember they were all pretty small tho: I dare say the Price will be large enough. There was a Gardiner in Bishoprick yt. wanted to come in with me on the same foot as Wooly has undoubtedly done with your nurseryman. But I did not only refuse him, But (as was just) told his master of him: this the Collonell knows to be true.'

So much for Switzer's side of the story; Woodman's view of the landscape gardener will emerge from his letters, which are here printed in full, together with the detailed accounts for plants and seeds which form part of the series.

To Henry Ellison Esqr. at Gateshead park near Newcastle upon Tyne
To Henry Elison Esqr. p. Henry Woodman

1729 Oct 18	£	s.	d.	£		
To 26 plumbs		13	0			
30 peaches & Nectarins	2	5	0			
34 pears	1	14	0			
20 Cherries		10	0			
15 aprecots		15	0			
48 Apples on paradise Stocks	2	8	0			
108 Gooseberys & Currants		18	0			
6 Berburys without Stone		6	0			
100 Early red Respberys		2	6			
100 White Do.		5	0			
				9	16	6
20 Damask roses		5	0			
4 White }						
4 red } Altheas		4	0			
8 Honysuckles		2	0			
4 almonds		6	0			
4 Persian Jesamins		1	4			
				0	18	4
				10	14	10
100 Ranunculas Comon		5	0			
100 Pollyanthus		16	8			
100 good Mixt Tulips		7	6			
1 lb. Dutch Emonies		5	0			
40 Strip't Lillies	2	0	0			
50 Do. Crowne Imperialls	2	10	0			
40 Persian Iris		2	6			
50 Hepaticas		16	8			
40 double Snow drops		2	6			
200 Dutch Crocus		2	0			
50 Ariculas		12	6			
400 Hautboy Strawberys		2	0			
6½ Single Matts		4	4			
2 Do. Double		2	0			
a Flasket for the Flowers		1	0			
Wharfedge & Sufference		2	0	8	11	8
	£19	6	6	£19	6	6

Henry Ellison Esqr. Dr. to Hen: Woodman

1729 29 Dec.		£	s.	d.
To Early Turnep	4 oz		2	0
Red Top Turnep	4 oz			8
Green Do.	4 oz			8
Yellow Do.	4 oz		2	0
Parsnep	6 oz			6
Orange Carrott	8 oz		1	3
Welch Onion	2 oz		1	0
Strasburgh Do.	8 oz		2	0
White Spanish Do.	8 oz		2	0
Italian Sellery	½ oz			6
London Leek	4 oz		2	0
Red & White Beet	6 oz		2	0
Large Nusturtion	2 oz		2	0
Dutch Asparagrass	4 oz		1	3
Collyflower	2 oz		10	0
Yellow Savoy	2 oz		2	0
Green Do.	2 oz		2	0
True Brocoli	2 oz		3	0
Brocoli	2 oz		2	0
Silesia Lettuce	1 oz		1	6
White Coss	2 oz		4	0
Browne Dutch Do.	2 oz		3	0
Red Coss Do.	2 oz		4	0
Cabbage	2 oz		1	0
Curld Endive	2 oz		2	0
Red Cabbage	2 oz		2	0
Early Cowcumber	2 oz		2	0
best Mellon 10 sorts	2 oz		5	0
Sweet sented Pease	2 oz		2	0
Scorzonera	2 oz		2	0
Salsify	2 oz		2	0
Batt(ersea) Cabbage	2 oz		3	0
Bush Bazell	½ oz		1	3
Sumer Swtt. Marjorum	1 oz		1	0
Winter Do.	1 oz		1	0
Venice Looking glass			1	6
Scarlet Lupins	2 oz		1	0
Cardoons	2 oz		2	0
Gourd & Meekin	1 oz		1	0
Double Larkspur	1 oz		2	0
Femal Balson & a deal Box			1	8
100 Asparagrass roots & matt			5	8
4 plumbs			2	0
Wharfedge			0	6
		4	12	11

No.		No. of Layers
1	Duke of Holsten	4
2	Glory of Reading	4
3	Bulls Blood	2
4	Topham's King George	2
5	Princes Sobiske	2
6	Princes Modenia	2
7	Curtis's No. 7	2
8	Sr. Robert Walpole	2
9	Topham's Prince of Wales	2
10	Glory of Windsor	4
11	Glory of London	4
12	Davis's Seedling	2
13	Elector of Brunswick	2
14	Lady Weymouth	2
15	St. Mary of Harrow	2
16	Island princes	2
17	Royall George	(2)
18	Randal's painted Layday	(2)
19	Superb	2
20	Crowne of Flowers Rectified	2
		Tot: 48

To 48 Carnation Layers transplanted	2	8	0
40 Double White Rockets	1	0	0
100 Hautboy Strawberys Basket & Sufferance		1	6
	3	9	6

Mr. Woolley   Xtmas Eve 1729

I have all your things in a Readiness & only waits for a Shipp there is a fleet up & some will be gowing at the latter end of this I was afraid you'd think this Delay was my Neglect but do ashure you I have made enquiry twice a Week ever since I had your Orders I have Bott. you a Case of good Instrumts. & will send all together & then will give you an acct. of all & by what Shipp & master they come by

           I am in great hast but
              nevertheless yr Humble Servt.
      ,   (signed) Hen: Woodman

Mr. Woolley   Janr. 1 1729(/30)

I have yesterday sent yr Seeds &c. on Board the Endevour Johnson Snowdon Master for Newcastle who saild directly & hope the things will have a speedy & safe passage & arive safe to Content. I could indeed have sent 'em sooner p. a small trader but some times they alter their port after they have gott in their Lading & carry them (away) to some other place wch is a disapointmt. (I hav)e bin servd so wch made me delay sending (un)till I had a Collier who always go directly The Seeds &c are all good & new but cou'd not have any small Baskets made for ye Cowcumbers I fancy small potts will do as well which may eaisely be had at Newcastle The Cowcumber & Mellon seed you may depend on to be as good (as) any in England haveing sav'd it all myselfe I have sent you pack'd up in the seeds a Case of good Usefull Instrumts. Bott. of Mr. Heath for wch I gave a Guinea & have his receipt The asparagrace plants I took up out of my owne ground & have prun'd them for the Conveniency (of car)raige but left roome to cut ye roots a little shorter when you plant them

I have for the safety of the seeds pack'd 'em up in a deal Box & am sorry the Emonies & Ranunculas suffer'd in their passage & am willing to make a Satisfection on my pt. if miscarried thro' me: herein you have an Acct. of the Charge of the seeds & am
Yr Humble Servt.
Hen. Woodman

Mr. Woolley   Strand on ye Green
21 March 1729/30
I have at last got a Newcastle Shipp the John & Edward John Dickenson Master who saild from London last Night by whome I have sent what things you requir'd I have also sent some Emonies & Ranunculas for which I have not charg'd any thing pray when you see Charles Fitzwater give my service to him I know Mr Gilroy very well but he being sometimes in the Country near Staines he is uncertain to be found in London if you rember (*sic*) I sent you 400 Hoboy Strawberryes in autum & have sent a 100 more now
I am not certaine wheather I shall be able to take so long a journey this sumer as Newcastle being obleg'd to take a tour Westward in August wch is the only time I can be from Home. I often see Mr Laurence & have sent a great many thing in ye North this season we have a great Flood now haveing raind almost every day for a fortnight You did not tell me how you like the Case of Instruments I sent to you p. the last parcle
I am wth. Humble Service
Yr Humble S(erv)t
Hen. Wood(man)

P.S. the Carnation layers are very good & are Number'd on yr papers as on the other sid wch numbers refers to the names My Waterman is good to London today to fetch a present of French Wine sent me by a Gentleman near Durham wth. which we shall remember all our Friends in the North on the other Sid is an (accoun)t of all yr Bills & if yr Master has a mind (tho' I am not in hast) may transmitt ye mony to me p. Bill sending a letter of advice
Yrs &c. H. Woodman

Mr. Woolly   Strand on the Green
                                                                    6 Octr. 1730

I fear you begin to think I have neglected sending you pease & beans tho' I put them on Board a good while ago but upon enquiry found the Shipp was not sail'd wth them the begining of last week by Reason of the strong Eastwardly Wind we have had a long time past but hope you will have them quickly tho' I wou'd not advise you to put 'em in to forward in yr Northern Climate I do assure you I sow'd last year upon the 17 day of November & gather'd pease ye 21 of April & you may depend upon them to be as good of each kind as any in England when you send for the rest of yr seeds will send you a few of a New sort of pea that Beats all I ever saw but you must not sow them till ye latter end of November being tender I had certainly seen you this sumer but that I have bin Bussey abt. Building a green House a Conveniency I very much wanted but next year God willing I will see you we have had vast plenty of all sorts of fruit this year & Exceeding Cheap I hope you have bin to vissit Mr Laurence at Weremouth.

I have had a gentleman of yr. Country wth. me today that wants & has agreed wth me for a great many trees his name is Reed & lives with 4 miles of Hexham he knowes your Master

           I am   Yr Lo(ving) Friend & Humble Servt.
               Hen: Woodman

The Shipps name is the Swan of Newcastle Thos. Youmen Master

Mr Woolley   Strand on ye Green
                                                                    19 Decr 1730

I recd yours & was willing to see Mr Boynd before I wrote to you who I find has another ½ Crowne to drink your Health wth wch is to be done the next opertunity as to my Bill wch is £27.14.5 he advises that I must have a Bill sent from the North payable to me in London 'tis no matter to me who your Master draws it up or what pt. of the Towne it is to be pd. in so that you send me a me a (*sic*) Letter of advice I am glad you Recd the pease & Beans the sorts I mentiond besides I had but a small quantity of but next year will send you some of them

as to the seeds you mention Onion Seeds is this year 3 shillings p. pound being Chard (*sic*) so yesterday by my Seeds man & Carrott 2 shillings Windsor Beans abt. 9 shillings p. Bushell if you have a mind to deall in that way I wou'd recomend Moses James to you of Stangate who I suppose you know for if I send 'em to you there will be farther Charges for I buy of him I hope God willing to see you next August

           I am in great hast
             Yr Humble Servt.
               Hen: Woodman

Mr. Woolley   Jan 30 1730(/31)

I yesterday Recd yr angery Letter & am sorry for yr oppinion of me that I slight you hoveer (*sic*) this I know that I allwayes was ready & glad to answer yr demands in every respect & allways shall I wrote you word abt. ye 25 of the delivery of yr Seeds & Trees on Board the Happy returne Edw. Hutchenson Mr. & Mr James wrote to you I believe a post before & we sent 'em asoon as a Shipp cou'd be procur'd Mr James & I both enquir'd for one my Waterman loads Barley at Bear Key every Market day & sees ye masters upon ye Gate & can be inform'd of ye first for any pt. I doubt not but before now you have Mr James's & my Letter & will quickly ye Seeds & Trees p. the Shipp because of this hard weather coales are dere & they will make what hast they can. as to the mony you need not have bin in hast to put yr selfe to any Inconveniency & as you was so kind to leave ye parke for me I shall be ye more carefull in obleging & tis mostly upon yr acct. that (god willing) I shall take a Journey into ye North next sumer

            I am Yr Humble Servt.
            Hen: Woodman

Mr Woolley   Strand on ye Green
                                        23 Feb 1730/31

I Recd. the Bill of 27.8.11 p. Mr Sisson as also an Order to send you downe p. first Shipp a parcle of Trees for yr owne use & accordingly deliverd them on Board last Saturday ye St. Michael John Strandrick Master who cleard last Saturday & hope you'l receive them safe to Content I hope you have Recd ye other things as these trees are for yr owne use & owne yr owne An(othe)r I have chargd you as I do ye Gard'ners who makes mony of them againe but you need not lett ye world know that

            I am Yr Humble Servt.
            Hen Woodman

P.S.   I have hereunder sent a Receipt as Mr Sisson desir'd

To	16 Cherryes	8	0
	6 pears	4	0
	8 plumbs	3	4
	2 matts	1	4
	Wharfedge		6
	Shill.	17	2

24 August 1731

    Recd of Mr Woolley seventeen shill. in full of the above Bill & all demands
                                          p. Hen. Woodman

Feb: 22 1730/31

    Recd of Hen: Ellison & Hen: Thos. Carr Esqrs. Twenty seven pounds Eight shill: & Eleven pence in full for Trees Seeds & Flowers & in full of all demands   p. Hen: Woodman

(The following memorandum shows where trees were to be planted at Gateshead Park)

19 8.br. (October) 1731 writt for p. T. W. (? T. Woolley) An Acct. what Hedge Plants & Fruit Trees will be wanted on the so. & so. west side of Parkehouse, both Standard Fruit trees & Dwarfes & Flowering Shrubbs for So. Front

The Numbrs.
    1500 Hornbeam for Hedging
     200 Dutch Elm for the Boundary if not walld
      20 Standard Cherries
      20 Standard Apples
      20 Standard Plumbs
      10 Standard Pears
      10 Damson Plumbs
       5 Standard Dutch Medlers
      10 Standard Almons
      10 Apples on Parradice Stocks
      40 Gooseberrys
      40 Currans
      40 Fillbutt Nutts

For the South Front of the House
      3 Jessamines
      3 Pumgrenetts
      3 Sweet Bryers
      3 Honey Suckles

For the New South wall if planted this winter
      4 Dwarfe
      4 Standart trees

For the Old Garden
      2 Standard Peaches
      4 Morrello Cherries

To Mr. Thos. Woolley at
Henry Ellison's Esqr. at
Gateshead parke near   Strand on ye Green
New Castle   Octr. 26 1731
Sr.

I Recd both your Letters as also yr Bill the wch. I here send you back againe being of No forse for want of your Indorsing your Name oon the back side there of please to write your Name on ye Backside & send it againe & may send it directly to Mr James for it cost me 9d being a double letter whareas if you had had ye bill Drawne upon a halfe sheet of paper you might have wrote what you had a Mind to under it I also desire to know ye Number of Dutch Elms you want for the Espalier yt being forgot too I shall take care to chuse shuch kinds as is proper for your Northern Climate & yt. every thing shall be good & will take Mr Gilroy's directions for a Shipp & it shant be long 'ere ye are s(en)t my serve. to all Friends & except ye same

from

yr. Lo: Friend & Humble Servt.

Hen: Woodman

Mr Woolley   Strand on ye Green

Novr. 25: 1731

I have at last shipp'd your trees I had indeed sent 'em almost a fortnight ago but because you was desireouse of Mr Gilroy procureing a Shipp I have from time to time almost every other day sent after him but to no purpose for when my waterman saw him he'd order him to call againe & then not to be found & at last saied he had a Shipp almost ready p. wch. he was to send some things him selfe by & promis'd more then once to send me a penny post letter but never heard of him & this way have trifled away near a fortnight to no purpose.

The person I have sent 'em by whose name is hereunder mencon'd sayes he lives at Newcastle & Mr Ellison & Family & have made inquiry of several people besides who all gree yt. he actually lives thare so yt. I hope you'l be under no difficulty of having yr trees thare shortly. The trees I have sent are all good & well chosen & have matted 'em well up & hope they'l all arive safe & answer yr. Expectation. fear not ye pomegranats but you must this winter screen 'em a little from rigerous frost & get som light rich soil for 'em to strike root into at first. I could not send ye 2 Stand. Newington peaches but have sent 2 Stand. Nectarins & hope that will be no detrement ye dryness of ye sumer has made Standard peaches & Nectarins very scarce. My humble service to Mr Sisson & all Friends & except ye same from

Yr Lo: Friend & Humble Servt.

Hen: Woodman

,

N.B.   ye inclos'd is ye Masters & Shipps Name of his own writeing but least it shou'd be mislaid here it is againe Jno. Weldon Mr. of ye Wm. of Newcastle my waterman saw him set Saile yesterday at high water

Mr James has Recd. his mony p. Bill you sent

To Henry Ellison Esqr p. Hen: Woodman

To 200 hedge Dutch Elms (6 foot high)		3 10	00
1500 Hornbeam	2 foot	3 15	00
34 Cherrys		17	00
20 Apples		10	00
31 plumbs & Damsons		15	6
17 pears		17	00
5 Standard Medlars		5	00
10 Standard Almonds		15	00
10 Apples on paradise		10	00
80 Gooseberys & Currants		13	4

40 Philbeards	13	4
8 peaches & Nectarins	12	00
4 white Jesamins	1	4
3 Sweetbryers	0	6
4 double flowering pomegranates	10	00
18 large double matts	18	00
Wharfedge &c.	5	00

Tot.   £ 15   8 00

Mr Woolley   Strand on ye Green
Xbr. (December) 15 1731

I Recd. yrs. yesterday & am sorry you have not yet Recd. the Trees &c. ye contrary Winds I suppose has hinder'd 'em but hope you'l receive 'em shortly in good order.

I am not att all surpris'd yt Mr Switzer has bin with you & in all yr. Neighbourhood seeing he has nothing else to recomend him (having not a foot of Nursery ground & wt. he sells must take of others) but his elaborate draughts & designs & as every man is to be comended for his diligince & Industry I would not here be thought to say any thing illnatur'd of him but confess 'tis a practice I was allways asham'd of to thurst my selfe in or indevour to surplant any person yt has bin us'd to serve a Gentleman (as you may in part remember when I was in yr Neighbourhood last autumn) but however I will boldly venture to say yt. what I have serv'd Mr Ellison wth. has allways bin good & right & shou'd be very loft (loath) to loose his favour without just acasion & at ye comon price I sell to every gentleman.

as to Flowering Shrubbs I have as great Variety as any of the trade & will sell 'em as cheap & perhaps as cheap as Mr. Switzer can bye 'em him selfe ye price I sell 'em in comon is 25 shillings p. 100 unless some curious & uncomon sorts wch. will be more.

you may if you think it proper wth. my Duty comunicate ye Contents above to yr Master & then he'll judge ye better what to do in the affair

I am in great hast but nevertheless

Yr Asshured Friend &c.

Hen: Woodman

Ps. I think I gave you ye perticulers of ye Bill wch. is £15 8 but if I did not let me know & I will

My service to Mr. Sisson & all Friends else

Mr. Woolley   Strand on ye Green
17 Feb. 1731/2

I Recd. yrs. dated ye 21st. of Janry for wch. I thank you I waited on your Master ye next day who seem'd to be be (*sic*) a little out of Humer I had not bin wth. him before but do asure you I never Recd any letter from you to that purpose till this I above mencon however he gave me (after waiting on him 2 days) a list of what he wanted wth. orders to gitt 'em ready directly &

he wou'd prouoide a Shipp but that he could not do so soon as he expected but Monday they ware put on Board a Newcastle Shipp by Mr. Gilroy's order but don't know ye Shipp nor masters name but that you'l have an Acct of by yr Master ye Quantity was 26 Bundles & a parcle of Seed I had indeed wrote to you before but was unwilling to put you to ye Expence of a letter till the things was deliverd which I thought wou'd have happen'd a week sooner

I need not send you ye perticulars of every thing but the 1000 flowering Shrubbs are distinguish'd as low & more hire (higher) kinds & tho' they are none of them very large because of sending so far & ye more middlin siz'd plants are ye likelyest to grow best yet I here under distinguish those kinds that will grow largest & those yt. are more dwarf

Viz.					
10 Bladder Senna			100 Spira Frutex		
100 Spanish Broom			100 Satisus		
100 Lelocks			100 St. John's Wort	Dwarf	
100 Syringas	Talest		100 Scorpian Senna	kinds	
40 Cornelian Cherrys	growing		50 Roses		
50 Guilder Roses	plants		50 Laurestynes		
20 Sumachs			———		
50 Yellow Jesamins			500		
30 Alltheas					
———					
500					
———					

besides 16 Laburnha(ms)

your Master wou'd have of the Flowering evergreens nothing but Laurestynes & of them but 50 he sayes he has no great Veneration for greens as I have on ye other side distinguish'd the high from the low kinds you'l better judge how to dispose of them in planting th(ey are a)ll fine yong thriving plants & securely pack'd in matts (&) hope all will arive safe to Satisfection Some of the peach trees are for an other place but I had orders to pack 'em all togeather so no doubt but you'l have an Acct. what is for Gateshead.

They are all directed to Mr. Sisson

I find Mr. Switzer has serv'd Coll Liddell with what he wants so I did not say any thing to yr Master abt. it I have taken care to send Mr. Ellison nothing but what is good & right (& hope you will think so) as being ye only & best recomendation a person can have

Jno. Shutt & I drank yr Health the other day wth. pt. of the ½ Crowne you was so kind to send

You'l not forgett my service & Respects to all Friends that are in your Neighbourhood that I know tell Charles Fitzwater when you see him I often see his Bror. Jo I set up my horse at his House allways when I go to Towne

I am

Yr Humble Servt

Hen: Woodman

To Henry Ellison Esqr. by Hen: Woodman 1731 Novr. 22

To 200 hedge Dutch Elems 1 foot	3	10	00
1500 Hornbeam 2 foot	3	15	00
34 Cherrys		17	00
20 Apples		10	00
31 plumbs & Damsons		15	6
17 pears		17	00
5 Standard Medlars		5	00
10 Almonds Standards		15	00
10 Apples on paradise		10	00
80 Gooseberys & Corrants		13	4
40 Philbeards		13	4
8 peaches & Nectarins		12	00
4 white Jesamins		1	4
3 Sweetbryers			6
4 double flowering pomegranats		10	00
18 large double matts		18	00
Wharfedge		5	00

Feb: 11 (1731/32)

100 Satisus (Cytisus)
100 St. John's Wort
100 Scorpian Senna
10 Blader Do.
100 Spanish Broom
100 Lealocks
100 Saringas
50 Yellow Jesamins } 1000   12 10   0
40 Cornelian Cherrys
30 Allthea Frutex
100 Spira Frutex
50 Gilder Roses
50 Roses several sorts
20 Sumachs
50 Laurestyness

16 Laburnhams		4	00
16 Woodbins		4	00
26 peaches & Nectarins	1	19	00
8 aprecots		8	00
3 oz wt. Coss Lettuce		4	6
4 oz Italian Brocoli		8	00
4 oz Cucumber		4	00
2 oz Mellons several best sorts		5	00
2 oz purslane			8
24 large double matts	1	00	00

(Feb.) 24

1800 small Hornbeam	4 10	00
2 Large matts	1	8

Tot.   £ 37. 7 10

(Copy of order sent by Thomas Sisson to Henry Woodman)

1732 Xbr (December) 29	What Seeds are wanting for ye
writt to Mr. Woodman	Kittchen Garden and nursery at Gates
for these Seeds	

        2 oz Red Gosk Lettice
        2 oz Wt Gosk Lettice
        2 oz Whitte Brockaley
        2 oz Green Brockley
        2 oz Red Beette
        2 oz Etalean Beete
        2 oz Coucumber
        2 oz melon
        1 oz Purslain
        4 oz ye Earley Green Topped Turnep
        4 oz ye Purple Topped Turnep
        2 oz Black Spanesh Radesh
        2 oz Whit Spanesh Radesh
        1 oz Swette marjam
        2 oz french maregold
        2 oz afreican maregold
            hornBeam seed ½ peck
            Bettch mast 1 peck
            hors Chesnutts 200
            Laburnum major 1 1.

To Mr. Hen: Woodman Nursery man at Strand on the Green near Old Brandford Midlesex vua (*sic*) London

To Mr Thos. Sisson at Henry Ellison's Esq at Gateshead Park near Newcastle upon Tyne

Strand on ye Green
12 Janry 1732/3

Sr.

    I Recd. yrs of the 29 of Xber & yesterday deliver'd on Board the Carr of Newcastle Robt. Lowgin Master all the Seeds you order'd in good order wch. are all good in the kinds & hope they'l arive safe to Content. under you have ye Charge of this parcle & those Trees &c sent last year a Bill of wch. I gave Mr. Ellison when in Towne.

I am Sr.
Yr Humble Servt.
Hen: Woodman

1731 Novr 22 To a parcle of Trees by Bill & date DD	15	8	00
Feb. 11 To Do.	17	7	2
24 To Do.	4	11	8

1732 Janry 11 To Red Coss Lettuce 2 oz 4s White Coss

⅂ .2 oz 4s		8	00
White Brocoly 2 oz 2s Green Do. 2 oz 2s		4	00
Red Beet 2 oz 6d Italian Do 2 oz 6d		1	00
Cucumber 2 oz 2s Mellon 2 oz 5s		7	00
Parsley 1 oz 6d Early Green Turnep 4 oz 18d		2	00
Purple Top Turnep 4 oz 4d			4
Black Spanish Radish 2 oz 1s White Do. 2 oz 1s		2	00
Sweet Marjorum 1 oz 1s French Marygould 2 oz 2s		3	00
African 2 oz 2s Hornbeam ½ pk 4s		6	00
Beech mast 1 pk 8s Hors Chesnutts 200 4s		12	00
LaBurnham major 1 li,		5	00
Box cord & Wharfedge		1	00

Tot.   £ 3(9 18 2)

To Mr. Thos. Sisson at Henry Ellison's Esqr at Gateshead Park near Newcastle (endorsed: 18 8br 1733 Mr. Woodman's lre. of his demd. on Mr. Ellison)

Strand on ye Green
18 8ber. 1733

Sr.

I Recd. yours of the 5th of this Inst. October & know that Mr. Woolley has left ye North (having seen him since his arival into the South) but as to his using his master ill I know nothing of but if he has I am sorry for it.

I am not a little surpris'd to here this Complaint of Mr. Ellison (being the first I ever had of this kind) of over charging any person he may remember I waited on him in Leicester Feilds twice abt. fixing the kinds & price of the trees & before he went out of Towne for the North I carryed my Bill & deliver'd it to his Servt. but did not see him I called againe before Mr. Ellison left London to know if he had any Comands nither did I see him then Sure if there had bin any just cause of this heavy Complaint of being so extravagently overcharg'd I shd. have heard of it then or at least befor Woolley left his Service I hope he has not suggested any shuch thing to him in prejudice of me but this I will say that I make but one price to every person & am ready & willing to shew my Books to any person to justify it & that the price I charg'd Mr. Ellison for the Goods he had of me is moderate & Comon I hope he don't deny ye Rect. of all the goods I charge him wth. if he does I am ready to make it apear by proper Vouchers I have by me & expect to be pd. the whole Sum of £39.18.2 without any abatemt. I have here under sent an abstract of the acct. & hope to have sortly (*sic*) the favour of an Answer

I am Sr.

Yr Humble Servt.

Hen: Woodman

			£	
Novr 22 1731	To sundry parcles of Trees &c	15	8	00
Feb. 11	To Do.	17	7	2
Feb. 24	To Do.	4	11	8
Janry 11 1732	To a parcle of Seeds	2	11	4

Tot.   £   39 18   2

(To Henry Ellison Esqr)

Strand on ye Green
5 Janry 1733(/34)

Sr.

About ye 12 of October last I Recd. a letter by the post from Mr Sisson dated the 5 of that Month wherein he mentions that you had order'd him to acquaint me that in my Bill of Trees Seeds &c you had been very much overcharged & that you expected a large abatement & wou'd not otherwise pay me.

I did on ye 18th of the same month write to Mr. Sisson that I was not a little surprised to here of your Complaint (being the first I ever had of the kind) & that I made but one price to every body & that the price I charged you for the Goods you had of me was Moderate & Comon & that I expected to be paid my whole Sum without any abatemt. I have since Recd. an other letter from Mr Sisson wherein he mentions that he had comunicated mine to you & that you was still pleased to think you had been overcharged & that without a consederable abatement you would not pay my Demands I am very sorry that any Gentleman should have ye Notion of my setting up a Demand in the least unreasonable & what I have not hereto met with before & am so far from thinking my Demand unreasonable on you at all that I would willingly submitt it to the Judgment of any indifferant person or otherwise leave it to the Determination of the Law & to that end hope you will please to give an order to some attorney at London to apear to an Action to save the Trouble & Expence of sending downe a Writt.

I should be glad to be favoured with your Answer

& am Sr
Yr most Humble Servt.
Hen: Woodman

(Copy of letter from Thomas Sisson to Henry Woodman)

Gateshead Parke Janr. 22 1733(/34)

Sr.

My Masr. recd. yours, and orders me to acquaint you He has writ to Mr. Jos. Geekie at Mr. Cha: Sanderson's Chambers in ye Temple concerning ye dispute between you & him by whose sentiments he is designed to be determin'd, & therefore as soon as Mr. Geekie is at Leasure he will let you hear from him

I am
Your Humble Servt.
Thos. Sisson

HENRY CLARK OF CHIPPING CAMPDEN, GLOUCESTERSHIRE

(A) Clark's claim of 1768 for his unpaid bills of 1750-1755 for plants supplied to the late Powell Snell Esqr. gives a good idea of the prices charged in the mid-century and also of the wide resources of a country nursery. (Gloucestershire Record Office, D 214 B 1)

To John Parsons Esqr.
To be Left at the Swan Inn in Tewkesbury

Court House In Campden:Gloucestershire
19 Novr. 1768

Sr.

I saw Derection In the newes paper. For the Late Powell Snell Esqr.* Creddeters To Send There bills Into Mr. Parsons — To the Swan Inn in Tewkesbury, I had The pleasure of Knowing your father uery well: as I was Sr. Will Keyts† Gardner & Stward, & I allso did a good deal of Busines for the Late Lord Tracy§ & sum for the present Lord** I hope Sr. you will doo me what Juestice is in your power for my Case is uery hard, and I am now in years, & cant gitt what I Was uest to Inioye In Great Plenty. & what makes itt The wors. The Gardner Walltr. Lodge as was then Mr Sneles gardner had all sorts of Kitchen garden seed & plants for severiall years and never paid me one shilling. tis uery near as Much as Mr. Sneals and i Cant Till wheare the man Is. So am a fraid I must Loos His money he appeared to me when he was Inn his place to be a uery Honest and Industres man &c

I am Sr. with Great Respect.
your Obedt. Humble Servt
(signed)   Henry Clark

a Line at your Lasure will much oblige me
Powell Snell Esqr Had of Henry Clark

* Powell Snell of Guiting Grange in Guiting Power, Glos., died 1767.
† Sir William Keyt, Baronet, succeeded 1702, died September 1741; he was succeeded by Sir Thomas Charles Keyt, who died 24 July 1755, but had sold the Ebrington estate to Sir Dudley Ryder soon after 1741.
§ the 5th Viscount Tracy, succeeded 1712, died 4 June 1756.
** the 6th Viscount Tracy of Toddington, Glos., died 10 Aug. 1792.

1750

Campden	ll	s	d
Decembr. 2 apricocks 2/ 6 Cherrys 4/6	0	6	6
1 dubble blossomed Cherry	0	1	0
2 pears 2/ 2 plumbs 1/6	0	3	6
3 peaches & Nectrines	0	4	6
2 black Currants	0	0	6
22 verigated Hollies	1	13	0
3 plain dito	0	1	0
22 Lorrels at /4	0	7	4
2 Hornets head Wall flowers	0	2	0
2 Larch 2/ 3 Spruce firs 1/6	0	3	6
3 Scotch firs 1/6 1 St. Johns Wort /4	0	1	10
2 virginian Rasberrys	0	0	8
6 Laburnams	0	2	0
2 St. Petters Wood /8 6 Honisuckles	0	2	2
4 Guilder Roses	0	1	4
4 Mezeriens	0	6	0
2 verigated Night Shades	0	0	8
£	4	4	10

1750

Decr. 2 Sumaks or Stags Horne	ll	s	d
	0	1	0
4 Spanish Jasamines	0	1	4
2 blush Hundred leaved Roses	0	3	0
2 double white Roses	0	1	0
2 red belgick Roses	0	1	0
2 yallow austrine Roses	0	2	0
2 York & Lancester Roses	0	3	0
2 Monthly Roses	0	1	0
2 double Red Roses	0	1	0
2 Childing or red province Roses	0	1	6
1 Maidens blush Rose	0	1	0
1 virginian or thornless Rose	0	1	0
1 red austrine Rose	0	1	6
1 Marbled Rose	0	1	6
1 Burnet Leaved Rose	0	1	0
1 Blush province Rose	0	0	6
1 double yallow Rose	0	1	6
2 Rose a Munda	0	1	0
1 sema double velvet Rose	0	0	6
1 great Royall Rose	0	0	9
	1	6	1

1750	ll	s	d
Decr. 1 dutch Hundred Leaved Rose	0	2	0
1 purple or frankford Rose	0	0	9
1 Moss province Rose	0	2	0
to Carriage	0	2	0
1750/1			
Jan: 25			
18 Lorestines at /4 18 Lorrels at /4	0	12	0
2 Speckled Hollies at	0	3	0
3 Standd. Cherries	0	3	0
60 Honisuckles at /3	0	15	0
Larkspur seed two sorts	0	1	0
Sweet sented pease two sorts	0	1	0
12 Hyacynths	0	12	0
a box	0	0	6
to Carriage from London	0	0	6
towards Carriage to Guiting	0	1	0
Feb: 18			
a little french & african Marygold	0	0	6
25			
2 sorts of Larkspur seed	0	1	0
2 sorts sented pease	0	1	0
6 Philareeas at /6	0	3	0
6 Tube rose roots	0	1	6
Mar 29:			
1 oz Small Nesturtion	0	0	8
£	3	3	5

1751	ll	s	d
Mar 29:			
Sweet sented pease two sorts	0	1	0
Lark Spur seed two sorts	0	1	0
3 oz White Canded tuft	0	1	0
2 oz Venus Looking Glass	0	1	3
4 oz Convolvolus Minor	0	1	8
2 oz Hollioak 1/ 2 oz Wall Flower	0	2	0
½ oz Sweet Bazill	0	0	6
1 oz Collumbine	0	0	8
1 oz Michelmas Daises	0	0	8
2 oz popy	0	1	0
some Sillver Periwincle a present			
May 14			
Scarlet Beans	0	1	0
two sorts sweet pease	0	1	0

Sepr. 13

200 picklings Cumrs.		0	1	0
ten Cumrs. for Mango		0	0	6
& 24 for Slicing: pd. John Phillips for Car.		0	1	0

Octr. 28

17 Dwarf pear Trees		0	17	0
2 apricocks		0	2	0
2 peaches		0	3	0

Novr. 5

34 Honisuckles at /3		0	8	6
200 Crocus		0	2	0
	£	2	7	9

		ll	s	d
1751				

Novr. 19:

60 Scotch firs at /6		1	10	0
6 french ash at /4		0	2	0
1 yew tree		0	0	9
toward Carriage		0	2	6

Decr. 17:

12 Large dubble Matts at		0	14	0
12 Hyacynths		0	12	0
24 Mix Narcissus polyanthus		0	6	0
100 Yellow dito blew		0	2	0
pd. to Carriage from London		0	1	0
Carriage to Guiting		0	1	6

1753

Mar: 26

4 dwf pears at 1/		0	4	0
12 dwf Nonparells at /6		0	6	0
7 peaches at 1/6		0	10	6

Apr. 27

1 apricock 1/ 6 Matts at 1/2		0	8	0

Novr. 13

12 peaches & Nectrines		0	18	0
1 pear Childs Early ⎫ Dubble Work:d 1 Murry Nectrine ⎬		0	5	0
6 Morella Cherries		0	3	0
3 Greaps		0	1	6
5 persion Jasamine 2 Yallow		0	1	8
	£	6	9	5

1753	ll	s	d
Novr. 13			
Mezerions 2ˢ. 100 White Lilly roots 12ˢ.	0	14	0
a box	0	1	6
1754			
to Horse Hire & Carriage	0	2	6
Decr. 11			
10 Arbeals 10/ 20 Sycemores 20/	1	10	0
15 beach 15/ 5 Oaks 5/	1	0	0
15 Witch Elms	0	15	0
5 birch 5/ 15 Wild Cherries	1	0	0
15 Limes	0	15	0
1755			
Mar: 6:			
Carnation seed /6 sweet William seed /6	0	1	0
pollyanthus /6 Queens Stock /6	0	1	0
Brompton Stock /6 Holioak /6	0	1	0
Levetrel* /3 poppys & Dutch /3	0	0	6
Sweet Scabyus /3 Dub: Ballsam /6	0	0	9
China Pink /6 Narsturtion /3	0	0	9
Sun flower /3 aricula /6	0	0	9
African Mary Gold /3 french dito /3	0	0	6
Marvel peru /4 Love lies Bleeding /3	0	0	7
Princess feather /3 Dub: Larkspur /6	0	0	9
Venation Mallo /6 Yallow Hawkweed	0	1	0
£	6	6	7

1755	ll	s	d
Mar: 6			
Scarlet or purple Hawk weed	0	0	6
purple China awster dubble	0	1	0
Love in a mist /3 sweet pease /6	0	0	9
Venus Looking Glass /2 Minonet 1/	0	1	2
Sweet Bazill	0	0	6
19			
15 Beach at 1/	0	15	0
10 Syckamores at 1/	0	10	0
25 Scotch firs at /6	0	12	6
6 Hollies at 1/	0	6	0
18 Large Dubble Bass Matts } by the teem at 1/2	1	1	0

*Presumably the annual *Lavatera trimestris*, grown in England for well over a century, but only recently named by Linnaeus.

Apr 22			
100 Scotch firs at /4	1	13	4
Novr. 26			
½ pk. Chalton pease	0	2	0
½ pk. Guine Beans	0	1	8
3 yew trees at 1/6	0	4	6
£	5	9	11

1st. page	4	4	10
2d	1	6	1
3d	3	3	5
4th	2	7	9
5th	6	9	5
6	6	6	7
7	5	9	11
sum total £	29	8	0

(B) Clark's letters, 1743-1771, preserved in the Harrowby MSS., were mostly written in his capacity of steward for the Burnt Norton estate in Aston Subedge, near Chipping Campden. Later his work extended to embrace all the Ryder estates in Gloucestershire, Warwickshire and Worcestershire. Clark acted as agent for other landowners in the region and travelled a good deal, making regular tours. In these he was probably able to transact business of his own as a nurseryman also. Sir Dudley Ryder, a great lawyer, became Lord Chief Justice of the King's Bench in 1754 and the king had just signed a patent creating him Baron Ryder of Harrowby when he died on 25 May 1756. Clark's letters, as a full record of country business over many years, are of extraordinary interest, but only a small selection of extracts can be given here; others have been printed in Christopher Whitfield, *A History of Chipping Campden* (1958). References are to the Harrowby MSS, Sandon Hall, by volume and folio; the letters were addressed to Sir Dudley Ryder except where otherwise stated.

1743 July 9   Henry Clark, as steward to Sir Thomas Keyt, Bart., to Mrs. Rutter; dated at Norton (CXIX, f. 49)
1752 Sep. 23   Norton. most estates, which had recently been selling at 24 years purchase, were now fetching 25 years; thanks Sir Dudley Ryder for his wishes for Clark's recovery, now almost well (CXXII, f. 115)
1752 Oct. 9   'Yesterday I com out of Warwickshire . . . I put my Last Letter into the poost the same day as it was dated there must be sum delay in sum of the infearer poost master in the Croos post, or it would a bean at Bath in two dayes.' (f. 118)
1752 Nov. 6   Norton. To Mr. Dudley Baxter. 'I am Removed to the Court

House in Camden where I haue a Room and a Bead at your service.' (CXXII, f. 122)

1753 Feb. 16   Court House, Camden. estates, if sold to a stranger, now costing 26 to 27 years purchase. 'I will send next Wednesday by the Camamden (*sic*) Carrier which I hop will be at the Croos keys a Wood Street a Saturday night.' (CXXII, f. 134)

1753 Apr. 25   Court House, Camden. 'This morning exactley at 10 I Recd. the Favour of yours jest as I was going to gitt a Horsback to go to my Lord Tracys.' (Clark had been asked to search records urgently in regard to the interests in Lady Langley's Charity of £20 a year to four poor widows, payable 25s. a quarter each) − difficult to answer in haste as 'the Regester in the Churches and graue Stones in the Church yards must be searched besids not find in them at homb'. (f. 143)

1753 June 25   Elizabeth Clark to Mr. Dudley Baxter. (Monday) 'my husband . . . ordered me to let you know he intended to set out early ys. (this) morning to Mr. Palmers of Olton end, but had buisness to do with Sr. Thos. (Keyt) first wch. detaind him till 4 oclock ys afternoon at wch. time he set out for ye above place & hopes to be in Town on Thursday if he meets with no hindrance at Mr. Palmers. . . .' (CXXII, f. 163)

1753 July 25   Court House, Camden. To Mr. Dudley Baxter. 'I shall go Into Warwickshire at the Latter end of next week, and to Coventry and a fryday am to go to Borton of the water to meet a Jentleman onnone (unknown) to me to seet out sum work. His name is ----- Ingram Esqr.' (The 'work' may perhaps have been agricultural or horticultural). (CXXII, f. 167)

1753 Aug. 18   Court House, Camden. To Mr. Dudley Baxter. 'Mr. Henry Darbys waggon the Camden Carrier seets out from the Cross Keys in Wood Street every monday morning. he is our Carrier and his father before him ever sence Norton House was begun, and I dear say will Take great Care of Sr. Dudley goods − the wagon Combs In to Camden thursdayes.' very bad wet weather for harvest − 'We will gitt the garden in as good order as we posable Can for the Reseption of Sr. Dudley and me Lady & Mr. Ryder but as the weather has bean so onfortunant Cant gitt it in such order as we otherwise should a dun.' (f. 170)

1753 Nov. 4   went to Stratford (on Avon) and took a view (i.e. surveyed) of every house & hedge &c. '27 years purches is sertainley a uery great price'. (XXXVI, f. 3)

1753 Dec. 3   the intention of making a 'tournpike from Bromsgroue to Alcester and to Stratford' − visits the Shattorey (Shottery) estate, on the north side 'of the Avon. Butyfull and fine to look at very Convenat to seend its produck into all parts of Europ by water'. (XXXVI, f. 5)

1754 Apr. 19   To Mr. Dudley Baxter. refers to 'Sr Dudleys advancement to be Lord Chief Justice.' 'Brest plowing and Burning was a subiect of discorse.' (XLVII, f. 1)

1754 June 9   Court House, Camden 'I was Taken very Ill with the gout in my left Lege, a wednesday was sennet. it is the first time I have had it sence the Compleating the Norton purchies. I was in great Hoops I had left it, but it was so strong upon me I could not posably Gitt out a doors till last fryday'. 'I was out againe a Saturday, but I mend but slowley — But thang god I am so well as to go out.' (CXXII, f. 186)

1755 Jan. 24 Court House, Camden. 'I was in Warwickshire, and did not return home till Sunday.' 'all the past season it has been such perdigous bad weather . . . I shant do any gleassing to the windows in the green House or House till jest before your Lordship coms for fear they should be brook againe . . .' 'If the frost is not very Hard to frees the apples in the Waggon I will send a Hampper of the best I can pick nex week by darby's waggon.' (CXXII, f. 196)

1755 Apr. 12 Court House, Camden. 'if we have a war with france Land Tax will rise and tis expectd Land will Sinck.' P.S. to the effect that an offer of 33 years purchase had been made for the Idleycot (Idlicote, Warwickshire) estate. (CXXII, f. 204)

1755 May 18 During a tour to collect the half-year's rents, Clark met tenants at Evesham Market who had suffered by 'Loosing all there Sheep, & the Haile storm as fell last Sumer had allmost destroid Halfe there Croops of Corne;' they want a postponement of rent until after Midsummer — 'this yare past has Been such a wan as I never knew in 30 yares . . .' (XXXVI, f. 7)

1757 Oct. 8 Court House in Camden. To Mr. Nathaniel Ryder. 'I am Returned well out of Sumersetshire . . .' went 'to Tanton and staid there . . . . . I went as fir as Exeter In Devon shire'. (CXXII, f. 227)

1769 Mar. 11 'We began faling (felling) Last monday and have got a good dale downe . . . . . euer Timber Tree is Numberd In his place and valued & all young growing Timber Tree — and all The young Saplings yt. are of aney sise but we have not Numbered the Pollord or Lopped Trees . . . . . the Wood Stealers, & other Theves, pesters me sadley, the World never was, for badnes as Tis now . . . . We haue a bad feaver In Campden & worss in The Vale.' (XXXVI, f. 12)

1771 May 27 Court House in Campden. To Nathaniel Ryder esq., Hill Street, London. 'I have been mending sence Thursday Last I can walk a Little my Head is as bad as my Limbs . . . ' (CXXIII, f. 71)

A letter in the Salt Library, Stafford (Salt MSS. 4 78) is from Nathaniel Ryder to Miss Clarke, daughter of Mr. Henry Clarke, Campden, Glos., dated 10 Oct. 1771. It is implied that Clark's illness had been very serious; 'I shall be heartily pleased to hear that he (your Father) is much better than when I saw him.' A letter of 20 Jan. 1773 (CXXIII, f. 95) shows that by then Francis Wheatcroft had become steward of the Norton estate. Wheatcroft died about 10 May 1784, and John Clarke, apparently son of Henry, was appointed Steward of all the Gloucestershire, Warwickshire and Worcestershire estates of Nathaniel Ryder, who had been created Baron Harrowby in 1776. John Clarke was to have £50 a year out of the rents from 11 May 1784 (CXXIII, f. 205).

APPENDIX IX

WILLIAM PENDAR'S ORDER OF 1766

The little that is known of William Pendar of Woolhampton, Berkshire, is told in the text (p.100). Below is his letter of 2 December 1766, apparently in the form of an estimate. It was addressed to Lord Bruce of Tottenham at Tottenham House, Savernake, near Marlborough, Wiltshire.

200 Flowering shrubs @	£2. 2s. p. 100
18 China Arbor Vite	2s. p. each
50 Small Cypress	6d. each
12 Lignum Vite	1. —
50 Small Larches	£2. 2s. p. 100
25 Ever-green Oaks	1. — each
25 True Phillyreas	6d. each
50 Phillyreas Strip'd & plain	£1. 10s. p. 100
10 Sumach's large	3d. each
200 English (sic) 4 feet	£1. 10s. p. 100
100 Plane's 6 feet	1. 11. 6
100 Roses 10 sorts — (200 order'd)	1. 10. 0
4 Shining-leav'd Sumach's	6d. each
6 Oriental Plane's	1s. each
20 Alaternus	6d. each
2 Large & 4 small Tulip Trees	£1. 1. 0
100 Sweet Briars	£1
100 Laurus Tinus	1. 5. — (200)
200 small Limes	2. —. — (none)
25 Strip'd & 25 plain large Box	£1
100 Laurels 4 & 5 feet	1. 10. —
A Bed of Spruce Firrs	10. —p. 100
50 Bays	6d. each
6 Portugal Laurels	1s. each (50)
6 Arbutus 2 feet	
6 Cedars of Lebanon	£1. 8. —
10 Large Cypress	12. 6
12 Junipers	4. —
200 English Elms 10 feet @	£4 p. 100
100 Plane's 10 & 12 feet	5. —. —
200 Spruce Firrs 3 & 4 feet	1. 10. —
100, or 150, or 200 Beeches 10 feet (if that Quantity)	1. 10. —
200 Silver Firrs 2 feet	2. —. —

4000 Quicksets	5. —
50 Red Cedars	1. each
25 Pinasters	1. each
25 Balm of Gilead Firrs	1. 6 each
200 small Larches (if that Quantity)	1. 0. 0p. 100
100 Moss Red Provence, Damask Provence ⎫	
Hundred-leav'd, Blush, Monthly, Double Yellow, ⎬	2. 10. —.
York & Lancaster and Velvet Roses 2 sorts ⎭	
2000 small Spruce Firrs	2. 10. —p. 1000

(signed) Wm. Pendar

Decr. 2d. 1766

My Lord, the Large Beeachs and Plains are to enlarge the Clumps in the Forist which your Lordship ordred — the Elms for the London road.

THE LONDON FIRMS OF 1786

John Abercrombie, in *The Gardener's Daily Assistant* (London, John Fielding), a book with preface dated 18 September 1786, gives at pp. 355-359 full lists of nursery gardeners and of seedsmen for the London area. Generally surnames only are provided, but in the following reprint the firms are fully identified wherever possible. A substantial minority of the firms listed cannot, however, be identified in the contemporary directories or in other sources so far available.

A
LIST
OF
NURSERY GARDENERS

In the Vicinity of LONDON, and within eight or ten miles thereof. Where the public may be supplied with all sorts of fruit trees, forest trees, ornamental trees, flowering shrubs, evergreens, herbaceous plants, bulbous and tuberous flower-roots, &c., green-house and hot-house plants; as likewise all kinds of kitchen garden, flower, tree, and shrub seeds, garden tools, mats, &c.

Adamson, Newcross, Deptford-road — *Kent*
Allport, Hackney road near Shoreditch — *Middlesex*. [John Allport -1807; Allport & Son, G. & J. Allport -1820; George Allport -1825]
Bassington, Hoxton near Shoreditch, London — *Middlesex*. [John Bassington, -1780-]
Bendel, Montpelier Gardens, Walworth — *Surry*. [John Bendel, Tea Garden, -1782-88-]
Bowstead, Highgate — *Middlesex*. [William Bowstread, 1769-1812]
Brinkworth, Ducking-pond lane, near Whitechapel — *Middlesex*.
Burchel and co., Fulham — *Middlesex*. [William Burchell, successor to Christopher Gray, 1764-1800; Matthew Burchell, 1800-10]
Campbell, Hampstead — *Middlesex*.
Chambers, Newington Butts — *Surry*. [? Richard Chambers, seedsman, -1762-]
Coleman, Tottenham — *Middlesex*. [William Coleman, -1777-1808]
Cunningham, Lisson Green, Paddington — *Middlesex*. [? Cunningham & Smith, nursery & seedsmen, 43 Oxford Street, -1797-]

Driver, Kent road, near the Borough of Southwark — *Surry.* [Samuel Driver, -1760-77-; Abraham P. & William Driver, -1785-1805-]

Duthie, Bethnal green near Whitechapel — *Middlesex.* [W. & A. Duthie, -1812-]

Eddie, East Sheen, near Richmond — *Surry.* [? Alexander Eddie, -1765-88]

Emmerson, Barnet — *Herts.* [Isaac Emmerton, 1760-89; Isaac Emmerton junior, -1823]

Gammock, Hoxton, near Shoreditch, London — *Middlesex.*

Gordon (James) and co., Mile-End near Bow — *Middlesex.* [James Gordon, 1742-70; James Gordon & Co., Gordon, Dermer & Thomson, etc., -1837]

Gordon (William), Mile-End near Bow — *Middlesex.* [William Gordon, -1780-]

Gregg, Crombie's Gardens, Halfway-house, Stepney — *Middlesex.*

Grimwood, Hudson and co., Brompton and Kensington — *Middlesex.* [Daniel Grimwood, successor to John Williamson & Co., 1783-95; Grimwood & Wykes, 1796-1804; William Malcolm & Co., etc., 1805-46]

Hay, Lambeth, and St. George's fields — *Surry.* [Walter Hay, 1780-1805]

Hay, Laytonstone — *Essex.* [John Hay, 1759-92; James Hill, etc., 1793-1888]

Hay, Tooting — *Surry.* [-1789-]

Harpur, Horse-ferry-road — *Westminster.* [? William Harper, florist and nurseryman, Covent Garden, -1789-97-]

Howie, Putney — *Surry.* [William Howey, successor to Francis Hunt, 1775-92; John & Robert Howey, etc., -1838]

Hewit and co., Brompton, near Chelsea and Kensington — *Middlesex.* [Henry Hewitt junior, successor to Henry Hewitt, 1771-91; John & Samuel Harrison, etc., -1833]

Hudson Grimwood and co., Brompton, and Kensington — *Middlesex.* [see Grimwood, Hudson and co., above]

Jefferies, Brompton-park nursery, near Kensington — *Middlesex.* [John Jeffreys, successor to John Swinhoe, 1756-88; Gray, Wear & Gray, etc., 1789-1851]

Kirk, Brompton, near Kensington — *Middlesex.* [Joseph Kirke, -1766-92; Kirke & Son, etc., 1793-1836]

Lane, Islington, near Sadlers-wells — *Middlesex.*

Lee and co., vineyard, Hammersmith — *Middlesex.* [Lee & Kennedy, successors to Lewis Kennedy & James Lee, 1780-1818; James Lee, etc., 1818-94]

Latin, Edgward-road, Paddington — *London.*

Lewis and co., Kingsland, Ball's-pond Road — *Middlesex.* [Lewis & Robert Mackie, -1800; Thomas Bassington, etc., 1800-44]

Loddiges, Mare-street, Hackney — *Middlesex.* [Conrad Loddiges, successor to John Busch, 1771-; Loddiges & Sons, etc., -1814-60]

Lowe, Kingston-wick, near Hampton-court — *Middlesex.*

Malcolm, Kennington, near Lambeth and Newington butts — *Surry.* [William Malcolm, -1757-88; William Malcolm & Son, etc., 1788-1815]

Mitchelson and Mitchelson, Kennington, near Lambeth, Newington-Butts, and Kingston — *Surry*. [James & George Mitchelson, 1785-1835]

Neale, near the Green Man turnpike, Kent-road — *Kent*. [G. Neal, Pineapple Nursery, -1802; William Cordery, 1803-1836-]

North, Lambeth, near Westminster-bridge — *Surry*. [William North, -1806]

Pringle, Sydenham — *Kent*. [? William Pringle, died 1813]

Prior, Paddington, near London — *Middlesex*.

Perkins, Holloway down — *Essex*. [William Perkins, Leyton, successor to Spencer Turner, 1776-1825]

Renton, Hoxton, near the Ivy-house — *Middlesex*. [John Renton, -1780-1810]

Ronalds, Brentford — *Middlesex*. [Hugh Ronalds, 1750-88; Hugh Ronalds Junior, etc., 1788-1880]

Richards, Kingsland, near Hackney — *Middlesex*.

Ross, Newington-road, between Kingsland and Stoke-Newington — *Middlesex*. [John Ross, Caledonian Nursery, -1837]

Russel and co., Lewisham, near Greenwich — *Kent*. [John Russell, 1760-94; Russell & Willmott, etc., 1794-1860]

Shepherd, Kent-street, Borough, and Southwark — *Surry*.

Smith's and co., Dalston, near Hackney — *Middlesex*. [Edward & Samuel Smith, etc., -1784-1849]

Stidolph, Bromley — *Kent*. [Godfrey Stidolph, 1768-1818]

Syborne, Lea-bridge road, between Hackney, and Low-Layton — *Essex*. [Richard Siborn, 1755-74; Joseph Hughes, etc., 1775-1869]

Shuport, Homerton, near Hackney — *Middlesex*.

Swindon, Brentford — *Middlesex*. [Nathaniel Swinden, -1768-1805-]

Swinton, Foreign nursery, Knightsbridge — *Middlesex*.

Townly, Walworth — *Surry*.

Thobourn, Brompton, near Kensington and Chelsea — *Middlesex*. [Frank Thoburn, 1784-88; Thoburn & Whitley, etc., 1788-1881]

Thomson and Gordon, Mile-end near Bow — *Middlesex*. [see Gordon (James) and co., above]

Watson and Watsons, Lower Street, Islington — *Middlesex*. [William Watson, -1769-76; William & James Watson, 1776-92; Thomas Watson, 1792-1821]

Watts, Lambeth Butts — *Surry*. [William Watts, Walcot Place, -1805-]

Whitlock, Fulham — *Middlesex*. [John Whitlock, successor to Bagley & Whitlock, -1782-c. 1790]

A

LIST

OF

SEEDSMEN

In and near London, including the City, Westminster, Southwark, and parts in the Vicinity.

Where all sorts of kitchen-garden seeds, tree, shrub, and flower seeds, flower-roots, grass seeds, &c. may be obtained in the best perfection, in their respective kinds, observing, that as there are many corn-dealers, and corn-chandlers who also sell some sorts of garden seeds, but not in full collection, this list therefore comprises principally those only who are professionally seedsmen, and such who being also in the corn way, as furnish likewise general supplies of garden seeds, &c. as above.

Bailey, Bishopsgate-street, without. [Isaac Bailey, The Rose & Crown, 82 Bishopsgate Street without, 1750-93; Elizabeth Bailey, etc., 1794-1813]

Beach, Blackman-street, Borough — *Southwark*. [George Beach, The Wheat-sheaf, 32 Blackman Street, -1789-97]

Bendel, Westminster-bridge Road, Lambeth — *Surry*. [? John Bendel, see above, nurserymen]

Cormack, Whitechapel road — *Middlesex*.

Cowie, Parliament-street — *Westminster*. [John Cowie, successor to John Webb, -1775-]

Cross, Fleet-street. [Edward Cross, 152 Fleet Street, -1768-1807]

Davidson, Tooley-street — *Southwark*. [John Davidson, 215 Tooley Street, 1789-97]

Davis, Snow-hill [William Davies, 61 Snow Hill, 1789-1809]

Dermer and Gordon, Fenchurch-street [see Gordon & Dermer, below]

Eddie and co., Strand [Alexander Eddie, 68 Strand, successor to Wilson & Sanders, etc., -1765-97; Wright & Beck, etc., 1798-1870]

Field and co., Thames-street [John Field & Co., 119 Lower Thames Street, -1763-1810; Field & Child, 1810-50]

Fisher, Haymarket, St. James's [James Fisher, successor to Samuel Gray and F. Gray, The Black Boy, 130 Pall Mall, -1785-]

Gordon and Dermer, Fenchurch-street [James Gordon & Thomas Dermer, etc., successors to James Gordon, 1775-1845] (see also Gordon and co. above, nurserymen)

Grimwood and Hudson, Piccadilly [Grimwood & Hudson, The Pineapple, Arlington Street — see above, nurserymen]

Hairs, Oxford-street, near the Pantheon. [John Hairs, 73 Oxford Street, 1780-1802]

Hairs and Hairs, St. James's-street. [James & Ivie Hairs, etc., 29 St. James's Street, -1777-1812]

Hay, Parliament-street — *Westminster.* [Walter Hay, see above, nurserymen]

Hill, Duke-street, Manchester Square

Kellet, Borough High-street — *Southwark.*

Lewis, Cornhill, opposite the Royal Exchange. [David Lewis, 28 Cornhill, -1785-94; Warner & Seaman, etc., 1795-1840]

Lucar and co., City Road, near Moorfields. [Luker, Smith & Lewis, successors to Warren Luker, The Sun, City Road, -1780-1849; see also above, Smith's and co., nurserymen]

Minier and co., Strand. [Minier, Teesdale, Minier & Oliver, successors to Minier & Mason, The Orange Tree, 63 Strand, 1781-1800; Minier, Minier & Nash, etc., 1801-80]

Mitchell, New Bond-street. [George Mitchell, 19 New Bond Street, -1789-98-]

North, Lambeth — *Surry.* [see above, nurserymen]

Oakley, near the Asylum, Westminster-bridge Road — *Asylum.* [Oakley, corndealer and seedsman, -1787-]

Post and Hunt, Borough High-street — *Southwark.* [Post & Hunt, 34 Borough High Street, -1783-; Walter Post, -1798-; John Hunt, etc., 1792-1824]

Ronalds, Brentford — *Middlesex.* [see above, nurserymen]

Robson, Holborn-Hill. [Adam Robson, 39 Holborn, successor to Nathaniel Powell, 1771-1802; John Allport junior, etc., -1805-1830]

Seaman, Monument-Yard. [? William Seaman, 16 Fenchurch Street, -1783-85-]

Shields, Brentford — *Middlesex.* [? James Shiells, 21 Parliament Street and Lambeth, 1766-88]

Thatcher, Fleet-street. [Samuel Thatcher, etc., The Raven, 147 Fleet Street, successor to George Ferne, 1780-1831]

Townly, Walworth — *Surry.* [see above, nurserymen]

Watt's, St. James's Street. [David Watts, 83 St. James's Street, -1786-88-]

White, Whitechapel. [James White, seedsman and cornchandler, 91 Whitechapel, -1785-97-]

Wilson, West-Smithfield. [James Wilson, 68 Smithfield, -1785-98; James Bassington, -1805-]

Wrench, Thames-street [J. Wrench & Son, etc., successors to Jacob Wrench, The Three Wheat Sheaves, 126 Lower Thames Street, 1785-1905]

N. B. As the foregoing list of nurserymen and seedsmen comprise the names of the present occupiers that as by removal, death, and other circumstances, they in the course of time will be succeeded by others, the same nursery grounds, and seed shops, being such as are mostly established in the different places annexed to the present names, the public will thereby readily know where to apply for the various nursery and seed articles, &c. required.

The earliest priced catalogues seem to have been published in 1775, and it is not easy to get a general impression of what was available at earlier dates. A few accounts of plants supplied to very large estates do, however, include such a wide range as to provide a partial substitute. Evidence of this kind regarding forest trees has appeared elsewhere (see John H. Harvey, 'Forest Trees and their prices before 1850', in *Quarterly Journal of Forestry*, LXVII, no. 1, January 1973, 20-37) and the several accounts printed below have been chosen for the information they provide on evergreen and flowering trees and shrubs, on varieties of roses, and on sources of supply for good pineapples and vines.

(A) An account of John and William Perfect of Pontefract, dated 7 November 1755, for plants supplied to the Countess of Oxford at Welbeck, Notts., closely follows the order of the later printed catalogues of the firm (for that of 1776 see *Early Gardening Catalogues*, 100-116). In the case of the roses it seems likely that this account includes all the varieties stocked at Pontefract at the time. Thirteen kinds listed in 1776 do not appear in this bill of 1755: Dwarf and Tall Burgundy, Crimson, White Damask, Dutch Hundred-leav'd, Thornless, Maiden's Blush, Semi-double Marbled, White Monthly, Single Yellow, Marbled Scotch, Full double Sweet Briar and Maiden's Blush or Evergreen Sweet Briar. The prices of those roses that appear on both lists remained the same, except for the Red Belgic which dropped from 1s. to 6d., and the Velvet. At only 4d. in 1755 this must have been a single rose, for the catalogue marked both Double Velvet and Semi double Velvet at 1s. each.

The highest priced rose in 1755 was the Moss Provence at 2s., and this had been available at Furber's Kensington Nursery by 1724; it has to be concluded that the middle of the eighteenth century was a period of stagnation in the rose trade. A marked quickening of tempo was soon to come. In 1768 Furber's successor John Williamson supplied Burgundy roses at the very high price of 7s. 6d. each to the Princess of Wales for Kew (*Early Gardening Catalogues*, 49) and by 1775 they were in the catalogue of Telford of York with the price of 5s. marked in ink. In 1787 Brunton of Birmingham listed both Dwarf and Tall Burgundy at 3s. each; the lists of northern firms from 1787 to 1797 marked the Dwarf at 1s. 6d. and the Tall Burgundy at 2s. The Rose De Meaux was also available at 5s. from Telford in 1775 and from Brunton by 1782; the price had fallen to 2s. in northern and Scottish catalogues of 1783-97. The next outstanding introduction was the Unique or White Provence, discovered as a bud-sport in East Anglia by Daniel Grimwood of Little Chelsea (and from 1783 Williamson's successor at Kensington) in

July 1775. In 1776 Grimwood arranged for propagation by his foreman Henry Shailer senior, who in three years had produced over 1200 plants, put on the market at a guinea each in 1780. By 1787 the Unique appeared in provincial catalogues but without a price in print; from 1790 onwards it was marked at 2s. 6d. (G. S. Thomas, *The Old Shrub Roses*, 4th edition, 1963, 112, quoting Henry Shailer junior, *Gardeners Chronicle*, 27 Nov 1852, 759; catalogues). The modern cult of rose-growing in England developed thenceforward.

Perfects' account (Nottinghamshire Record Office, DD.5P 6/ 10/3/18) was receipted by William Perfect on 5 June 1756 in the sum of £10. 11. 0 'in full of this Bill & all Demands', knocking 5d. off the total.

The Right Honble. the Countess of Oxford of Jno. & Wm. Perfect
7 Novr. 1755

	£	s	d
2 Tripple Thorn'd Acacias		4.	0
6 Double blossom'd Dwarf Almonds		3.	0
4 Single blossom'd Dwarf Almonds		2.	0
6 Red ⎫			
6 Purple ⎬ Althea Frutex			
6 White ⎭			
6 Strip'd flower'd	12.	0	
2 Arbor Judae		2.	0
2 Arbutus		5.	0
4 White Barberrys		1.	4
2 Red Poded Bladder Sena's		2.	0
10 Gold Edg'd Box trees		2.	6
4 Dwarf Branching Brooms		1.	0
8 Sweet Gales		4.	0
15 Shrub Cinquefoils		3.	9
2 Willow leav'd Cistus with white flowers		2.	0
2 Willow leav'd Cistus with Spotted flowers		3.	0
4 Sage leav'd Cistus with Purple flowers		3.	0
2 Gum Cistus or Rock Rose		1.	6
6 Virginian Creepers		1.	6
10 Goosberry leav'd Currants		2.	6
15 Cytissus Secundus		3.	9
4 Evergreen Honeysuckles		2.	0
10 Red Dutch ⎫			
10 Long blowing ⎪			
6 Red Roman ⎪			
6 Early Red ⎬ Honeysuckles		8.	4
6 Early White ⎪			
6 Late white ⎪			
6 Oak leav'd ⎭			
4 Trumpet Honeysuckles		4.	0

6 Hydrangulas	2.	0
20 Hypericum Frutex	5.	0
10 White Jassamines	2.	6
10 Yellow Jassamines	2.	6
20 Persian Jassamines	6.	8
2 Cut leav'd Persian Jassamines	1.	0
2 White flower'd Persian Jassamines	1.	0
4 Spurge Laurels	1.	0
20 Laurus Tinus	5.	0
10 Red ⎫ Mesereans 6 White ⎭	5.	4
4 Strip'd Nightshades	1.	0
2 Candleberry Myrtles	2.	0
6 Myrtle leav'd Sumach	2.	0
2 Oleasters	2.	0
6 Periplocas	2.	0
4 Evergreen Privets	0.	8
6 Broad leav'd Sage trees	3.	0
2 Narrow leav'd Sage trees	1.	0
10 Scorpion Senas	2.	6
20 Spirea Frutex	5.	0
5 Spirea Frutex with Purple flowers	2.	6
2 Storax or Liquid Ambers	5.	0
10 Dwarf Syringas	2.	6
4 Creeping Toxicodendrons	1.	0
2 Upright Toxicodendrons	1.	0
6 Diervellas	2.	0
6 Travellers Joys	1.	6
6 Upright Tutsans	1.	6
5 Spanish Brooms	1.	3
6 Single Sweet Bryars	1.	0
4 Double Sweet Bryars	2.	0
2 Yellow Austrian Roses	2.	0
2 Red Austrian Roses	2.	0
2 Apple bearing Roses	1.	0
4 Blush Belgick Roses	4.	0
4 Red Belgick Roses	4.	0
2 Blush Cluster Roses	2.	0
2 Blush hundred leav'd Roses	2.	0
4 Burnet leav'd Roses	1.	4
4 Childing Roses	1.	4
4 Double Cinamon Roses	1.	4
2 Single Cinamon Roses	1.	0
2 Damask Roses	0.	8
2 Evergreen Roses	1.	0
4 Frankfort Roses	1.	4

2 Marbled Roses	2.	0
2 Monthly Roses	0.	8
2 Strip'd Monthly Roses	1.	0
4 Rosa Mundi	1.	4
2 Double Musk Roses	2.	0
2 Pensilvanian Roses	1.	0
4 Province Roses	1.	4
2 Blush Province Roses	2.	0
2 Moss Province Roses	4.	0
4 Double Red Roses	1.	4
4 Great Royal Roses	1.	4
2 Red Scotch Roses	2.	0
4 White Scotch Roses	1.	4
2 Velvet Roses	0.	8
4 Virgin Roses	1.	4
2 Double White Roses	0.	8
2 Double Yellow Roses	2.	0
4 York & Lancaster Roses	1.	4
Spreading Tutsans & Periwinkles of Sorts	7.	6
3 Large Bass Matts & Package	3.	0
£ 10. 11.		5

(B) Sir William Lee, Bart., of Hartwell, Buckinghamshire, in 1759-60 had a new garden, greenhouse and pinery designed by Richard Woods of Chertsey, Surrey. Trees, shrubs and pineapples were all supplied by Woods from his nursery and his account shows that he also paid many visits to Hartwell to supervise the work. This account (Buckinghamshire Record Office, D/LE/11/10) is of unusual importance because it shows the very wide selection of stock kept by Woods as a nurseryman as well as the handsome fees he could command as a landscape gardener.

Sir Willm. Lee Bart. Dr. To Richd. Woods.
1759

Octr. 10th	£	s	d
200 Laurels £2.10 / 100 Laurastinus £1. 5	3.	15.	0
100 Philerays £1. 5 / 25 Piracanthas 6s. 3	1.	11.	3
50 Savan 12s. 6 / 50 Rough yews £2.10	3.	2.	6
100 Plain Hollys £1. 5 / 6 Stript Do. 9s	1.	14.	0
20 Phlomas 5s / 20 Gumsistus 10s	0.	15.	0
50 Spanish Broom 12s. 6 / 35 Evergreen Sistus 8. 9	1.	1.	3
50 Tongue Laurels 12s. 6 / 12 Seagreen Purslain 3s	0.	15.	6
25 Spirafrutex 6s. 3 / 25 Hyperciam Do. 6s. 3	0.	12.	6
50 American Roses 12s. 6 / 50 Second best Sorts 12s. 6	1.	5.	0
50 Lalocks in Sorts 12s. 6 / 50 Syringoes 12s. 6	1.	5.	0

50	Blader Senas 12s. 6 / 50 Lyburnums 12s. 6	1.	5.	0
50	Sweet briers 12s. 6 / 50 Virginian Rasps	1.	5.	0
20	St. Peters wort 5s. / 100 Privet £1. 5	1.	10.	0
25	Yellow Jesamin 6s. 3 / 4 Large Gilder Roses 1s	0.	7.	3
50	Looker Broom 12s. 6 / 10 Toxicodendarons 3s. 4	0.	15.	10
10	Fiveleav'd Bladernuts 2s. 6 / 8 Maiden Barberries 4s.	0.	6.	6
10	Pencylvania Cherries 5s. 6 / 100 Fine young Oaks £2. 2	2.	7.	6
100	Do. Beech £1 / 100 Do. Hornbeam 15s.	1.	15.	0
2	Bastard Indigoes 4s. / 2 Oley aster 4s.	0.	8.	0
2	Tripple thornd Accacia 4s. / 2 Catalphers 4s.	0.	8.	0
2	Carolina Poplars 4s. / 2 Sweet Gums 5s.	0.	9.	0
2	Scarlet Maples 2s. / 2 Virginian Do. 2s.	0.	4.	0
2	Sugar Do. 2s. / 2 Ashleav'd Do. 2s.	0.	4.	0
2	Scarlet Oaks 2s. / 2 Dwarf Red Do. 2s.	0.	4.	0
1	Champaign Do. 1s. / 1 Stript Do. 2s. 6	0.	3.	6
2	Carolina Tulips 8s. / 2 Scarlet horse Chesnuts 10s.	0.	18.	0
2	Agnas Castus 4s. / 2 Double Peach 3s.	0.	7.	0
4	Double Cherries 6s. / 2 Double thorns 3s.	0.	9.	0
2	Bitter Almonds 2s. / 2 Sweet Do. 3s.	0.	5.	0
6	Dwarf Do. 6s. / 6 Arberjudea 6s.	0.	12.	0
2	Sorbus 2s. / 2 Yelloberried Thorns 2s.	0.	4.	0
2	Cockspur Do. 2s. / 2 Lord Elys Do. 2s.	0.	4.	0
2	Glasenbury Do. 4s. / 2 Red azarolas 2s.	0.	6.	0
2	Yellow Do. 2s. / 2 Double Pears 3s.	0.	5.	0
2	Benjamin Trees 3s. / 2 Tackmahaca 2s.	0.	5.	0
2	Win Leav'd Toxacodendrons 2s.	0.	2.	0
2	Angelica Trees 2s. / 10 Stript Laurels 10s	0.	12.	0
20	Plain Hollys 6s. 8 / 20 Stript Do. £1.10s	1.	16.	8
20	Bays £1. / 4 Systus in Sorts £1.10s	2.	10.	0
4	Portugal Laurels 16s. / 4 Arbutus £1.	1.	16.	0
10	Stript Laurastinus 10s. / 3 Stript Rosemary 1s. 6	0.	11.	6
10	Do. Box 5s. / 2 Cork Trees 2s.6	0.	7.	6
50	Shumacks £1. 5s. / 20 White Mazerians £1.	2.	5.	0
20	Althea frutex 10s. / 20 Percian Lalocks 6s. 8	0.	16.	8
16	Deavila 8s. / 2 Double Pomgranats 4s.	0.	12.	0
2	Single Do. 3s. / 6 Threeleav'd Bladernuts 3s.	0.	6.	0
10	Oriental Coluta 7s. 6 / 10 Etheopian Do. 7s. 6	0.	15.	0
10	Mountain Ash 10s. / 10 Flowering Do. 10s.6	1.	0.	6
100	Honeysuckles in Sorts	1.	5.	0
2	Indigo Sweetmeats	0.	3.	0
2	White Cedars 6s. / 4 Red Do. 10s.	0.	16.	0
2	Carolina Do. 15s. / 2 Cedars of Labanus 12s.	1.	7.	0
2	Barmudas Do. 10s. / 2 Hemlock Spruce firrs 8s.	0.	18.	0
2	White Spruce firs 5s. / 2 Black Do.	0.	10.	0
2	Common Do. 2s. / 2 Weymoth pines 10s.	0.	12.	0
2	Balm of Gilliad Firrs 8s. / 2 Pineasters 4s.	0.	12.	0

2	Cluster Pines 4s. / 2 Jersey Do. 4s.	0.	8.	0
2	Foxtail Do. 4s. / 2 Silver Firrs 2s.	0.	6.	0
100	Laurels £1. 5 / 50 Philerays 12s. 6	1.	17.	6
20	Phlomas 5s. / 20 Upright Cypress £1.10	1.	15.	0
2	China Arbervita 6s. / 2 Canada Do. 4s.	0.	10.	0
2	Common Do. 3s. / 2 Evergreen Oaks 3s.	0.	6.	0
2	Candleberry myrtles 8s. / 100 Oaks £2. 2	2.	10.	0
100	Beech £1. / 100 Hornbeam 15s.	1.	15.	0
20	Pencylvania Cherries	0.	10.	0
10	Virginian Wallnuts 10s. / 40 Plains £2.	2.	10.	0
2	Virginian Cypress 5s. / 2 Percemian Plumbs 3s.	0.	8.	0
10	Common Junipers 5s. / 2 Sweedish Do. 3s.	0.	8.	0
	Matts and Baskets	0.	16.	0

Feb. 20th

50	Succession Pineapple plants at 2s/6 each	7.	10.	0
40	Fruiting Plants of Do. at 7s.6 each	15.	0.	0

July 9th

25	Large Store plants of Do. at 6s each	7.	10.	0
2	Large Basketts & Carriage &c	0.	11.	0
	A Waggon and 4 horses to Hartswell	3.	0.	0

Aug: 28th To a Journey to Hartwell	1.	1.	0
Sepr: 18th To a Journey and time from the 18th to the 22d 5 Days	5.	5.	0
Octr. 18th. To a Journey and time from the 18th to the 21st 4 Days	4.	4.	0
Novr. 7th To a Journey to Hampton Court	1.	1.	0
To a Journey and Time from ye 13th to the 17th 5 Days	5.	5.	0
Decr. To a Journey and Time from the 15th to the 17th	2.	2.	0

N.B.

Jan. 1760 To a Journey and Time from the 2d to the 7th 5 Days	5.	5.	0
April To a Journey and Time from the 23d to ye 26 4 Days	4.	4.	0
May To a Journey and Time from the 19. to ye 20th 2 Days	2.	2.	0
June To a Journey and Time from 30th to ye 2d of July 3 Days	3.	3.	0
Sepr. To a Journey and Time from ye 11th to the 12th 2 Days	2.	2.	0
To Design for the New Garden Greenhouse and			

Pinery		12. 12. 0

		148. 17. 11 *
Rec'd in part		55. 5. 0
Ballance Due		£ 93. 12. 11

Octr. 20, 21, 22 For my self to Journey and Time 3 days	3. 3. 0
My Clark 2 Days	0. 12. 0
N.B. A Mistake from the other Side	1. 1. 0

Total due	£ 98. 8. 11
deducted	12. 12. 0
	£ 85. 16. 11

Recd. ye 4th May 1761 the full Contents of this
account & all Demainds

By me (signed) Richd. Woods

(C) Whereas Sir William Lee obtained pineapple plants for his new pinery
from the nursery of Richard Woods, other estates frequently got them, and
choice sorts of grapevines, from head gardeners of specialist status. One such
gardener was Robert Teesdale senior (died 1773) at Castle Howard in
Yorkshire, father of the botanist Robert Teesdale (c. 1740-1804). It is of
particular interest that William Speechly (c. 1734-1819), head gardener to the
Duke of Portland at Welbeck and later the author of the two standard
treatises *On the Culture of the Pineapple* (1779) and *On the Culture of the
Vine* (1790), should have obtained supplies of both from the elder Teesdale.
The accounts (Nottinghamshire Record Office, DD 5P/14/19, 21, 22, 23)
show that in 1767 carriage was paid on 20 May on 'some Pine Plants from
Castle Howard' (6s. 2d.) and again on 18 September on 'some Pine Succers
from Cas. Hd.' (5s. 5d.); on 18 February 1768 the sum of £29 7s. 5d. 'To Mr.
Teesdale for a New stock of Pine-plants Suckers &c. as pr. Bill'; and on 5 Nov-
ember 1770 an item of £1. 10s. to 'Mr. Teesdale for some Vine Plants (new
Sorts)'. The detailed bill for Pineapples has survived and is printed below.

To Robt. Teesdale	
1767 May 11th	
To 100 Best pick'd Pine plants to fruit the next Year at 4s.	20. 0. 0
19 Sugar Loaf Pine Plants ⎫ 1 King Do. ⎬ at 4s.	4. 0. 0
Hamper, Basket & package	0. 4. 2

* This total should read £148.14.11

Aug. 19th 100 Strong Pine Suckers   5. 0. 0
    Hamper & Package   0. 3. 0
Dec. 3d. Best Red Beet Seed
    Bag   0. 0. 3
                                                            _____
                                                         £ 29. 7. 5
                                                            _____

Received the 18th of Feby. 1768 of Mr. Speechly by
the Hands of Mr. Wm. Mason the Contents of the above
                            p. me (signed) Robt. Teesdale

BIBLIOGRAPHY WITH ABBREVIATIONS

The following bibliography includes only a few works of special importance, and authorities frequently mentioned in the Notes; these latter are supplied with abbreviations.

AgHR	*Agricultural History Review*
Amherst	A. Amherst *A History of Gardening in England* (1895)
AO	Archives Office
BM	British Museum, London (PD Dept of Prints & Drawings)
Bodl	Bodleian Library, Oxford (JJ John Johnson Collection)
Cal LPH	*Calendar of Letters and Papers of the reign of Henry VIII*
Cal PatR	*Calendar of Patent Rolls*
Cal SPDom	*Calendar of State Papers, Domestic*
Cal TrB	*Calendar of Treasury Books*
	A. M. Coats, *Flowers and their Histories* (1956/1968)
	Garden Shrubs and their Histories (1963)
	The Quest for Plants (1969)
CRO	County Record Office
Flor Cab	*Floricultural Cabinet*
Gard Chron	*Gardeners Chronicle*
Gard Mag	*Gardener's Magazine*
Gent Mag	*The Gentleman's Magazine*
GLRO	Greater London Record Office
Gorer 1970	R. Gorer, *The Development of Garden Flowers*(1970)
Hadfield	M. Hadfield, *A History of British Gardening* (1969)
Harvey 1972	J. Harvey, *Early Gardening Catalogues* (1972)
Harvey 1973	*Early Horticultural Catalogues — a Checklist* (University of Bath Library, 1973)
HMC	Historical Manuscripts Commission
JRHS	*Journal of the Royal Horticultural Society*
	K. Lemmon, *The Covered Garden* (1962)
	The Golden Age of Plant Hunters (1968)
Linn Trans	*Linnean Society's Transactions*
Loudon 1822	J. C. Loudon, *Encyclopaedia of Gardening* (1822)
Lysons 1811	D. Lysons, *The Environs of London* (2nd ed., 1811)
MinL	Minet Library, Lambeth
NL Wales	National Library of Wales, Aberystwyth
PCC	Prerogative Court of Canterbury (Probate)
PRO	Public Record Office, London
RCHM	Royal Commission on Historical Monuments (England)

Royal Horticultural Society, *Dictionary of Gardening* (2nd ed., 1956)

RO Record Office

Soc Gen Society of Genealogists, London

Thompson 1937 G. Scott Thompson, *Life in a Noble Household* (1937)

VCH Victoria County History

R. Webber, *The Early Horticulturists* (1968)

Whitting 1965 P. D. Whitting ed., *A History of Hammersmith* (Hammersmith Local History Group, 1965)

Whitting 1970 ed., *A History of Fulham to 1965* (Fulham History Society, 1970)

Willson 1961 E. J. Willson, *James Lee and the Vineyard Nursery, Hammersmith* (Hammersmith Local History Group, 1961)

NOTES TO THE TEXT

References are not given for the very extensive matter derived from directories, nor from catalogues included in Harvey 1973.

PREFACE

p. ix   HENLEY — E. Lamond ed., *Walter of Henley's Husbandry* (1890), 19

HOLBORN — Amherst; B. D. Jackson ed., *A Catalogue of Plants cultivated in the Garden of John Gerard* (1876)

INTRODUCTION

p. 2   PLANE — *Guide to the Oxford Botanic Gardens* (Oxford, 1971), 6; M. Hadfield in Gard Chron, 5 July 1968, 7-8; 22 Oct, 29 Oct and 5 Nov 1960, 422-3, 443, 462-3; in *Country Life*, 19 Nov 1964, 1338-9; in *Country Life Annual* 1969, 118-20

p. 3   CATALOGUES — see Harvey 1972 and, for a checklist of surviving copies, Harvey 1973

SCOTLAND — T. Donnelly, 'Arthur Clephane, Edinburgh Merchant and Seedsman, 1706-30', AgHR, XVIII.ii (1970), 151-60

p. 4   HILL — A. Leighton, *Early English Gardens in New England* (1970), 190; will PCC 53 Fairfax, PRO Prob 11/207

LUCAS — catalogue reprinted in Harvey 1972, 65-74; will PCC 132 King, PRO Prob 11/361; will of Elizabeth Lukas, PCC 52 Bence, PRO Prob 11/350

MEAGER — *The English Gardener* (1670), copy in BM, 41.a.5

SEEDSMAN — in *Oxford English Dictionary* given first in 1691, but occurs in 1678 (Cal TrB 1676-79, ii.1006)

p. 5   WHITECHAPEL — *Survey of London*, XXVII (1957), 123, 278-80

p. 6   GARDENERS' COMPANY — *Adam armed: or an Essay . . .* (n.d.)

CANALS — C. Hadfield, *The Canal Age* (Newton Abbot, 1968)

p. 7   MILNE'S MAP — J. H. Harvey, 'The Nurseries on Milne's Land-Use Map', *Transactions of the London & Middlesex Archaeological Society*, XXIV (1973), 177-98

p. 8   LYSONS — Lysons 1811, 839-42

           MANGLES — I am very deeply indebted to Miss Alice M.
           Coats for her generous loan of this important book; her
           article on the Mangles family is in *Garden History*, I, no. 3,
           Summer 1973, 42-6

p. 9   WOOD & SONS — In 1842 William Wood & Son issued a
           catalogue in which it was stated that Mr. Wood had resided
           upwards of 30 years abroad, had more than 200 varieties of
           Roses on over 14 acres out of a total acreage of 40. The
           remote situation was overcome as there was 'a most
           excellent Posting Inn at Maresfield, conducted by James
           Bourner, replete with every accommodation, and where the
           best horses, were kept. 'There is a Coach, Bourner's "True
           Blue", from Brighton to Tunbridge Wells and Maidstone
           every Monday, Wednesday and Friday morning, returning
           the following day, which passes daily through Maresfield'. I
           am indebted to Mr. Peter A. Hyypio of the L. H. Bailey
           Hortorium, Cornell University, for this quotation from
           Wood's catalogue

p. 10   OSBORN — Miss E. J. Willson in Whitting 1970, 241

p. 11   BEAUMONT — Mrs. A. Bagot in *Archaeological Journal*,
           CXXVII for 1970 (1971), 261-4

           MINIER — Pedigrees in Wagner Collection, Huguenot Society
           of London. For access and information I am greatly
           indebted to Miss Irene Scouloudi and Mr. C. F. A. Marmoy

           ORDOYNO — T. M. Blagg, *Newark as a Publishing Town*
           (1898)

           NORTHERN BOTANISTS — J. G. Baker, *Botanical Trans-
           actions of the Yorkshire Naturalists' Union*, I (1885),
           185-201

p. 12   MADDOCK, CURTIS — W. H. Curtis, *William Curtis*
           (Winchester, Warren, 1941); information on the Maddock
           family from the Librarian, Society of Friends, Friends
           House

                                    CHAPTER I

p. 15   BABUR — *The Babur-Nama in English*, translated by A. S.
           Beveridge (1922/1969), 215, 321

           SELIM II — A. Baker in JRHS, LVI, 238

           COUTANCES — V. Mortet ed., *Recueil de textes relatifs à
           l'Histoire de l'Architecture* (Paris, 1911), 72-3

           WOODSTOCK — T. Arnold ed., *Henrici Huntendunensis
           Historia Anglorum* (Rolls Series 74, 1879), 244

p. 16   ROMSEY — Amherst, 7

PEYVRE — H. R. Luard ed., *Matthaei Parisiensis Chronica majora* (Rolls Series 57, 1872-84), v, 242-3

CHESTER — City of Chester records, CR 63/2 (Earwaker MSS); R. H. Morris, *Chester in Plantagenet and Tudor Reigns* (1894), 99, 570; I am indebted to Professor A. R. Myers and to Mr. R. G. C. Desmond for their help over the word 'restingtre'.

p. 18   NONSUCH — M. Hadfield, 'The long-lived Oriental Plane', *Country Life Annual* 1969, 120

'FROMOND' LIST — Harvey 1972, 58-64

PEACH — PRO, E.101/467/6/2, m. 9, kindly communicated by Mr. R. E. Latham

ARDERNE — BM, Add. MS. 29301; Westminster Abbey Muniments, 19356

JOHN GARDENER — A. G. Rigg in *Notes & Queries*, CCXI (1966), 326-7

p. 19   MENAGIER — E. Power, *The Goodman of Paris* (1928), 203-4

BRAY — BM, Sloane MS. 282, ff. 167v-173v

CARTHAMUS — R. E. Latham ed., *Revised Medieval Latin Word List* (1965), 74

STOCKHOLM MS — G. Stephens and T. J. Pettigrew in *Archaeologia*, XXX (1844), 386-7

p. 22   IMPYARD etc. — *Oxford English Dictionary*, s.v. Imp; *English Place-Name Society*, XXV, 280; VI, 117; X, 210; XI, 226; XII, 244, 446, 583; XIV, 247; XVII, 286; XIX, 40, 365; XXII, 480; XXXI, 82, 133-4; XXXIII, 30, 35; XXXVI, 213

p. 23   DURHAM — Durham, University Department of Palaeography, Accounts of Master Forester of the Bishop of Durham, 1438-1536. I have to thank Mrs. J. L. Drury for information from these accounts

GLYNDE PLACE — R. F. Dell, *The Glynde Place Archives* (1964), 78, 240

p. 24   LYDGATE — H. Bergen, ed., *Lydgate's Troy Book* (Early English Text Society, Extra Series XCVII, 1906), lines 1265-75, 1202-11

p. 25   WINCHESTER — College Muniments; Bursar's annual account rolls, and notes by the late C. W. Little

CHAPTER II

p. 27   BURGHLEY — Cal SPDom 1547-80 (1856), 171: orders of 7 March 1561

RUSSELL — Bodl., MS. Engl. hist. b.192, f. 27

p. 28   LE LEU — Cal LPH, XXI.ii, 728, 770(56); XIII.i, 887(2); ii,
         1280 (ff. 3b, 15, 20, 30); XIV.i, 904(3); ii, 781 (ff. 58b,
         59b); XV, 380 (f. 114), 1489 (f. 171b); XVII, 88 (f. 13);
         XIII.i, 981 (p. 362)
         GREENWICH — Ibid, XXI.ii, 700, 769.iv, 4
p. 29   SOUTHWARK — Ibid, XXI.ii, 769.ii, 18, 19
         WEST HORSLEY — Ibid, XXI.ii, 769.ii, 15; iv, 3
         HANWORTH, ELTHAM — Ibid, II.i, pp. 1448, 1474
         BEAULIEU — Ibid, V, pp. 747, 750, 751, 752, 755
         LOVELL — Amherst, 90-1; Cal LPH, V, pp. 305, 748, 751,
         760; XIII.ii, 1280 (f. 9b); XIV.ii, 781 (f. 66); XX.ii, 1035
         (f. 18); will, GLRO, DW/PA/5, Archdeaconry of Surrey, 27
         March 1550; Cal PatR, Edward VI.iii, p. 308; 1555-57, p.
         182; Surrey Parish Register Society, I
p. 30   CHAPMAN — *Journal of the British Archaeological
         Association*, 3rd series, VIII (1943), 53; M. Sands, *The
         Gardens of Hampton Court* (1950), 13, 14, 41, 45;
         Amherst, 88
         WANSTEAD, WINDSOR — Cal LPH, V pp. 324, 752-3, 762
         GREENWICH — Ibid, V, p. 759
         MOUNTEYN — Ibid, XX.ii, 1035 (f. 23)
         JENNINGS — Amherst, 127; L. Stone in *Archaeological
         Journal*, CXXII (1956), 103, 125, 126
p. 31   ANTWERP — Cal LPH, XXI.i, 523
         FLEMINGS — Ibid, XXI.i, 147(2)
         MONEY — G. G. Coulton, *The Meaning of Medieval Moneys*
         (Historical Association Leaflet No. 95, 1934); E. V.
         Morgan, *The Study of Prices and the Value of Money*
         (Historical Association, Helps for Students of History, No.
         53, 1950); articles in *The Amateur Historian*, II, nos. 8, 9,
         10, pp. 238-44; 271-3; 304-8; J. Harvey, *The Gothic World*
         (1950), 42-3
         HAMPTON COURT — Sands (above, note p. 30)
p. 32   DURHAM — J. T. Fowler, *Extracts from the Account Rolls of
         the abbey of Durham* (Surtees Society, XCIX), i, 92
p. 33   KENILWORTH — J. H. Harvey in *Archaeological Journal*, CI
         (1946), 97, 101-4, 106; *History of the King's Works*
         (1963), II, 685
p. 34   HAVERING — *History of the King's Works*, II, 956
         LANGLEY — L. F. Salzman, *Edward I* (1968), 99; *History of
         the King's Works*, II, 970-77
         DOMINICANS — J. H. Harvey in *Archaeologia*, XCVIII
         (1961), note 1
         DUNSTABLE — *Monasticon Anglicanum* (1817-30), VI.i, 239;
         History of the King's Works, II, 925
p. 35   DURHAM — J. T. Fowler, *Extracts . . .*, i, 34, 84, 91, 115,
         261

CLARE — Westminster Abbey Muniments 12167

THORNBURY — PRO, E.36/220, p. 8

YORK — F. Collins ed., *Register of the freemen of the city of York* (Surtees Society, XCVI, 1897); N. Bartlett, *The Lay Poll Tax Returns for the City of York in 1381* (London and Hull, A. Brown, 1953), 53, 54, 65

ISABELL — J. H. Harvey in *The Northern Gardener*, XXIV no. 5 (September 1970), 155 note 6

p. 36   DONCASTER — S. Appleby in *Doncaster Gazette*, 18 May 1866, reprinted in *Sheardown's Pamphlets*, III, 183-90; cf. P. Skidmore in *The Naturalist*, no. 921 (1972), 55-7

OXFORD C. E. Doble, D. W. Rannie and H. E. Salter, edd., *Remarks and Collections of Thomas Hearne* (Oxford Historical Society, 1885-1921), viii, 355; ix, 126, 137, 291; xi, 250

GORDON — *Kalm's Account of his Visit to England,* translated by Joseph Lucas (1892); I am indebted to Miss Alice M. Coats for this reference

p. 37   NORWICH — Loudon 1822 quoting Linn Trans, II, 226

RENCH — Loudon 1822; E. J. Willson in Whitting 1970, 244

MALPAS — Amherst

p. 38   STAMFORD -- Bodl, JJ, Horticulture box 1

YORK FLORISTS — Archives deposited in York City Library

EXETER — J. Caldwell in *Transactions of the Devonshire Association*, XCII (1960)

CHAPTER III

p. 40   ROGER — Amherst, 31; PRO, C.47/3/31

WILLIAM —PRO, E.101/467/6/6; 467/5/2, m. 9

RUSSELL, BANBURY — *Registers of St. Margaret's Westminster*; will of John Banbery, Westminster Public Library, Peculiar Court of Westminster, 163 Bracy; probate of Henry Banbury, T.ii, 141(7); cf. J. Gerard, *Herball* (ed. 1633), 1456

p. 41   ARNOLD BANBURY — HMC, *Egmont,* I.ii, (1905), 531

WARNER — wills PCC 8 Rudd, PRO Prob 11/125; 85 Barrington, Prob 11/154

POINTER — Amherst, 147, 172; will PCC 49 Parker, PRO, Prob 11/133

p. 42   CROFTON — Twickenham Public Library, Glover's map; Soc Gen, transcript of Twickenham parish registers

TUGGIE — *Registers of St. Margaret's Westminster*; wills, Westminster Public Library, Peculiar Court, A.iv, 7, 8; PCC 66 Penn; cf. J. Parkinson, *Paradisus Terrestris* (1629), 312, 314; Gerard, *Herball* (ed. 1633), 161, 589, 785

p. 43   COLLIN — Amherst, 151; COLLINS — G. R. Batho, ed., *Household Papers* . . . (Royal Historical Society, Camden 3rd series, XCIII, 1962), 151

MOULART, MOULLAR — NL Wales, Bettisfield MS. 1663; will, PCC 166 Mico, PRO Prob 11/322

TURNER — will, PCC 103 Laud, PRO Prob 11/308

p. 44   MORGAN — M. Allan, *The Tradescants* (1964), 175; *Registers of St. Margaret's Westminster*; R. H. Jeffers in *Proc. Linnean Society*, CLXIV, 102-33; CLXVIII, 96-101

MILLEN — Parkinson, *Paradisus* (1629), 574-5; Gerard, *Herball* (ed. 1633), 1324, 1448, 1456, 1496, 1506; wills, St. Paul's Cathedral Library, St. Paul's Peculiar Court, Reg. E, ff. 50, 94v, 150v, 232

p. 45   HARMAN — HMC, *Egmont*, I.ii, 531

GURLE L. Meager, *The English Gardener* (1670), 82; *Survey of London*, XXVII (1957), 123, 278-80; Vicar General's Marriage Licences; Soc. Gen, Boyd's 'Citizens of London', 17765; Hadfield, 128-9, 146; R. T. Gunther, *The Architecture of Sir Roger Pratt* (1928), 305, 307-8; Thompson 1937, 248-50; Cal TrB, V.i, 828-9; VIII.i, 290; PCC administration 1685, PRO Prob 6/61, f. 48v; will of Joyce Gurle widow, PCC 78 Exton, PRO Prob 11/391

p. 46   ROSE — Wiltshire RO, Court Rolls of Amesbury, 20 Sept 1638; will of Stephen Rose, proved in court of Archdeacon of Sarum, 21 Nov 1638; I am grateful to Mr. Maurice G. Rathbone and to Mr. K. H. Rogers for these references; *Wiltshire Archaeological Magazine*, XLII, 252-3; Cal TrB 1660-67, 294; V.ii, 1377; will PCC 93 Hale, PRO Prob 11/354; cf. Thompson 1937, 241

p. 47   CROUCH — Cal TrB 1676-79, ii, 1006

FULLER — J. Woolridge, *Systema Horti-culturae* (3rd ed., 1688, 4th ed., 1719), 271-8

TURNER — John Turner as a seedsman occurs from 1695 in accounts for Newby Hall, Yorks., in Northumberland RO, Blackett of Matfen MSS, ZBL,273/8, ff. 20, 46, 48, 50, 92; cf. T. Donnelly in Ag HR, XVIII.ii (1970), 152-4, 157; S. Switzer, *A Compendious Method* . . . (4th ed., 1729), x; Turner subscribed to Switzer's *Practical Husbandman and Planter* in 1734

MINIER — Charles Minier (I; c. 1710-1790) was son of Matthieu and Jeanne Minier, Huguenots of St. Paul's, Covent Garden; in 1742-44 he was receiving payments from Switzer (Switzer's bank account, a reference for which I am grateful to Mr. William Brogden); will, PCC 196 Bishop

p. 48   POWELL — W. Roberts in Gard Chron, 1918.i, 223, advertisements from 1731; in 1733 subscribed to Robert Furber, *A*

Short Introduction to Gardening; died 1 March 1773 at Bristol (Gent Mag)

NOBLE *—Survey of London*, VIII (1922), 24, 68; H. J. Bradley, *The History of Shoreditch Church* (1914), 131; will PCC 193 Grey, PRO Prob 11/218

RICKETS — *Survey of London*, VIII, 68; Thompson 1937, 253; W. Roberts in JRHS, LXIII (1938), 425; will, PCC 184 Eedes, PRO Prob 11/490

PEARSON — J. Gibson in *Archaeologia*, XII (1796), 191; parish register of St. Leonard Shoreditch (Guildhall Lib, MS. 7499/3); will of Samuel Peirson, PCC 42 Dyer, PRO, Prob 11/459; will of Edward Pearson, St. Paul's Cathedral Library, St. Paul's Peculiar Court, Reg. K, f. 290; *Surrey Apprenticeships 1711-1731* (Surrey Record Society, X, 1921), nos. 1993-4

p. 49   DARBY — J. Cowell, *The Curious and Profitable Gardener* (1730), part ii, 14; Peter Collinson in Linn Trans, X, 271; J. E. Dandy, *The Sloane Herbarium* (1958), 123-4

FAIRCHILD — *The City Gardener*, 5; parish registers of Aldbourne, Wilts., kindly communicated by K. H. Rogers, esq.

FOSTER — MinL, P2/34, 35

VERSPRIT — J. Gibson, *Archaeologia*, XII, 185, 190; MinL, P2/34

'MORDAN' — Hadfield, 129; Thompson 1937, 251-2

p. 50   FULHAM — E. J. Willson in Whitting 1970, 238, 243-5; will of Nathaniel Dauncer, (PCC 338 Ruthen); PRO, Prob, 11/267; will of Thomas Rench, (PCC 121 Brook) PRO, Prob. 11/621

MARSH E. J. Willson in Whitting 1965, 96; I. Scouloudi & A. P. Hands, *London Topographical Record*, XXII (1965), 86

MARSHFIELD — Bedfordshire CRO, L 31/296

PUTNEY — J. H. Harvey, 'The Putney Nursery: an early Plant Centre', *Surrey Archaeological Collections*, LXIX (forthcoming), 135-42

GRIGSON — Soc Gen, transcript of Twickenham parish registers

p. 51   CEDAR — Hadfield, 99, 141

BROMPTON PARK — BM, Harleian MS. 6273, ff. 50-6; will of Roger Looker, see Appendix VI

p. 52   WILLIAM LOOKER — Thompson 1937, 247-8; Soc Gen, transcript of Hatfield parish registers

COOK — *The Manner of Raising* . . ., 8, 26; W. Minet, Registers of Little Hadham, Herts., 1559-1812 (1907); P. Morant, Essex (1768), II, 291; I am much indebted for this reference and other information to Miss Nancy Briggs

p. 53   FIELD – *Bedfordshire Parish Registers,* vol. III
           LONDON – S. Switzer, *The Nobleman, Gentleman, and Gardener's Recreation* (1715), 60; will, PCC 31 Aston PRO Prob 11/538; Soc Gen, Boyd's Marriages, transcripts of registers; J. E. Dandy, *The Sloane Herbarium* (1958), 158

CHAPTER IV

p. 59   COOK – *The Manner of Raising . . .*, 84
           PERCY – T. Percy ed., *The Earl of Northumberland's Household Book* (1770), 45, 255, 328; L. T. Smith ed., *The Itinerary of John Leland* (1907/1964), I, 53-4
           SYON, PETWORTH – G. R. Batho ed., *The Household Papers of Henry Percy, 9th Earl of Northumberland* (Royal Historical Society, Camden 3rd series, XCIII, 1962), 150-1, 158, 161, 164; 36, 55, 91, 95, 99
p. 60   NAWORTH – G. Ornsby ed., *Selections from the Household Books of Lord William Howard* (Surtees Society, LXVIII, 1878), 87, 92, 108, 136
           WILLESDEN – Society of Antiquaries, MS. 133, f. 1
           CREAKE – Amherst, 182
p. 61   OXFORD – above, note to p. 36; M. G. Hobson & H. E. Salter, *Oxford Council Acts 1626-1665* (1933); M. G. Hobson, *Oxford Council Acts 1665-1701* (1939); J. E. T. Rogers, *Oxford City Documents* (1891), 82, 84; W. H. Quarrell & W. J. C. Quarrell, *Oxford in 1710* (Oxford, Blackwell, 1928), 60
p. 62   TAGG – *Remarks and Collections of Thomas Hearne,* XI, 250; VIII, 342, 355, 392; IX, 126, 137, 291; Oxfordshire CRO, DIL XXVI/4; Bodl R.Top. 731 (Jackson's Oxford Journal synopsis)
p. 63   AUSTEN – A. Lawrence & J. Beale, *Nurseries, Orchards, Profitable Gardens, and Vineyards encouraged* (1677), 5
           YORK J. H. Harvey in *The Northern Gardener,* XXIV No. 5 (Sep. 1970), 153-5; XXV No. 2 (March 1971), 50-7; PRO, C.142/125/74, a reference for which I am obliged to Dr. D. M. Palliser
           WHARTON – E. Bulmer ed., *The Parish Registers of St. Martin-cum-Gregory, York* (1897), 112; York City Archives, D.13, f. 26; C.34, f. 9; Yorks. Archaeological Society, Parish Register Section, *St. Mary Castlegate Registers,* ii, 215; York Wills, vol. 128, 76; Prerogative, March 1784
p. 64   TELFORD – J. H. Harvey, 'The Family of Telford, Nurserymen of York', *Yorkshire Archaeological Journal,* XLII (1969), 352-57

p. 65   ROCK, FALLADON — E. Gibson ed., *Camden's Britannia* (1695), 873

              NORTHALLERTON — H. Phillips, *The Companion for the Orchard* (1831), 184

              KNAVESMIRE — R. H. Skaife in *Yorkshire Archaeological Journal*, XIV (1897), 454; RCHM, *City of York*, III (1972), 51

p. 66   PERFECT — York Minster Library, MS. Poll-Book of 1708; Leeds City Archives Dept., VR/285, 286 A.2 etc.; Pontefract Library, George Fox MS., vol. 3, 42ff., 57; *The Practical Husbandman and Planter*, I (1733), ii, 116-29; M. Brockbank, *Pictures . . . at Nostell* (1915), a reference for which I am grateful to Mr. William Brogden

              BANKS — J. W. F. Hill ed., *The Letters and Papers of the Banks Family* (Lincoln Record Society, XLV, 1952), 237-8

p. 67   TEMPLE NEWSAM — Leeds City Archives Dept., TN/EA/12/11

              KIVETON — Yorkshire Archaeological Society, Duke of Leeds MSS, DD.5, box xxxiii

p. 68   NOBLE — ibid, box xxxii; Lincolnshire AO, Monson 11/25/30; York Wills, Sep. 1756

              MANSFIELD — Soc Gen, Apprentices 1710-62; Notts RO, DD.BM (Mansfield Court Rolls), information from the County Archivist

              COWLISHAW — Notts RO, DD 5P/6/5/2 no. 2; DDN/212/115; York Wills, Reg. 121,449

              WINTER & FOX — Cusworth Hall Museum, Goodchild Loan MSS, box M/8, information from John Goodchild esq.

              JOYCE — *Newcastle Journal*, 12 Jan 1754; *Newcastle Courant*, 1 Jan 1757, from Gateshead Public Library

p. 69   BEVERLEY — for the Sigston family I am obliged to the Borough Librarian and to David Neave esq. for information from the Burgess Roll and Apprentices Register

              RIPON — York Poll Books; York City Archives, D.13; York City Library, records of the Ancient Society of York Florists, vol. 1

              LINCOLN — Lincs AO, Monson 11/25/27

              DERBY — Glover's Directory

              REA — *Kinlet Parish Registers* (Shropshire Parish Register Society, XVII), vii, 18, 25

p. 70   BATES — I am greatly indebted to Dr. D. M. Palliser for information from the MSS of Edward Mainwaring (died 1703) at Whitmore Hall, Staffs.; cf. J. G. Cavenagh-Mainwaring in *Staffordshire historical Collections for 1933* (1934), 70-79

              LAWRENCE — op. cit. (above, note to p. 63, Austen), 2

SEEDSMEN — ibid, 27

p. 71   BROMPTON PARK — T. Donnelly in AgHR, XVIII.ii, 154, 157

COLCHESTER — wills of the Agnis family in Essex RO; P. Morant, *History of Colchester* (1st ed., 1748), 8; (2nd ed., 1768), 92; will of Henry Stow, PCC 356 Trevor. I am greatly indebted for material from the *Ipswich Journal* and other sources to John Bensusan-Butt esq., who regards the 'John' Stow of 1748 as a mistake for Henry Stow

WOODBRIDGE — *Notcutts Plants* (1969), 2-3; GLRO, B/HRS/13, p. 176

SOUTHAMPTON — information from Mayor's Accounts and All Saints Rate Books from the City Archivist; cf. A. T. Patterson, *A History of Southampton 1700-1914* (Southampton Records Series, XI), i(1966), 43

EXETER — Hadfield, 236; Soc Gen, transcripts of parish registers of St. Thomas, Exeter; Powderham; Devon Marriage Licences; information from Exeter City Library

p. 72   LUCOMBE OAK — Buckinghamshire RO, D/LE/D/2/55; the County Archivist informs me that, although the year of the Claxton letters is not given, days of the week are often stated and, with external evidence, make 1774 virtually certain. The only other *possible* years would be 1768 and 1785, yielding (by subtraction of 11) dates for the Lucombe Oak of 1757 or 1774, both of which are out of the question

p. 73   BRISTOL — J. Dallaway, *Antiquities of Bristow* (1834), 29

BERRY — Gloucester City Library, Diocesan Archives, B4/T2/18.4; Gloucester Wills, Sep. 1727

CLARK — Harrowby MSS, CXXII, f. 178v (12 Dec 1753)

p. 74   WARWICK — VCH, *Warwickshire*, VIII, 471; information kindly sent by M. W. Farr esq

CHAPTER V

p. 76   BEAUMONT — Guillaume/William Beaumont is evidenced in the Levens Hall muniments from 1684 and about 1688 had a considerable forest tree nursery at Bagshot Lodge, Surrey, where he was working for James II. Beaumont's wife Ann is also mentioned, and they were living at Levens until 1729. It is possible but not certain that the Levens gardener was identical with the William Beaumont, gardener of New Windsor, Berks., who made his will on 17 August 1729, leaving all his estate to his wife Anne, son William, and a daughter (proved 3 Nov 1730; PCC 296 Auber, PRO Prob 11/640)

FAIRCHILD — will, PCC 269 Abbott, PRO Prob 11/632; *The Practical Husbandman and Planter*, I (1733), ii, 199-209; see also note to p.49 above

p. 77 BACON — W. Roberts, JRHS, LXIII (1938), 424; administration, St. Paul's Cathedral Library, St. Paul's Peculiar Court, 1725-65, f. 71

SIMPSON — Roberts, loc. cit., 426

p. 78 FURBER — *Faculty Office Marriage Licences* (British Record Society, XXXIII, 1905), 219; Soc Gen, Apprentices 1710-62 (9/186); *Autobiography and Letters of Mrs. Delany* (series I, vol. i, 265; I owe this reference to Miss Joan Edwards; PRO, Prob. 11/824 (PCC 244 Glazier)

GRIMWOOD — *Gentleman's Magazine* and Burial Book at Kensington Library, by kind information of Miss R. J. Ensing

GRAY — E. J. Willson in Whitting 1970, 239-40; will of William Gray, Guildhall Library, Commissary Court of London, 2 Nov. 1745; will of Christopher Gray, (PCC 426 Simpson), PRO Prob. 11/903

p. 79 WALPOLE — P. Toynbee ed., *Strawberry Hill Accounts* (1927), 58

p. 80 ALSTON — letter of 30 Oct 1749, Osborn Collection, Yale University Library

SINGLETON — will, Middlesex RO, Archdeaconry Court of Middlesex, vol. 6, 355

THOMPSON — Chelsea Rate Books, from the Librarian

DRIVER — National Register of Archives, *Architectural History*, List 2 (1970), no. 1351; Newington Rate Books

p. 81 HOLT — Leyton Rate Books and parish records, from the Reference Librarian; Hadfield, 169; C. O. Moreton, *The Auricula* (1964), 27; (PCC 295 Greenly), PRO Prob 11/782; Soc Gen, transcript of Wanstead register

BUTT — possibly identical with Richard, son of Francis and Margaret Butts, born at Barnes, Surrey 20 Dec 1699 (Soc Gen, transcript of Barnes register); Bucks. RO, D/LE/C6/9, 17; Staffs. RO, D.603/F/1976

SPYERS — PRO, Prob 3/29/111; P. Toynbee ed., *Strawberry Hill Accounts* (1927), 1, 3, 44; 'the wife of Joshua Spires' was buried at Twickenham on 30 April 1740 (Soc Gen, transcript of registers)

MASON — Soc Gen, transcript of Isleworth registers; administration, PCC 1730, Prob 6/106; inventory, Prob 3/29/111; B. Langley, *New Principles of Gardening* (1728), 151

p. 82 MASTERS — PRO, Prob 3/21/77

WOODMAN — Chiswick Rate Books, information kindly sent by Mrs R. K. Judges and by Librarian; Bishop of London's

Marriage Licences; will, PCC 138 Hutton, PRO, Prob 11/837

p. 83   HENRY SCOTT – Gard Chron, LVIII, 317; BM, PD, trade card in Banks Collection; MinL, transcript of Weybridge registers

JAMES SCOTT – Gard Chron, LVIII, 317; J. Justice, *The Scots Gardiners Calendar* (1754). 119. 176. a reference for which I am indebted to Miss P. Minay; BM, PD, trade card in Banks Collection

p. 84   GORDON A. M. Coats, *Garden Shrubs and their Histories* (1963), 384-5; Hadfield, 235; Flor Cab, XI (1843), 49-53; Tower Hamlets Borough Library, Stratford-Bow Rate Books, from the Librarian; will, PCC 20 Webster; Gent Mag, LI (1781), 46

KENNEDY & LEE – Willson 1961; R. Meredith, 'The Eyres of Hassop', *Recusant History*, IX (1967-8), 276, a reference for which I am grateful to Mr J. S. W. Gibson; Windsor Castle, The Royal Archives, 55584; will of Lewis Kennedy (1721-1782), PCC 415 Gostling, PRO Prob 11/1094; *Aberford Parish Registers 1540-1812* (Thoresby Society, XXXVI)

p. 85   KIRKE – T. Faulkner, *History and Antiquities of Kensington* (1820), 18, 21-2; Kensington Central Library, MSS. 2739, 2844, and Rate Books, information from the Reference Librarian

HEWITT – Bucks. RO, D/LE; Notts. RO, DD 5P/6/4/3 no. 15; Yorks. Archaeological Society, Duke of Leeds MSS, DD.5, box xxxii; GLRO, B/HRS/1-753

p. 86   PARKINSON – Linn Trans, X, 271; MinL, P2/34, 35; GLRO, Archdeaconry of Surrey, original will Nov 1719 in DW/PA/5

LUCAS – Essex RO, will, Archdeaconry of Middlesex, Essex and Herts. division, D/AMR 11/56

EMMERTON – Soc Gen, great card index; Herts. RO, DE 4408/3; B. E. Coates in *Transactions of the Hunter Archaeological Society*, VIII (1963), 303 note 24; wills, Middlesex RO, MDR, 1823/9/2, 3

CLARK – Herts. RO, 52600; see J. H. Harvey, 'The Stocks held by early Nurseries', in AgHR, XXII pt.i (1974), 18-35

p. 87   LEYTON – Rate Books, from the Reference Librarian; Gard Mag, XI (1835), 686-7; wills of John Hay, James Hill, Spencer Turner, Richard Siborn: PCC 568 Fountain, PRO Prob 11/1225; 301 Tenterden, Prob 11/1800; 41 Bellas, Prob 11/1015; 203 Bargrave, Prob 11/998

NORTH - MinL, P2/52; Deeds (XXII), 5292; *Museum Rusticum*, VI (1766), 77ff.; 287-94

SHIELDS — Northumberland RO, 2 DE.34/6/3, 5, 6, 7; MinL, P2/96, p. 14

p. 88   RONALDS — Gard Mag, V, 736; X, 96; Middlesex RO, PLT/1560-1596; Soc Gen, great card index; T. Faulkner, *The History and Antiquities of Brentford* . . . (1845), 65, 145-6, 149-50, 153; Oxfordshire CRO, J VIh/1-4; Wilts. CRO, Savernake Papers

MALCOLM — MinL, P2/51, /56, /96, pp. 61, 429, 480; James Edwards, *Companion from London to Brighthelmston,* part ii, 4, 6; H. Andrews, *Botanist's Repository,* III, t. 200; Gard Mag, XI (1835), 720

LUKER — Soc Gen, great card index; will PCC 607 Rockingham, PRO Prob 11/1123

LEWISHAM — Loudon 1822; H. H. Drake ed., *Hasted's History of Kent: Hundred of Blackheath* (1886), 262 note, 265-6; *Register of St. Mary, Lewisham*; Lysons 1811, II.ii, 842; F. H. Hart, *The History of Lee* (1882); Lewisham Library, Rate Books, Tithe Map, from the Borough Librarian; will of John Russell PCC 164 Holman, PRO Prob 11/1243

p. 89   HACKNEY — W. Robinson, *History of Hackney* (1842), I, 90; Lysons 1811, II.ii, 842; J. Mangles, *The Floral Calendar* (1839), 32, 96, 97; Knight & Perry, *A Synopsis of the Coniferous Plants* . . . (1850), 1; Hadfield, 285-6; information from Hackney Borough Archivist

ASHE — P. Toynbee ed., *Strawberry Hill Accounts* (1927), 45

CHAPTER VI

p. 92   KENNEDY — Borthwick Institute, York, Wills, Prerogative, August 1790

p. 93   PERFECT — Gateshead Central Library, Ellison Papers

BARNES — Leeds City Archives Dept., Harewood vouchers 376; catalogue in National Library of Ireland, Fingall (Plunket) Papers, MS. 8036(2); for knowledge of this I am greatly indebted to Dr Eileen McCracken

PONTEY — Lincs. AO, Massingberd of Gunby 4/5/12, pp.403-8, 455-8; York Wills, Reg. 183, f. 332

HAYNES — Lincs. AO, 3 Anc 6/25; catalogue 3 Anc 9/8/6

p. 94   WHITTINGHAM — Staffs. RO, D.593/F/3/2/33; Northants. RO, ASL 1128; information from Coventry Libraries; Shifnal parish registers from information kindly sent by Shropshire County Archivist; Soc Gen, Apprentices 1710-62 (42/65)

p. 95   THOMPSON — *The Registers of Pickhill-cum-Roxby* (Yorks.
         Parish Register Society, XX, 1904); Durham CRO, Vane
         deposit
         SIMPSON — *Knaresborough Wills* (Surtees Society, CX, 1905),
         ii, 308

p. 96   CROWDER — Borthwick Institute, York, York Wills, Reg.
         185, f. 83; Reg. 184, f. 462; P. Skidmore in *The Naturalist*,
         No. 921 (1972), 55; Phillimore's *Yorkshire Marriage
         Registers*, IV; *Doncaster Gazette*, 18 May 1866, reprinted
         in *Sheardown's Pamphlets*, III, 183-90; information from
         Doncaster Public Libraries
         HANBURY — A. M. Coats, *Flowers and their Histories* (1968),
         326; Hadfield, 239; catalogue, for a photocopy of which I
         am extremely grateful to Professor J. Ewan

p. 97   DORKING — PRO, C.110/174, a reference for which I am
         obliged to Mr. M. F. Thick; and see J. H. Harvey in AgHR,
         XXII pt.i (1974), 18-35
         CREE — Surrey RO, Land Tax returns, from information
         kindly supplied by the County Archivist; Court Books of
         Chertsey Beamond, Surrey RO, 97/1/1-21, and Enclosure
         Award; PRO, MR 1158; from information most generously
         supplied by B. F. J. Pardoe esq; information from the
         Reference Librarian, Chertsey; Gard Mag, VI, 381; VII,
         359; PCC 8 Effingham, PRO, Prob. 11/1588
         WOODS — Court Books of Chertsey, as above; Bucks. RO,
         D/LE/11/10, 61; H. Prince, *Parks in England* (Pinhorns,
         1967), 8, 44-5; Leeds City Archives Dept., BW/MA/10; and
         information kindly sent by Dr. Hugh Bilbrough

p. 98   HERTFORD — Herts. RO, DE 3857; Bodl, JJ, Horticulture,
         box 8
         SANDY — R. Webber, *Market Gardening* (Newton Abbot,
         1972), 42-4
         COTTRALL — Wilts. RO, Savernake Papers; *Ampthill Parish
         Register* (Beds. Parish Registers, XVII); cf. C. S. Higham,
         Wimbledon Manor House (1962), 29; NL Wales, Wynnstay
         MS. 170, ff. 42-3; 172, f. 1
         GIBBS — Beds. RO, B.313-17, 318/15-20; QSR 1827/316,
         318, from the County Archivist; Bodl, JJ, Billheads, box
         13; Agriculture, box 1; Gard Mag, III, 126
         MACKIE — Gard Mag, IX (1833), 751, and Harvey 1972,
         142-51
         LINDLEY — Norwich Central Library, information from the
         Librarian

p. 99   CLARKE — W. P. W. Phillimore, *Cambridgeshire Parish
         Registers*, II (1908), 45; Soc Gen, J. H. Bloom, 'Cambridge
         Monumental Inscriptions' (MS., Ac. 106), 39

WOOD — Gard Mag, VII, 384

SMALL, SILVERLOCK — Soc Gen, Apprentices 1763-74 (56/72); West Sussex CRO, Add. MS. 10600-604; 10620-622, from the County Archivist; Loudon 1822

NEWMAN — will, West Sussex CRO, Peculiar of the Dean of Chichester, vol. 8, 229; cf. F. W. Steer in *Sussex Archaeological Collections,* CIII (1965), 35 note 1

KEEN — Southampton Public Library and Civic RO, information kindly sent by the Librarian and by the City Archivist; Winchester College Muniments 32543

ROGERS — H. M. Gilbert ed., *A Sketch of the Life and Reminiscences of John Rogers* (1889); Gard Mag, XI (1835), 61-3; information from G. F. Verdon esq.

PAGE — Gard Mag, XI (1835), 60-1; Flor Cab, VII (1839), 53; cf. IX, 66; Willson 1961, 52-4

p.100 WARNBOROUGH — Winchester College Muniments 32544; H. Andrews, *Botanist's Repository,* II, t.114; Flor Cab, II (1834), 263-4 and plate at 241; Hants RO, 4 M52/237

SWALLOW — Reading, Rate Books and parish registers from information kindly sent by Trevor J. Falla esq.; W. Roberts in JRHS, LXVI (1941), 15 note

PENDAR — Wilts. RO, Savernake Papers; for entry of 1721 see J. A. Neale, *Charters and Records of Neales of Berkeley, Yate, and Corsham* (1907), p. 181, by kind information of Mr K. H. Rogers.

p.101 TOTTY — will, PCC, 80 North PRO Prob 11/366

BAKER — *Wiltshire Apprentices . . . 1710-60* (Wilts. A. & N. H. Society, Records Branch, XVII), no. 1055

GEARY — Soc Gen, great card index; Loudon 1822

BIGGS — C. O Moreton, *The Auricula* (1964), 36-7

DODDS — Somerset RO, DD/SF, Books/101.i; Flor Cab, I (1833), 70

p.102 BRISTOL — information and photocopies from the City Librarian and from the City Archivist

SPIRING — Bristol AO, 12881(9)

MAULE — information kindly sent by Terence Maule Oliver esq.; Gard Chron, 17 May 1884

MILLER & SWEET — Gard Mag, XI (1835), 159; information kindly sent by Messrs. Brown & Son Seeds Ltd.; Wilts. RO, Savernake Papers; Glos. RO, D.1799/A 154; Berks. CRO, D/E By C.41

p.103 HARRIS, POOLE — Somerset RO, DD/SP, boxes 41, 42

YOUNG — Somerset RO, Tithe Map; John Wood's plan of Taunton; Gard Mag, XIX (1843), 63

p.104 HAMMOND & STEPHENS — Somerset RO, DD/SF/Books/ 101.i; John Wood's plan of Taunton; Tithe Map

FORD — J. Caldwell in *Transactions of the Devon Association,*
XCIV (1962), 411-12, Soc Gen, transcript of St. Thomas's
registers, 10235, 29907; 16065, 23984, 28019, 28255

POPE — M. Hadfield, 'Camellias at the Hawthorns', Gard
Chron, 27 Jan 1962, and details generously supplied by Mr.
Hadfield; information kindly sent by G. C. Baugh esq.

BRUNTON — Staffs. RO, D.593/F/3/2/33; Gent Mag, April
1803, 382; books of Messrs. Caldwells, Knutsford; Gard
Chron, LVIII, 318; BM, PD, Trade Card in Banks
Collection; Bodl, JJ, Trade Cards, box 18

FORBES — Notts RO, DDE/42/34

p.105   HUNTER — information from Miss Alice M. Coats and from
Birmingham City Library; books of Caldwells, Knutsford

HUBBARD — Northants RO, I.L.4153; Leics RO, will of 25
June 1785 proved 14 Feb 1787, from the County Archivist

TURNBULL — Northants RO, YZ 4767 q1-5, 4768 kl-3;
Warwicks RO, CR 1355

MURRAY — Burghley House muniments, from information
kindly supplied by Dr E. C. Till; Lincs AO, 3 Anc 6/24, 25

MADDOCK — *Lincoln, Rutland and Stamford Mercury,* 13
Nov 1801

CHAPTER VII

p.107   FOREST TREES — J. H. Harvey, 'Forest Trees and their
Prices before 1850', *Quarterly Journal of Forestry,* LXVII
(1973), 20-37

HAMMOND — Rugeley parish registers, from information
kindly sent by Douglas Johnson esq.; books of Caldwells,
Knutsford

p.108   PLANT — Flor Cab, III, 239, 273-4; IV, 179, 216; V, 72

WELTON — Staffs. RO, D.543/E/25

HAYWOOD — Staffs RO, D.593/F/3/2/85, 86

SMITH — information from the Borough Librarian, Burton-
upon-Trent

PEARSON — Flor Cab, VIII (1840), 68, 94; will, York Wills,
Reg. 171, f. 197; JRHS, XIII.i (1891), adverts., 7; Bodl, JJ,
Billheads, box 13; Gard Chron, 1876.ii, 278-9, 290-1

p.109   ORDOYNO — Borthwick Institute, York Wills, April 1796;
July 1812; R. P. Shilton, *The History of Newark-
upon-Trent* (1820), 201-2; Soc Gen, great card index;
GLRO, B/HRS/3; T. M. Blagg, *Newark as a Publishing
Town* (1898); information from the Borough Librarian

p.110   SAXE — Bodl, JJ, Trade Cards, box 1; Notts RO, DDE/42/38

PENNELL — Lincs AO, deposited records; information kindly

supplied by Messrs. Pennell and by Lincoln City Librarian
WOOD — Lincs AO, 3 Anc 6/25; GLRO, B/HRS/3
CROWDER — information kindly supplied by W. A. B.
Crowder, esq.
ROGERS — books of Caldwells, Knutsford; will, Cheshire RO,
WS.1799 (see Appendix VI)

p.111 DICKSON — Gard Chron, 1866, 272; Flor Cab, III (1835),
117-18; VII (1839), 287
MULLOCK — books of Caldwells, Knutsford

p.112 VICKERS — B. Maund, *The Fruitist*, no. 10 (1846)
MORLEY — L. T. Smith ed., *The Itinerary of John Leland*
(1907/1964), IV, 7
KNUTSFORD — books preserved by Messrs. Caldwells; a
highly compressed version of a detailed study which it is
hoped to publish later
NICKSON — Cheshire RO, Knutsford parish register, P7/1/4;
DET/Acc. 1424/5, no. 44; Sessions Book, 27a, p. 182; will,
WS.1809 April; will of Margaret Nickson, WS.1823 March

p.113 PICKEN — Gard Mag, XII (1836), 164

p.115 CUNNINGHAM — Brown Library, Liverpool: James Hoult,
'Notes and Articles on Local History'; Paxton's *Magazine of
Botany*, IV (1836), 5
WHALLEY — books of Caldwells, Knutsford
BLUNDELL — will, Lancs RO, 1798 April
RAFFALD — wills, Cheshire RO, WI.1790 Sep; WS.1805 Dec

p.116 McNIVEN — wills, Lancs RO, 1815 June; 1818 March; R.
Webber, *The Early Horticulturists* (1968), 112

p.117 HENDERSON, FURNASS — Westmorland RO, Morland MSS.
SANDER — H. V. Taylor, *The Apples of England* (1948), 138;
E. Hughes, *North Country Life in the 18th century*, II
(1965), 237
CLARK — Bodl, JJ, Silviculture; West Riding Deeds Registry,
Wakefield, EU 245.315; FP 87.85; books of Caldwells,
Knutsford; Westmorland RO, Morland MSS., bills 1798,
1800
GREENER — E. Hughes, *North Country Life . . .* , II (1965),
236; Royal Agricultural Society, Pamphlets, vols. 132, 135
DICKSON — E. Hughes, loc. cit.; R. Agr. Soc., Pamphlets,
vols. 132, 135; Durham CRO, D/Sa/E 746.3

p.118 HANKS — Westmorland RO, WD/Rad/Morland MSS, bills
1798; West Riding Deeds Registry, Wakefield, EU 246.316;
GN 108.86; J. Tomlinson, *Doncaster* (1887), 259
LITTLEWOOD — J. Tomlinson, *Doncaster*, 258-9; will, York
Wills, Prerogative Oct. 1825; vol. 172, 171; West Riding
Deeds Registry, IN 296.280
FISHER & Co. — Flor Cab, I, 216; III, 213; Paxton's *Magazine*

of Botany, III (1836), 1, 147; J. Hunter, *Hallamshire* (ed.
A. Gatty, 1869), 490

p.119   MARTIN — information from Hull City Library and from Mr
J. R. Whitehouse

PHILIPSON — *Hull Advertiser*, 31 Aug 1811, p. 2; 14 March
1812;.books of Caldwells, Knutsford

TINDALL — East Riding RO, (Pennington-Ramsden)
DDWA/10/94; /6/95; DDBC/16/368, 423; /17/36; /20/9;
/30/454-66; /37/65; G. Oliver, *Beverley* (1829), 295-7, 419;
G. Poulson, *Beverlac* (1829), II, 782-3; information from
Beverley town records, kindly sent by the Borough
Librarian and by David Neave, esq.

p.120   BEAN — Lincs AO, Monson 11/37; *Journal of the Society for
the Bibliography of Natural History*, VI.3 (1972), 152-61; I
am greatly obliged to R. G. C. Desmond, esq. for this
reference

HARTLEPOOL — R. Surtees, *Durham*, Hartlepool vol. (1910),
132

CLARKE — W. Roberts in Gard Chron. LXII, 135-6

p.121   CALLENDERS — Northumberland CRO, Delaval MSS, 650 K

JOYCE — Durham University, wills 1767; Edinburgh Register
House, Exchequer: Forfeited Estates, E 730/31/5,
information for which I am grateful to Miss P. Minay; Soc
Gen, Apprentices 1763-74 (57/132)

p.122   DALE — Gateshead Central Library, Cotesworth MSS,
CN/9/111; information from newspapers etc. kindly sent
by the Borough Librarian; Durham CRO, Vane deposit
(1780); will, Durham University, wills 1781

p.123   FALLA — Gateshead Central Library, Durham Marriage Bonds
(typescript); Durham CRO, Vane deposit (1776);
Gateshead Library, Cotesworth MSS, CA/15/17; Hebburn
Estate Rentals; Ellison MSS., EB/12/71; wills, Durham
University 1804 June; 1830 Dec; 1832 April; 1837 Dec;
information kindly sent by the Borough Librarian,
Gateshead, and by Trevor Falla, esq.; V.C.H., *Durham*, II
(1907), 381; Durham CRO, D/Sa/C.123.2, 3; R. Surtees,
Durham, Gateshead vol. (1909), 43; E. Mackenzie & M.
Ross, *View of Co. Durham*, I (1834), 105; Gateshead
Library, Brockett MSS, vol. IV, 145; Sykes, 'Local
Records', vol. III, 57

EPILOGUE

p.129   MADDOCK — Friends House, information kindly sent by the
Librarian; Newington Library, Rate Books; J. Edwards,
Companion . . . , 10

CURTIS — *Botanical Magazine*, I-XIV

DAVEY — Loudon 1822; books of Caldwells, Knutsford; T. Faulkner, *Chelsea and its Environs* (1829), II, 162-3; Flor Cab, I, 95, 183-4; II, 48

WATSON — Islington Central Library, Rate Books; Willson 1961, 26-7; will of William Watson, PCC 119 Dodwell, PRO Prob 11/1229

p.130 COLVILL — Chelsea Rate Books, from the Librarian; MinL, Colvill archive 1797-1835 (Deeds IV/39); will of James Colvill (II), PCC 621 Tenterden, PRO Prob 11/1806; Gard Mag, VIII (1832), 256

SWEET — Gard Mag, XI (1835), 159

WHITLEY — GLRO, B/HRS/50; Gard Mag, XI (1835), 160; *Horticultural Journal*, III (1835), 79-80

FRASER — Hadfield, 289-90; A. M. Coats, *The Quest for Plants* (1969), 281-5, 340; Chelsea Rate Books, from the Librarian; BM, PD, Banks Collection (trade card in Russian, English and French)

MACKIE, BASSINGTON — Islington Central Library, Rate Books

BUNNEY — Paxton's *Magazine of Botany*, II (1835), 75, 186; IV (1837), 75; W. Robinson, *History of Hackney*, I (1842), 6-7; R. Gorer, *The Development of Garden Flowers* (1970), 149

BARR — Islington Central Library, Rate Books; Loudon 1822

ROLLISON — Loudon 1822; Gard Mag, III, 362; VI, 620; XVIII, 12, 336; Wandsworth, West Hill Library, information kindly supplied by the Local History Librarian

NAPIER & CHANDLER — Flor Cab, I (1833), 24; Paxton's *Magazine of Botany*, IV (1837), 114-15; Gard Mag, III, 126; X, 279; XIX, 373

HAIRS — F. Birrell ed., *Diary of a Scotch Gardener at the French Court* (1931), 132-4, 136, 138; Surrey RO, Land Tax returns, from information sent by R. G. C. Desmond esq.

COLEMAN — Haringey Borough Libraries, Tottenham Rate Books, from the Controller; Middlesex RO, Acc. 695/7, pp. 24, 38, 290; will, PCC 717 Ely, PRO Prob 11/1485

CROMBIE & CORMACK — Gard Mag, VI, 379; XIX, 65; Bodl, JJ, Trade Cards, box 1

p.131 RIGG — York City Library, newspaper index; Borthwick Inst., York Wills, Reg. 188, f.100; Reg. 1835 pt. i, f. 266; R. Davies, *The Freeman's Roll* (York, 1835); books of Caldwells, Knutsford; Loudon 1822; *Transactions of the Yorkshire Agricultural Society*, no. 8 (1845), 131

BARRATT — Cusworth Hall Museum, Goodchild Loan MSS,

box Misc. 45; box Misc. Local Govt.; information kindly
sent by John Goodchild, esq; Flor Cab, II (1834), 176-80,
202-3, 218-19; III (1835), 84-5, 93, 116, 181, 290-1; IV
(1836), 107; V (1837), 12, 72, 140-1, 202

p.132   ELY — Flor Cab, XI (1843), 245, 250-8; *Parish Registers of
Rothwell* (Yorks. P. R. S., XXVII, XXXIV, LI); Borthwick
Institute, York Wills, original Aug. 1843 (Pontefract)

BONNOR — Cal SPDom 1611-18

p.133   BARTERAM — Huguenot Soc. Library, G. L. Gwynn, 'Notes
on Huguenot Gardeners', quoting return in BM, Lansdowne
MS. 202

VERBADHOME — NL Wales, Wynnstay MS. 167, f. 3v

COBBETT — Gard Mag, III, 363

INDEX

This index includes all names and main subjects except plants in the body of Appendix IV. Scientific identification is not attempted; it is, therefore, necessary to search, e.g. both under *Delphinium* and Larkspur for plants of the same genus. For biographical material see the collected entries Artists, Botanists, and Gardeners etc.; see also collected entries Books and Journals; and Nurseries.

'Abeal', abele, 'arbeal' — see Poplar
Aberford, Yorks., 85
Abies alba, 147
——— ———*nana*, 111
Acacia, 96, 146
——— Triple-thorned, 202, 205
   See also Robinia
Acanthus mollis, 139
Acer, 96, 141
——— *saccharinum*, 94
Ache, 140
Achillea millefolium, 144
Ackres, George, 55
——— Thomas, 55
Aconite, 146
Adcock, John, linenweaver, 69
Adder's Tongue, 139, 142
Addlestone, Surrey, 97
Advertisement, 91-2, 113
Aeonium arboreum, 146
Aesculus hippocastanum, 146
——— *pavia*, 151
Africa, South, Plates 9, 12, 15
Agnus castus, 205
Agricultural seeds, 82, 98, 100
Agriculture, Board of, 80, 98
——— ——— ——— of Sweden, 98
Agrimonia eupatoria, 142
Agrimony, 142
Ailesbury, earl of, 88, 98, 100

Aislabie, John, 66, 85
Ajuga reptans, 142
Alaternus, 96, 147, 194
Alcester, Warwicks., 192
Aldbourne, Wilts., 12, 49, 77n.
Alder, 96, 141
Alexanders, 20, 142
'Aleys' — see Service
Allington, lord, 46
Allium ampeloprasum porrum, 142
——— *ascalonicum*, 142
——— *cepa*, 142
——— *sativum*, 142
Almond, 18, 96, 165, 170, 178, 179, 182, 205
——— dwarf, 147, 202, 205
Alnus, 96
——— *glutinosa*, 141
Alnwick, Northumberland, 124
Aloe, American, 49
Alpine plants, 2, 111, 115
Alpinia officinarum, 19
Alps, 2
Althaea, 143
——— *cretica*, 139
——— *officinalis*, 139
——— *rosea*, 139
Althea frutex, 95, 134, 139n., 147, 165, 172, 181, 182, 202, 205
Alton, Hants., 129

Amaryllis, 101
Ambleside, Westmorland, 117
America, 19, 115, 119
—— North, 2, 51, 96; Plate 11
American Independence, War of, 130
Amesbury Wilts., 12, 46, 54
Amherst, Alicia (Lady Rockley), x, 138, 139, 140
Amygdala flore Africano, 147
Amigdalus, 96
Amomum Plinii, 146
Ampthill, Beds., 82, 98
Anagallis arvensis, 140, 143
—— *monelli*, 103
Ancient Society of York Florists, 38, 69, 96
Andover, Hants., 101
Andrews, Henry Charles (fl. 1794-1833), 100
Androsaemum, 96
Anemone, 56, 92, 115, 145, 148, 172, 175
Anemone coronaria, 148
Anemone Spermos, 150
Angelica Tree, 205
Anglo-Saxon period, 16, 34, 60
Anise, 18, 30
Anne queen of England, Plate 6 of Bohemia, queen of England, 34
Anthemis nobilis, 142
Antwerp, 17, 27, 31
Apium, 140, 143
—— *graveolens*, 139, 140, 142
Apple, 18, 21, 28, 31, 41, 46, 56, 67, 68, 73, 85, 101, 116, 117, 123, 138, 141, 145, 149, 163-4, 165, 172, 178, 179, 182
—— Blandurel, 34
—— Crab, 163
—— double-flowering, 95
—— Golden Pippin, 62
—— Keswick Codlin, 117
—— Paradise stock, 101, 172, 178, 179, 182
—— Ribston Pippin, 120
—— stocks, 164, 165

Apprenticeships to gardening, 101, 133
Apricot, 28, 41, 44, 46, 62, 67, 73, 98, 101, 116, 149, 165, 172, 182, 187, 189
Aquifolium, 96
Aquitaine, 34
Aragon, 34
Arbor Judae, 202, 205
Arbor Vitae, Canada, 206
—— —— ('Arbervita'), Chinese, 194, 206
—— —— common, 105, 165, 206
—— —— sweet-scented Chinese, 105
Arboretum, 89
Arboriculture, 15, 22
   See also Forestry
Arbour, 16, 25-6, 30, 40
Arbutus, 79, 96, 194, 202, 205
Archives, nurserymen's, x, 9-10, 94, 110
Arctotis aspera, 150
Arderne, John (fl. 1349-78), surgeon, 18, 19, 20, 135, 139, 140
Aria Theophrasti — see Whitebeam
Aristolochia clematitis, 19
Arlington, earl of, 54
Arsesmart, 139
Artemisia abrotanum, 18, 143
—— *absinthium*, 144
—— *vulgaris*, 143
Artichoke, 19, 60
——, Jerusalem, 126
Artists, botanical, 54, 88
   See also Andrews, Danckerts, Edwards, Frankcom, Lavorgne, London (Henrietta), Merian
Arum maculatum 139
Ash tree, 21, 67, 68, 119, 138, 141
—— Flowering, 205
—— French, 189
—— Mountain, 205
Ashley, Staffs., 70
Ashley, J., 94
Ashton, Nicholas, 118

Index

Asparagus, 4, 48, 100, 173
Aspen, 141
Asperula odorata, 144
Asphodel, Red, 148
——— Yellow, 148
Asphodeline lutea, 148
Asphodelus fistulosus, 148
Aster, China, 190
Aster grandiflorus, 151
Aston Subedge, Glos., 191
'Astralogia longa, rotunda', 19
Atamasco Lily, 150
Atriplex hortensis, 143
Auricula, 1, 2, 43, 50, 71, 81, 92,
    101, 115, 121, 145, 148, 172,
    190
Australia, 8, 9, 100; Plate 10
Avens, 142
Avenues, 1, 75
Azalea, 109
——— Pontic, 130; Plate 16 .
Azarole, Red, 205
——— Yellow, 205
Azedarach, 51

Babbes, Richard, poulterer, 168
Babur (1483-1530), Mogul emperor,
    15
Bachelor's Button, Purple, 95
Bacon, John, 77
Baker, Colonel, 101
Ball, Thomas, 72
Balsam, 173
——— double, 190
Bankruptcies, 10, 86, 90-1, 127, 160
Banks, Sir Joseph, 66
——— William, 66
Banksia serrata, Plate 10
Banqueting house, 33
Barberry, 46, 165, 172, 202, 205
Barbour, John, capper, 168
Barking, Essex, 84, 167
Barkley, Mr, 168
Barley, ix
Barnet, Herts., 86, 97, 128

Basil, 173
——— Sweet, 188, 190
Basketmaking, 40
Bath, Som., 6, 191
Batho, Mr G. R., 59
Battersea — see London
Bawtry, Yorks., 110
Baxter, Dudley, 191-2
Bay, Sweet (Laurel), 18, 32, 73, 105,
    141, 147, 164, 165, 194, 205
Bead Tree, 51
Beale, John, 70, 71
Bean, ix, 20, 138, 176
——— Broad, 141
——— Guinea, 191
——— Scarlet, 188
——— Windsor, 176
Bean Tree, French, 151
Bean, William (1787-1866),
    geologist, 120
Beaufort, duke of, xiii; Plate 9
Beaulieu (New Hall), Essex, 29
Bedale, Yorks., 95, 124
Bedford, 98
Bedford, earls and dukes of, xiii, 45,
    47, 49, 53, 55, 58
Bedfordshire, 54, 98
Beech, 68, 119, 141, 165, 183, 184,
    190, 194, 195, 205, 206
——— Brown, 115
Beet, 20, 138, 173, 183, 184, 208
Belford, Northumberland, 124
Bellflower, 149
——— Steeple, 148
Bell-flowered Tree, dwarf, 151
Bellis perennis, 142
Benjamin Tree, 205
Bermuda Cedar, 51
Berwick-upon-Tweed, 124
Betony, 142
Betula, 141
Beverley, Yorks., 69, 119-20
Bewdley, Worcs., 5
Bible in English, 28
Biggleswade, Beds., 99
Bigold, 142

Bills, prompt payment of, 69
Birch, 68, 111, 141, 165, 190
Bird's-Eye, 151
Birmingham, 89, 95, 104-5, 107, 113, 118
Birthwort, 19
Blackett, Sir Edward, Bart., 68
Blackmore, R. D., 133
Bladder-nut, five-leaved, 165, 205
——— ——— three-leaved, 205
Blair, James, 108
Blathwayt, William, 102
Blenheim Palace, Oxon., 75
Blith, Walter, improver, 63
Blyth, Notts., 68, 160-4
Bog plants, 102, 115
Bolas — see Bullace
Bolsover, Derbyshire, 108
Books, botanical, 54, 109
——— by nurserymen, 93-4
Books and Journals cited:-
    Abstract of North American Trees (Lawson), 87
    Adam in Eden (Coles), 44
    Agricultural History Review, 160
    A most briefe and plesaunt treatyse (Hill), 30
    Beverlac (Poulson), 120
    Botanical Cabinet (Loddiges), 89, 92
    Botanical Magazine (Curtis), 12, 129, 130; Plates 12, 13, 14, 16
    Botanist's and Gardener's New Dictionary (Wheeler), 93
    Botanist's Repository (Andrews), 100; Plates 11, 15
    Britannia (Camden), 65
    Catalogus Plantarum, 5, 38, 77, 78, 80
    Chronicles (Holinshed), 23
    City Gardener (Fairchild), 49, 77, 150
    Compleat Florist, 77
    Complete Seedsman (Townsend), 82
    Complete Treatise on Land

    Surveying, 113
    Coniferous Plants (Knight & Perry), 111
    Cumberland Pacquet, 118
    Curious and Profitable Gardener (Cowell), 49
    Description of England (Harrison), 23
    Development of Garden Flowers (Gorer), xi
    Dictionary of Gardening (R.H.S.), xi, 138, 145
    Dutch Florist (Thompson), 121
    Early Gardening Catalogues (Harvey), 66, 96, 97, 135, 145, 201
    Early Horticulturists (Webber), 116
    Eboracum (Drake), 65
    Encyclopaedia of Gardening (Loudon), x, 8
    English Flower Garden (Robinson), 2
    English Gardener (Meager), 4
    English Vineyard Vindicated (Rose), 46
    Essay upon Gardening (Steele), 112, 119, 125
    Feat of Gardening (John Gardener), 18, 22, 138
    Flora, Ceres and Pomona (Rea), 43
    Flora Londinensis (Curtis), 80
    Flora of Nottinghamshire (Ordoyno), 109, 110
    Floral Calendar (Mangles), 8
    Floricultural Cabinet (Harrison), 103, 108, 111
    Florist's Vade Mecum (Gilbert), 69
    Flower Garden Display'd (Furber), 81
    Forest Pruner (Pontey), 93
    Fruit Cultivator (Rogers), 99
    Fruitist (Maund), 112
    Garden History (G.H.S.), xii, xiii, 135

Gardener to Queen Anne (Green), 150
Gardener's Chronicle, 8, 202
Gardener's Daily Assistant (Abercrombie), 7, 196-200
Gardener's Dictionary (Miller), 65, 78, 82, 84, 87, 160, 171
Gardener's and Florist's Dictionary (Miller), 78, 79, 80
Gardener's Magazine (Loudon), 88
Gardener's Universal Calendar (Whitmill), 49
General View of the Agriculture of Hampshire (Driver), 80
Gentleman's Magazine, xiii
Guide to the Orchard and Kitchen Garden (Lindley), 93
Herball (Gerard), 30, 43, 139, 145
History and Antiquities of the Town and Minster of Beverley (Oliver), 120
History of British Gardening (Hadfield), xi, 76, 116
History of Chipping Campden (Whitfield), 191
History of Gardening in England (Amherst), x
Hortus Kewensis (Aiton), 128
Hull Advertiser, 119
Improved System of Nursery Gardening (Haynes), 93
Introduction to Botany (Lee), 93
James Lee and the Vineyard Nursery (Willson), xi, 84
Journal Kew Guild, xiii
Journal R.H.S., 151
Kalendarium Hortense (Evelyn), 47
Kalm's Account of his Visit to England (Lucas), xiii
Kit and Kitty (Blackmore), 133
Leeds Mercury, 93
Life in a Noble Household (Thomson), 53
Lincoln, Rutland & Stamford

Mercury, 106
London Gazette, 64
Lorna Doone (Blackmore), 133
Magazine of Botany (Paxton), 103
Manchester Gooseberry Book, 112
Manner of Raising, Ordering and Improving Forest Trees (Cook), 52
Metamorphosis Insectorum Surinamensium (Merian), 54
Monthly Register of Experiments . . . (Bradley), 150-1
Museum Rusticum, 67, 87
New Method of Propagating Fruit-trees and Flowering Shrubs (Barnes), 93
New Orchard and Garden (Lawson), Plate 3
Newcastle Chronicle, 125
Nobleman, Gentleman and Gardener's Recreation (Switzer), 51
Nurseries, Orchards, Profitable Gardens and Vineyards encouraged (Beale & Lawrence), 70
Old Shrub Roses (Thomas), 202
Oxford English Dictionary, 47
Oxford Journal (Jackson's), 62
Page's Prodromus (Kennedy), 100
Paradisus Terrestris (Parkinson), 86
Philosophical Transactions (Royal Society), 77
Plain and practical Treatise on the culture and management of the Auricula (Emmerton), 86
Pomona (Evelyn), 47
Pomona Britanica (Driver), 80
Practical Husbandman and Planter, 65, 66, 77, 87
Practical Treatise of Lucern (Rocque), 93
Profitable Planter (Pontey), 93
Pyrus Malus Brentfordiensis

(Ronalds), 88

Quarterly Journal of Forestry,
201

Rhodon and Iris, 37

Romaunt of the Rose, 18, 138

Rural Improver (Pontey), 93

*Short Hints on Ornamental
Gardening* (Forbes), 126

Short Introduction to Gardening
(Furber), 53, 77, 78, 80, 84

Sylva (Evelyn), 47, 63

*Synonoma de nominibus
herbarum* (Bray), 19

Systema Horti-Culturae
(Woolridge), 5, 145-9

Theatrum Botanicum (Parkinson),
86

Theory and Practice of Gardening
(James), 80

Tradescants, The (Allan), 145

*Treatise on the Culture and
Management of Fruit-trees*
(Forsyth), 116

*Treatise on the Culture of the
Pineapple* (Speechly), 96, 118,
207

*Treatise on the Culture of the
Vine* (Speechly), 105, 108,
113, 118, 125, 207

Treatise on Forest Trees
(Boutcher), 121

Treatise of Fruit-Trees (Austen),
63

Treatise of Fruit-Trees (Hitt), 82

*Treatise on Grasses and the
Norfolk Willow* (North), 87

Treatise upon Planting (Kennedy),
85, 92, 95-6, 109

Troy Book (Lydgate), 24-5, 33

Twelve Months of Flowers
(Furber), 78, 121

Universal British Directory, 103

Vegetable Cultivator (Rogers), 99

York Courant, 64, 92

Borage, 18, 20, 142

Borago officinalis, 142

Botanical artists — see Artists

Botanists, 11-12, 37, 113
    for individuals, see Gardeners etc.,
        and Burchell, W. J.; Catesby;
        Collinson, P.; Hailstone;
        Jackson; Johnson; Lindley;
        Linnaeus; Lyte; Maund;
        Morgan; Ordoyno; Turner;
        Watson

Botany, 9

Bottesford, Leics., 83

Bourton on the Water, Glos., 192

Bower, 25-6

Box, 105, 141, 163, 165, 194, 202
––– Dutch, 164
––– striped, 205

Boynd, Mr, 176

Bradbury, John, 112

Bradley, Richard, 77, 150-1

Bramston, Anthony, 55
––– Sir John, 55

Branke ursine, 139

Brassica nigra, 143
––– *oleracea,* 142

Bray, John (d. 1381), physician, 19,
    22, 135, 140

Brayton, Yorks., 23

Brazil, 131

Breast ploughing, 192

Brechin Castle, Forfarshire, 102

Brentford, Middlesex, 59, 82, 88, 97,
    125, 128, 183

Bridlington, Yorks., 120

Bright, Richard, 102

Brisewort — see Daisy

Bristol, 5, 9, 60, 73, 102-3
––– Great Orchard, 73
––– Hobson's Gardens, 73

Broad, James, 116

Broccoli, 173, 182, 183, 184

Brome, John, 29

Bromley, Gerards, Staffs., 69-70

Brompton Park — see London, and
    under Nurseries

Bromsgrove, Worcs., 192

Broom, 202

——— Lucca ('Looker'), 205
——— Spanish, 147, 150-1, 165, 181, 182, 203, 204
——— ———, white, 150-1
Bruce, lord, 194
Buckingham, Edward Stafford duke of, 35
Buckthorn, 141
Bugle, 142
Bugloss, 140
——— Pearl, 151
Building over nurseries, 45, 84
Bulbs, ix, 1, 2, 3, 40, 43, 50, 56, 68, 69, 74, 103, 106, 114, 115, 125, 128, 148-9, 150, 172
——— Dutch, 4, 12, 75, 172
Bullace (Bolas), 18, 141
Burchell, William John (1781-1863), 79
Burghley House near Stamford, 27, 38, 105, 107
Burghley, lord — see Cecil, Sir William
Burlington, earl of, 83, 84, 167
Burnt Norton, Glos., 74, 191-3
Burslem, Staffs., 108
Burton, Lincs., 68
Burton-upon-Trent, Staffs., 108
Buttonwood (American Plane), 2
Buxus sempervirens, 141
Byfleet, Surrey, 80
Byron, lord, 109

Cabbage, 20, 21, 24, 112, 173
——— Battersea, 173
——— Early York, 131
——— Savoy, 173
Calais, 23, 33
Calamint, 142
Calamintha ascendens, 142
Calceolaria, 104, 131
Cambridge, 52, 99
Camden, William, 65
Camellia, 72, 109
Camomile, 142
Campanula, 149

Campanula pyramidalis, 148
Campden, Chipping, Glos., 73-4, 186-93
Campernello — see Jonquil
Campion, Red (Flos Campi), 142
Canals, 6-7, 106
Canarina campanula, 51
Canary Bellflower, 51
Candleberry Myrtle, 203, 206
Candytuft, Shrubby, 95
——— Tree, 151
——— White, 188
Cannabis, 35
Cannon Hall, Yorks., 98
Canons, Middlesex, 50
Cape of Good Hope, 2, 54, 100
Capel, Arthur, earl of Essex, 47, 52
Capitals, regional, 60-1
Caraway, 30
Cardinal's Flower (Lobelia), 51, 148
Cardoon, 173
Carlisle, Cumberland, 60, 117, 118
Carlton-in-Lindrick, Notts., 68
Carnation, 1, 20, 43, 76, 109, 129, 132, 139, 145, 148, 174-5, 190
Carpenter, William, 26
Carr, Henry Thomas, 177
Carrot, 24, 30, 138, 173, 176
Carshalton, Surrey, 18, 135
'Carsyndyllys', 138-9, 142
Carthamus, 19
Cary, John, Surveyor, 87
Caryll, John, 85
Caryophyllum, 139
'Cassia' — see Acacia
Cassiobury, Herts., 52
Castanea sativa, 141
Castile, 34
Castle Howard, Yorks., 38, 75, 207
Castor-oil plant, 19
Catalogues, 4, 5, 8, 38, 51, 62, 65-6, 79, 80, 85, 89, 92, 93, 94, 95, 96, 97, 98, 101, 102, 103, 108, 111, 113, 115, 116, 118, 120-1, 125, 133-4
——— book-form, 91, 103, 108, 115,

116, 120-1, 125
——— botanical, 11, 88, 89, 104, 125
——— of gooseberries, 112
——— priced, xiii, 2-3, 7, 89, 92, 93,
    104, 106, 107, 109, 113, 115,
    118, 121, 125, 129, 133-4, 201
——— scientific, 11, 93, 109
——— specialized, 89
Catalpa, 134, 205
Catapuce — see Spurge
Catesby, Mark (1679-1749), 77, 151
Catton, Norfolk, 93, 98
Cauliflower, 84, 173
Cave, Yorks., 129
Cecil, Sir William (lord Burghley), 27
Cedar, Bermuda, 205
——— Carolina, 205
——— of Lebanon (Libanus), 51, 68,
    79, 105, 147, 194, 205
——— Red, 95, 195, 205
——— White, 205
Cedrus libani, 51, 147
Celery, 140, 173
——— Wild, 139
Centaurium umbellatum (erythraea),
    139, 142
Centaury, 139, 142
Cereus, 49
Chaenomeles japonica, 102
Chandlers Ford, Hants., 99
Charlecote, Warwicks., 80
Charles I, king of England, 9, 69;
    Plate 4
——— II, 5, 45, 46, 54; Plate 1
Chaucer, Geoffrey, 17-18, 24, 33,
    138, 140
Cheadle, Staffs., 108
Cheam, Surrey, 18, 135
Checkley, Staffs., 108
Cheiranthus cheiri, 20
Chelsea — see London
Chephant, Thomas, 167
Cherry, 18, 20, 40, 41, 44, 46, 56,
    64, 67, 68, 73, 101, 116, 141,
    145, 149, 163, 165, 172, 177,
    178, 179, 182, 187, 188

——— Bird, 165
——— Black, 56
——— Cornelian, 148, 165, 181, 182
——— double-blossomed, 94, 147,
    187, 205
——— Morello, 178, 189
——— Pennsylvania, 205, 206
——— stocks, 64, 68, 163, 165
——— wild, 190
Chertsey, Surrey, 97-8, 204
Chervil, 140
Cheshire, 11, 37, 110-13
Cheshunt, Herts., 86, 97, 98
Chester, 36, 41, 113
——— Castle garden, 16, 17, 110
——— earls of, 16
——— Nuns' Gardens, 36, 110-11,
    167, 170
Chestnut, Horse, 1, 68, 146, 165,
    183, 184
——— ——— Scarlet-flowered, 151,
    205
——— Spanish, 18, 62, 67, 68, 94,
    119, 141, 163, 164, 165
Chichester, Sussex, 99
Chilwell, Notts., 108, 113, 114
China, 139
Chiswick — see London
Cholmondeley, marchioness of, Plate
    1
Chopwell Woods, Co. Durham, 125
Christ's Thorn, 147
Christmas Rose, 18
Chromosome count, 14, 131
Chrysanthemum, 130; Plate 14
——— Tree, 151
——— ——— from Carolina, 151
Chrysanthemum frutescens, 151
——— *indicum*, Plate 14
——— *segetum*, 142
Chulmleigh, Devon, 103
Church Langton — see Langton
Cinquefoil, Shrub, 202
Cistus, 202, 205
——— evergreen, 204
——— Gum, 94, 204

––– Spotted, 94
Citrus limonia, 146
––– *sinensis*, 146
Civil War, 37, 43, 44, 45, 46, 48, 61, 65, 75
Clare Castle, Suffolk, 35
Clarendon, earl of, 167
Clark, Elizabeth, 192
Clarke, John, 193
––– Sir Samuel, 81
Clary, 20, 142
––– Wild (Oculus Christi), 42
Claxton, John, 72
Clematis, 110
––– Hungarian, 157
Clematis integrifolia, 147
–*viticella*, 147
Clementhorpe, Yorks., 35
Clennell, John, 123
Clifton near Bristol, 102
Clifton, Yorks., 92
Climate, 14
Climbing plants, 76
Clove Gilliflower, 139
Coal smoke, 150
Coats, Miss A. M., xi, 57
Cobham, lord, 31
Cockington, Devon, 102
Coddington, Notts., 109
Coddrington family, 102
Colchester, Essex, 5, 71, 96, 106
Colchicum, 43, 148
Colchicum autumnale, 148
Colewort, 142
Collectors, 130, 131
Collinson, Peter (1694-1768), botanist, 86
Columbine, 188
Colutea, Ethiopian, 205
––– Oriental, 205
Colutea arborescens, 146, 165
Colutea odorata, 146
Coma Aurea, 151
Comfrey, 142
Compton, Henry, bishop of London, 54, 55, 68, 71, 75, 78

Convolvulus minor, 188
Cook, Captain Edward, 52
––– Rev. Moses, 53
Cooke, John, 22
Corbet, Richard, bishop, 42
Coriander, 18, 30, 142
Coriandrum sativum, 142
Cork Tree, 205
Corn, 138
Cornbury, Oxon., 167
Cornel (Wippeltree), 141
Cornus mas, 148, 165
––– *sanguinea*, 141
Coronilla emerus, 147, 165
––– *valentina*, 146
Coronopus squamatus, 144
Corydalis cava, 151
Corylus avellana, 141
Cottingham, Yorks., 113, 119
Cotyledon decussata, xiii
Courgette – see Custard Marrow
Coutances, Normandy, 15, 22
Coventry, Warwicks., 36, 74, 94-5, 113, 114, 192
–––Charterhouse, 36, 74
Cowpen, Northumberland, 123
Cowslip, 20, 98, 142
Crab, 163
––– stocks, 68
Crataegus, 141
Creake, Norfolk, 60, 98
Cress, 20, 139, 142
Crewkerne, Som., 5, 71
Crimes against nurseries, 62, 64
Crocus, 101, 149, 189
––– Dutch, 172
Crocus sativus, 143
Crofton, Robert, 42
Cromwell, Oliver, 43, 75
Crosse, Peter, 169
Crown Imperial, 172
Croxdale, Co. Durham, 85
Crusades, xiii, 139
Cucumber, 'Cumr', 4, 24, 29, 30, 173, 175, 182, 183, 184, 189
Cullen, viscount, 167

Cultural notes, 17, 20-2, 94, 135-7
Cumberland, 117
Cumin, 60
Cupressus sempervirens, 147
Currant, 20, 56, 67, 101, 123, 149,
    165, 172, 178, 179, 182
——— Black, 187
——— Flowering, 131-2
——— Gooseberry-leaved, 202
Curwen, John Christian, 117
Custard Marrow (Courgette, Meakin),
    173
Cusworth Hall, Yorks., 86, 97
Cutberdole and Cutbertill, 139
Cuttings (slips), 19, 25, 60, 136-7
Cydonia oblonga, 141
Cyperus longus, 19
Cypress, 32, 46, 56, 57, 73, 79, 105,
    147, 165, 194, 206
——— Virginian, 206
Cytisus, 181, 182
——— lunatus, 146
——— secundus Clusii, 147, 202
Cytisus sessilifolius, 147

Dacre, Mr, 60
Daffodil, 20, 142
Dahlia, 115
Daisy (Brisewort), 142
——— see also Michaelmas Daisy
Dalhousie, earls of, 102
Damson, 29, 64, 165, 178, 179, 182
Danckerts, Henry, painter, 54; Plate 1
Daniells, Bartholomew, 132-3
Danyell, Henry, O. P., 17, 34
Daphne laureola, 143
——— *mezereum*, 147
Darlington, Co. Durham, 123
Date, 18, 21
Daventry, Northants., 94, 105
Davis, William, 113
Dawley Lodge, Middlesex, 81
Delany (Pendarves), Mrs, 78, 91
Delaval, lord, 121
Delphinium chinense, 100
Denbigh, 112

Derby, 69, 108
Devil's bit scabious, 140
Dézallier d'Argenville, Antoine
    Joseph — see Le Blond
Dianthus caryophyllus, 20, 142, 148
Dickenson, John, master mariner,
    175
Dictamnus albus, 148
Diervilla ('Deavila'), 203, 205
Digitalis purpurea, 142
Dill, 18, 139
Dipsacus sylvestris, 144
Directories, 3, 7-8
Dissolution of monasteries, x, 36, 39,
    59
Distilled waters, 29
Ditcheat, Som., 47
Ditchley Park, Oxon., 62
Dittander, 139, 142
Dittany, 139, 142
Ditton, Long, Surrey, 55; Plate 1
Dixon, William, 96
Doddington, Cheshire, 112
Dodecatheon meadia, 99
Dodington, Glos., 102
Dominican Order, ix, 34
Doncaster, Yorks., 36, 86, 96, 110,
    118, 119
Dorking, Surrey, 97
Doronicum pardalianches, 146
Downham, Norfolk, 46
Dracunculus vulgaris, 139
Drake, Francis, 65
Drawings of plants, 54, 128, 129
Dumfries, Scotland, xiii
Duncan, James, 121
Dunn, Daniel, 79
Dunstable, Beds., 34
Durham, 22, 35, 175
——— bishop of, 23
——— cellarer of, 32, 35
Durham, earl of, 126
Dwarf (bush) trees, 57, 117
Dyrham Park, Glos., 102

East Anglia, 98-9

Easter, High, Essex, 23
Eblet, Mr, 125
Ebrington, Glos., 73, 186n.
Ebulus, 140
Echium vulgare, 140
Eden, Garden of, 14
Edinburgh, 3, 66, 69
Edward I, king of England, 16, 18, 24, 40, 63
——— III, 19
——— IV, 24
——— VI, 40
Edwards, Sydenham, Plate 16
Egerton, Hugh, 168
Eglin, Mr, 52
Egypt, 19
Elaeagnus angustifolia, 146
Elden, Robert, 63
Elder, dwarf, 140
Eleanor of Castile, queen of England, 34
——— of Provence, 34
Elecampane (Horsel), 142
Elford, Richard, 54
Elizabeth I, queen of England, 27, 42
Ellison, Cuthbert, 122, 126
——— Henry, 82, 93, 122, 124, 171-85
Elm, 31, 60, 62, 64, 67, 68, 74, 119, 141, 163-4, 165-6, 194
——— Dutch, 119, 165, 178, 179, 182
——— Exeter, 104
——— Wych, 163, 165, 190
——— yellow, 165
Eltham, Kent, 84
——— Palace, 29
Ely, Matthew, 132
Emildon, Northumberland, 65
Endive, 173
Enniskillen, lord, 115
Epilobium angustifolium, 151
Erfurt, Germany, 8n.
Erica ampullacea, Plate 12
Erythrina crista-galli, 131
Erythrolena conspicua, 108

Essex, 141
Essex, earl of, 47, 52
Euphorbia lathyrus, 143
Evelyn, John, 37, 44, 47, 52-3, 63, 93, 94
Evergreens, 51, 68, 81, 86, 94, 101, 111, 119, 126, 146, 147, 181, 201
Evesham, Worcs., 193
Ewell, Surrey, 42
Exeter, 5, 6, 9, 60, 71, 104, 106, 132, 193
——— Horticultural Society, 38
Exeter, earl of, 105
Exotics, x, 1, 49, 51, 52, 54, 55, 58, 67, 72, 75, 79, 84, 89, 128, 129, 130
Experimental agriculture and horticulture, ix, 17
Exploration, x, 8, 9, 15, 79
Eyre, Francis, 85, 91
Eyres, William, printer, 116

Fagus ferruginea, 115
——— *grandifolia,* 115
——— *sylvatica,* 141
Fairchild, John (d. 1668), 49, 77n.
Falla, Myler (c. 1808-1881), 125
——— Mr Trevor, 124
Falladon, Northumberland, 65
Fanshaw, Sir Thomas, 167
Farlam, Cumberland, 22
Feasts of florists etc., 37, 50, 90
Felling Hall, Co. Durham, 126
Felwort, 142
Fennel, 142
Fens, draining of, 11
Ferns, 89
Fig, 18, 21, 46, 101, 165
——— Indian, 146
Filbert, 29, 73, 178, 180, 182
Financial backing of nurseries, 10, 12-13, 128
Fir, 18, 68, 73, 105, 111, 141, 163-4
——— Balm of Gilead, 195, 205
——— Black Spruce, 205

—— Hemlock Spruce, 205
—— Norway, 147
—— Scotch — see Pine, Scots
—— Silver, 147, 165, 194, 206
—— Spanish, 56, 57
—— Spruce, 46, 56, 81, 85, 94,
   118, 165, 187, 194, 195, 205
—— White Spruce, 205
Fisher, Christopher, 132
Fisherton, Wilts., 101
Fitzwater, Charles, 175, 181
—— Jo., 181
Fitzwilliam, earl, Plates 2, 3
Flanders, 30
Flintshire, 110
Florence Court, Ireland, 115
Florists, 1, 4, 6, 15, 37, 38, 42-3, 48,
   69, 86, 91, 92, 112, 120, 121,
   129, 131, 132, 150
Florists' Flowers, 1, 15, 30, 62, 129
Flos Campi — see Campion, Red
Foeniculum vulgare, 142
Forest trees, 1, 15, 16, 17-18, 22, 23,
   31, 58, 65, 86, 87, 96, 101, 102,
   103, 107, 110, 111, 118, 119,
   121, 126, 138, 141, 201
Forestry, 35
   See also Arboriculture
Fosse Way, 6
Foxglove, 20, 142
Fragaria vesca, 143
Frampton Cotterell, Glos., 73
France, 17, 28, 30, 57, 59n., 60,
   110, 135
Francklyn, Sir John, 60
Frankcom, Daniel (fl. 1700-05), xiii
Fraxinella, 148
Fraxinus excelsior, 141
French Willow, 151
Friars, ix, x, 17
Fritillaria, 149
Fritillary, 149
'Fromond' list of plants, 18, 19, 135,
   139
Fruit, 1, 16, 20, 29, 35, 36, 40, 45,
   59n., 60, 65, 80, 88, 112

—— trees, 22, 23, 41, 42, 45, 48,
   53, 58, 60, 61, 62, 63, 68, 70, 81,
   82-3, 85, 98, 100-1, 102, 103,
   106, 111, 116, 117, 119, 121,
   123, 125, 138, 141, 145, 177-80
Fruiterer, 4, 16, 120
Fuchsia, 130, 131
Fuchsia elegans, 119
—— *magellanica globosa*, 119
Fulham — see London
Fumaria officinalis, 142
Fumitory, 142

Gale, Sweet, 202
Galingale, 19
Garden design, 9
Garden History Society, xii
Gardeners, 16-17, 92
   for individuals, see below
Gardeners, Nurserymen, Seedsmen
   Abercrombie, John (1726-1806),
      7, 196
   Adams, Charles (fl. 1770), 124
   Adamson, —— (fl. 1786), 196
   Adcock, John (fl. 1733-84), 69
   —— William (fl. 1740-84), 69
   Agnis (Agnes), John (fl.
      1771-1808), 71
   —— Robert (d. 1782), 71
   —— Thomas (d. 1733), 71
   Aiton, William (1731-1793), 128
   —— William Townsend
      (1766-1849), 128
   Allerton, Joseph (fl. 1733), 87
   Allport, G. & J., 196
   —— George (fl. 1810-25), 196
   —— John (fl. 1787-1820), 114,
      196
   —— John junior (fl. 1805-30),
      200
   Alston, John (fl. 1730), 80
   Anderson, Robert (fl. 1763-82),
      65-6
   Appleby, Samuel (1806-1870),
      36, 96
   Aram, Peter (c. 1660-1735), 11,

68
——— William (c. 1689-fl. 1763),
68
Armstrong, John (fl. 1782-96),
100; Plate 15
Ashe, Thomas (fl. 1741-d. 1779),
89
Atte Watyr, John (fl. 1435), 26
Austen, Ralph (c. 1612-1676), 63,
70
Ayde, Jacob de (fl. 1546), 31

Backhouse, T. & J., 131
Bacon, Stephen (1709-1734), 77,
78, 81
Bagley & Whitlock, 198
Bailey, Elizabeth (fl. 1794-1813),
199
——— Isaac (fl. 1750-93), 199
Baker, John Totty (fl. 1723), 101
Banbury, Arnold (1598-1665),
41, 45
——— Henry (1540-1610), 40-1
——— John (d. 1561), 40
Barnes, Thomas (fl. 1758-95), 93,
121
Barnes & Callender, 93, 95, 121
Barr, Thomas (fl. 1791-1820),
130
Barratt, John (c. 1770-1829), 131
——— William (fl. 1822-41), 131-2
Barteram, Peter (fl. 1568), 133
Bartram, John (1699-1777), 133
Bassington, James (fl. 1805), 200
——— John (fl. 1780), 196
——— Thomas (fl. 1806), 130, 197
Bates, Richard (fl. 1683-86), 70
Beach, George (fl. 1786-97), 199
Bean, William (fl. 1790-d. c.
1801), 120
Beasar, ———, 43
Beaulieu, Jasper of — see Jasper
Beaumont, Guillaume (fl. 1684-d.
1730), 11, 57, 76
Beck, John & Co., 114
Bendel, John (fl. 1782-88), 196,

199
Benet, John (fl. 1427-31), 26
Bentham, John (fl. 1731), 64
Berry, John (fl. 1714-d. 1727), 73
Bert, Stephen (fl. 1729), 77
Bettridge, William (fl. 1798), 95
Bickerstaff, Thomas (fl. 1730), 80
Biggs, James (fl. 1798), 103
——— Thomas (fl. 1782-93), 101
Billings, Nathaniel (fl. c. 1640),
48
Bishop, John (fl. 1413), 26
——— William, 26
Blackwell, Charles (fl.
1688-1719), 5, 47
Blaikie, Thomas (1758-1838), 130
Blair & Co., 114
Blakesley, John (fl. 1794-1801),
105
Blundell, James (fl. 1784-d.
1798), 115
Bonnor, John (fl. 1618), 132-3
Bourne, Nathaniel (fl. 1623-27),
59
Boutcher, William (fl. 1734-81),
121
Bowstread, William (fl.
1769-1812), 196
Brames, Peter (fl. 1801-d. 1834),
79
Bridgeman, Charles (fl. 1795), 98
Brinkworth, ——— (fl. 1786),
196
Brockbank, Thomas (fl. 1795),
117
Broke, Gerom Somme de (fl.
1546), 31
Brookes, Samuel (fl. 1805-32),
130
Brown, Lancelot (1716-1783), 11,
15
Brown & Sons Seeds, 102
Brunton, ——— (fl. 1759), 94
——— John (c. 1721-1803), 89,
95, 104-5
Brunton & Co., 105

Brunton & Forbes, 104

Brunton, Forbes, Forbes &
    Hunter, 104

Brunton & Hunter, 105

Buchanan, James (fl. 1790-1821),
    130

Bunney, George Hockley (fl.
    1825-44), 130

Bunyard, George & Sons, 116

Burchell, Matthew (c. 1751-d. c.
    1829), 79, 196

——— William (c. 1725-1800), 79,
    196

Busch, John (c. 1730-c. 1790),
    11, 88-9, 197

Butt, Richard (fl. 1729-51), 77,
    81

Caldwell, James (fl. 1789-d.
    1795), 114

——— Thomas (fl. 1795-1801),
    114

——— Thomas (fl. 1796), 113

——— William (1766-1844), 95,
    108, 112-14, 115, 118, 119

——— William (1789-1852), 114

——— William George
    (1824-1873), 114

Caldwell, William & Co., 111

Callender, Ebenezer Romain (fl.
    1795), 93

——— Michael (fl. 1794-95), 121

——— William R. (fl. 1794-95),
    121

Campbell, John (fl. 1774-d. 1804),
    196

Carpenter, Joseph (fl.
    1700-1730), 10, 71

Carr, John (fl. 1780-d. c. 1803),
    112-13

Carr & Caldwell, 113

Carter, James (fl. 1834-1856), 8

Casy, Thomas (fl. 1539), 40,
    167-8

Chambers, Richard (fl. 1762- ?
    1786), 196

Chandler, Alfred senior (fl.
    1800-28), 130

——— Alfred junior (1804-1896),
    130

Chapman, John (fl. 1515-39), 30,
    32

——— Samuel (fl. 1711), 95

Clark, George (fl. 1807-32), 110

——— Henry (c. 1702-1778), 73-4,
    186-93

——— Henry (d. 1782-3), 86-7

——— Thomas (fl. 1787-1811),
    117

Clark, Thomas & Co., 117, 118

———William (fl. 1805-11), 117

———William & Co., 110

Clark & Atkinson, 117

Clark & Stevenson, 117

Clarke, James (fl. 1767), 97

——— James (fl. 1779), 120-1

——— Richard (c. 1757-1836), 99

Clements, ——— (fl. 1691), 5,
    49

Cobbett, William (1762-1835),
    133-4

Coe, Robert (fl. 1839), 102

Cole, Richard (fl. 1730), 80

Coleman, William (c. 1743-1808),
    130, 196

Coles, William (fl. 1657), 44

Collin, Pierre (fl. 1607), 43, 132

Collins, Peter (fl. 1617-30), 43, 59

Colvill, James senior (c.
    1746-1822), 130, 131, 133;
    Plate 14

——— James junior (c.
    1777-1832), 130, 131, 133

Constable, Timothy (fl. 1798), 99

Cook, Moses (fl. 1664-d. 1715),
    11, 45, 47, 52-3, 59n., 93

Corbet, Vincent — see Pointer

Cordery, William (fl. 1803-36),
    198

Cormack, ——— (fl. 1786), 199

Cormack, Son & Sinclair, 130

Cotterell, John (fl. 1643-49), 98n.

Cottrall (Cotterel), John (fl. 1676-d. 1708), 98
Coussin, Laurence (fl. 1641-49), 98n., 132
Cowell, John (fl. 1717-30), 49, 50, 76, 93
Cowie, John (fl. 1775-86), 199
Cowlishaw, Henry (fl. 1746-d. 1777), 68
Cox, William senior (fl. 1678-d. 1704), 50, 67, 81
––– William junior (1680-1722), 50, 81, 82, 160, 164
Cree, John senior (c. 1738-1816), 97; Plate 11
––– John junior (c. 1800-1858), 97
Crick, James (fl. 1798), 99
Crofton, Robert (1603-fl. 1638), 42
Crombie & Cormack, 130
Cross, Edward (fl. 1768-1807), 199
Crouch, ––––– (fl. 1678), 47
Crowder, Abraham (c. 1734-1831), 96
––– Anderson (1793-1873), 110
––– Rowland Wood (fl. 1789-1807), 96
––– William (fl. 1792-d. 1836), 110
––– William Law (c. 1780-fl. 1851), 96
Crowder, W. & Sons, 110
Cunningham, George senior (fl. 1794-1800), 115
––– George junior (fl. 1802-36), 115
Cunningham, George & Son, 115
Cunningham & Johnson, 115
Cunningham & Smith, 196
Curtis, William (1746-1799), 12, 80, 129, 132
Cussings, Thomas (fl. 1730-51), 97

Dale, George (c. 1705-1781), 5, 68, 95, 120, 122-3, 124, 125
––– George (c. 1738-fl. 1762), 123
––– George (fl. 1781), 123
––– (Deel), James (fl. 1733), 122, 123
––– James (fl. 1780), 123
––– Joseph (d. 1781), 123
Dancer, Nathaniel (fl. 1625-d. 1657), 50
Darby, William (fl. 1677-d. c. 1713), 5, 49, 50, 55, 76
Davey, Thomas (c. 1758-1833), 129
Davidson, John (fl. 1786-97), 199
Davies, William (fl. 1786-1809), 199
Dayesye, Thomas (fl. 1399), 25
Deel, James – see Dale
Dennison, Henry & T., 117
Dermer, Thomas (fl. 1775-d. 1799), 199
Dickinson, William (fl. 1726-74), 92
Dickson, Archibald senior (fl. 1744-1808), 118
––– Archibald junior (fl. 1783-1814), 118
–––Francis (1793-1866), 111
–––Francis & James, 111
––– James (1738-1822), 129
––– Robert (fl. 1728-44), 117, 125
Dobie & Son, 32
Dodds, William (c. 1808-1900), 101
Douglas, James (fl. 1757), 121n.
Drake, Nicholas (fl. 1436-40), 26
Driver, Abraham Purshouse (fl. 1787-1812), 80, 197
––– Samuel (fl. 1717-30), 80
––– Samuel (fl. 1760-77), 80, 197
––– William (fl. 1787-1812), 80, 197

Dunhill, Richard (fl. 1784-d. c. 1816), 118
Duthie, W. & A., 197

Eddie, Alexander (fl. 1765-88), 197, 199
Eddie & Co., 199
Ely, Benjamin senior (1779-1843), 132
——— Benjamin junior (1810-fl. 1845), 132
Ely, Benjamin & Son, 132
Emmerton, Isaac senior (c. 1736-1789), 86, 197
——— Isaac junior (c. 1769-1823), 86, 197
——— Thomas (fl. 1741-63), 86

Fairchild, Thomas (1667-1729), 5, 12, 49, 51, 55, 76-8, 81, 93, 131, 150-1; Plate 7
Falla, John (fl. 1793-1808), 125
——— Thomas (c. 1736-181), 124
——— William (c. 1739-1804), 3, 11, 68, 95, 120, 121, 123-4
——— William II (1761-1830), 124-6; Plate 8
——— William III (1799-1836), 125-7
Falla, William & Co., 106, 116, 122, 124
Falla, William & Son, 116, 124, 125
Ferne, George (fl. 1765), 200
Ferrok, Nicholas (fl. 1432-34), 26
Field & Co., 199
Field, James (fl. 1793), 53
——— John (fl. 1662-d. 1687), 47, 53
——— John (fl. c. 1750-84), 53, 199
——— William (1678-1734), 53
Field & Child, 53, 199
Finney, Samuel (fl. 1838-47), 124-5
Finney, Samuel & Co., 125

Finneys Seeds, 125
Fisher, Charles (fl. 1822-59), 118-19
——— George (fl. 1838), 119
——— James (fl. 1785-86), 199
——— William (c. 1680-1743), 66, 132
Fisher, Holmes & Co., 119
FitzSalomon, Geoffrey (fl. 1200), 34
——— Ralf (fl. 1160), 34
Flanagan ———, 11
Forbes, Alexander (fl. 1782-95), 105
——— Alexander (fl. 1810-62), 105, 126
Forbes, Alexander & Co., 105
——— John (fl. 1805-08), 105
Forbes & Blakesley, 105
Ford family, 132
Ford, Ann (fl. 1831), 104
——— Joseph (1737-1796), 104
——— William (1760-1829), 104
Ford & Please, 104
Forrest, Richard (fl. c. 1812-46), 78
Forsyth, William (1737-1804), 116
Foster, Captain (fl. 1690-1703), 49
——— James (fl. 1838-48), 119
Fountain, Robert (fl. 1798), 110
Fox, George (fl. 1722), 161
——— John (fl. 1776), 68
Fox & Oldham, 108
Franklin, ——— (fl. 1787), 129
Fraser, John (1750-1811), 130
Frebern, Philip (fl. 1412), 26
Fuller, Edward (fl. 1680-c. 1720), 5, 47, 169
Furber, Robert (c. 1674-1756), 53, 77, 78, 79, 80, 81, 91, 93, 121, 133, 151, 201
——— William (fl. 1722-56), 78
Furnass, William (fl. 1786-1800), 117

Gammock, Alexander (fl. 1764-92), 197

Garaway, James (fl. 1828-50), 102

Garaway, Mayes & Co., 102

Gardener, Master John (fl. c. 1400), 18-22, 24, 138, 140

——— John (fl. 1546), 29

Garland, Thomas (fl. 1784), 121

Geary, Andrew Chapman (fl. 1783-d. 1792), 101

——— J. & P., 101

——— William (fl. 1783), 101

Geary & Moody, 101

Gerard, John (1545-1612), ix, 11, 37, 41, 42, 43, 50, 92, 139, 140, 145

Gibbs, Thomas (fl. 1787-1836), 82, 98

Gibbs & Co., 82, 98

Giddings, Robert (fl. 1822), xiii

Gilbank, Thomas (fl. 1657-d. 1684), 44, 49-50, 53

Gildon, John (fl. 1722), 161

——— Robert (fl. 1743), 69

Goldesburgh, Robert de (fl. 1351), xii-xiii

Gordon, 114, 129, 131

——— James (1708 ?-1780), 11, 36, 49, 84, 89, 197, 199

——— William (fl. 1780-86), 197

Gordon & Dermer, 199

Gorton, John, 111, 170

Gott — see Greening, (Sir) Henry Thomas

Gray, Christopher (c. 1694-1764), 78-9, 91, 196

——— Samuel & F., 199

——— William senior (fl. 1700-33), 78-9

——— William junior (fl. 1724-d. 1745), 79

Gray & Clark, 117

Gray, Wear & Gray, 114, 197

Greener, John (fl. 1776-1808), 117

——— Peter (fl. 1829-34), 117

Greening, (Sir) Henry Thomas, later Gott (fl. 1761-d. 1809), 132

——— Thomas (fl. 1735-d. 1757), 132

Gregg, ——— (fl. 1786), 197

Griffith (Gryffyn), Edmund (fl. 1533), 30

Grigson, Thomas (fl. 1688-d. 1724), 50

——— William (fl. 1686-94), 50

Grimwood, Daniel (c. 1725-1796), 78, 129, 197, 201-2

Grimwood, Hudson & Co., 197, 199

Grimwood & Wykes, 197

Gryffyn — see Griffith

Gurle, Leonard (c. 1621-1685), 4-5, 45-6, 50, 51, 55

Hairs, Ivie (fl. 1788-1812), 130, 200

——— James (fl. 1777-1812), 130, 200

——— John (fl. 1780-1802), 199

Hairs, Hairs & Smith, 130

Ham, George (fl. 1723), 101

Hammond, Henry senior (fl. 1780-1811), 107-8

——— Henry junior (1790-fl. 1835), 108

Hammond, Henry & Son, 108

——— Thomas (fl. 1798), 103

Hammond & Stephens, 104

Hanbury, Rev. William (1725-1778), 96

Hankin, James (fl. 1790-1821), 115

Hanks, James (fl. 1798-1822), 117, 118

Hanks, James & Co., 118

Hanks & Dunhill, 118, 119

Hanks & Muscroft, 118

Harman, William (fl. 1653), 45

Harper, William (fl. 1789-97), 197

Harpur, William (fl. 1786), 197
Harris, John senior (fl. 1782-c.
   1816), 103
—·— John junior (fl. 1811-16),
   103
Harrison, John (fl. 1788-1814),
   86, 197
——— Samuel (fl. 1790-1833), 86,
   95, 110, 197
Harrison & Bristow, 86
Hay, ————— (fl. 1786-89), 197
——— John (fl. 1759-d. 1792), 87,
   197
——— Walter (fl. 1780-1805), 197,
   200
Haynes, Thomas (fl. 1802-21),
   93-4, 106
Haywood, Daniel (fl. 1795-1812),
   108
——— John (fl. 1794-97), 108
Heap, William (fl. 1784-93), 108
Helyar, John (fl. 1440-48), 26
Henderson, A. (fl. 1782-95), 117
Hewitt, Henry (fl. 1730-d. 1771),
   85-6, 197
——— Henry (fl. c. 1750-d. 1791),
   86, 197
——— Samuel (fl. 1738-d. 1793),
   85-6
Hill, ——— (fl. 1786), 200
——— Charlotte (fl. 1832-38), 87
——— James (c. 1761-1832), 87,
   197
——— Robert (fl. 1631-d. 1649), 4
——— Thomas ('Didymus
   Mountain') (fl. 1558-d. c.
   1599), 30
Hillier & Sons, 32
Hirst, Robert Michael (fl. 1822),
   118
Hitt, Thomas (fl. c. 1739-d. c. 1760),
   82-3
Hodgkinson, Edmund (fl. 1722),
   161
Hoggarth, Henry (fl. 1795), 117
Holloway, Robert (fl. 1822), xiii

Holmes, John (fl. 1751), 93
Holt, Adam (fl. 1710-d. 1750),
   81, 87
——— Simon & Son, 109
Hood, William (fl. 1730-33), 80
Howey family, 50, 197
——— John (1762-1798), 197
——— Robert (1764-1800), 197
——— William (c. 1729-1792), 197
Hubbard, William (fl. 1778-d.
   1787), 105
Hughes, Joseph (fl. 1775-82), 87
   198
Hulme & Raffald, 115-16
Humphries, —————, 43
Hunt, Francis III (1691-1763),
   50, 78, 80
——— Francis IV (c. 1729-1775),
   197
——— John (fl. 1786-1824), 200
——— Samuel (fl. 1730-d. 1763),
   78, 80
Hunter, James Augustus (fl.
   1813-28), 105
Hutton, William & Thomas, 117

I'Anson, Charles (fl. 1840-47),
   124
I'Anson & Finney, 125
Ilkeley, Gilbert de (fl. 1335), 35
Innis, James (fl. 1793), 120
Irwin, George (fl. 1743-75), 71,
   99

James, Moses (fl. 1719-31), 78,
   82, 86, 176, 177, 178, 179
Jasper, of Beaulieu (fl. 1530), 29
Jeffreys, John (fl. 1756-88), 197
Jennings, Mountain (fl. 1607-12),
   30
Joyce, John (fl. 1757-1827), 121
——— John & William, 121
——— Stanley (fl. 1757-78), 68,
   121
——— William (fl. 1754-d. 1767),
   68, 120, 121, 124

—— William (fl. 1826-34), 121-2

Keen, Isaac (fl. 1780-1818), 99
Kellet, —————— (fl. 1786), 200
Kennedy, 11, 84
—— John (fl. 1760-d. 1790), 85,
96, 109
—— John (1759-1842), 85,
99-100
—— Lewis (d. 1743), xiii
—— Lewis (1721-1782), xiii,
84-5, 91, 197
—— Lewis (c. 1757-1810), 85
—— Thomas (d. 1721), xiii
King, Samuel (fl. 1784), 105
Kirke, John (fl. 1719), 66, 85
—— John (fl. 1822-36), 85
—— Joseph senior (fl. 1753-90),
85, 197
—— Joseph junior (fl.
1793-1825), 85
—— Mary (fl. 1793), 85
—— William (fl. 1793-1805), 85
—— William (fl. 1789-91), 113
Kirke & Caldwell, 113
Kirke & Son, 197
Knight, —————— (fl. 1726), 82
—— Joseph (1777-1855), 82
Knight & Perry, 111
Knowlton, Thomas (1692-1781),
84
Knyght, Henry (fl. 1398), 25

Lance, ——————, 43
Lane, —————— (fl. 1786), 197
Langfitt, Ralph (fl. 1722), 161
Langley, Daniel (fl. 1695), 82
Lapidge, William (fl. 1759), 97
Latin, —————— (fl. 1786), 197
Lauder, Peter (fl. 1792-1814),
102, 116
—— Peter junior (fl. 1803-05),
102
Lee, James (1715-1795), 11, 84,
87, 89, 129, 131, 197; Plate 10
Lee & Kennedy, 197

Leeson, William (fl. 1716-d.
1722), 68, 160-4
—— William II (fl. 1722-51), 160
—— William III (fl. 1744-50),
160
Le Notre, André (1613-1700), 47
Lewis, —————— (fl. 1786-1800),
197
—— David (fl. 1785-94), 200
Lindley, George (fl. 1796-1831),
93, 98
Little & Ballantyne, 117
Littlewood, John (fl. 1779-d.
1825), 118-19
Loddiges, Conrad (1743 ?-1826),
11, 87, 88-9, 92, 129, 131, 197
—— George (1784-1846), 89, 92
Loddiges & Sons, 197
Lodge, Walter (fl. 1750-55), 186
London, George (fl. 1673-d.
1714), xiii, 10, 52, 53-5, 71,
76, 85, 93; Plates 1, 9
Looker, Roger (fl. c. 1660-d.
1685), 43, 52, 53, 88, 167,
168-9
—— William (fl. 1667-d. 1685),
52 & n., 168-9
Lovell, John senior (fl. 1519-d.
1550), 29, 34
—— John junior (fl. 1550-c.
1590), 29
Lowe, —————— (fl. 1786), 197
Low(e), Obadiah (fl. 1724-30), 80
Lucas, Robert (fl. 1725-d. 1734),
86
—— William (fl. 1672-d. 1679),
4, 5, 37, 47, 51, 70, 145
Lucombe family, 72, 104, 132
—— William (1696-1794), 72
—— William (c. 1716-fl. 1795),
72
Lucombe & Pince, 9
Lucombe & Son, 72
Luker, Warren (fl. 1758-d. 1784),
88, 200
Luker, Smith & Lewis, 88, 200

Mackey, Robert (fl. 1770), 124
Mackie, Frederick (fl. 1833-54), 98
——— John (fl. 1773-d. 1797), 98
——— Robert (fl. 1787-1800), 130, 197
McNiven, Charles (fl. 1776-d. 1815), 116
——— Peter (fl. 1783-d. 1818), 116
Maddock, 12, 129, 132
——— James senior (c. 1715-1786), 112, 129
——— James junior (1763-1825), 129; Plate 13
——— John (fl. 1795-1834), 102
——— William (fl. 1796-1801), 105
Malcolm, William senior (fl. 1757-d. c. 1800), 11, 88, 89, 129, 197
——— William junior (1769-1835), 78, 88, 134, 197
——— William & Co., 114, 197
Malcolm & Doughty, 114
Marsh, Henry (1665-1741), 50, 132
Marshfield, ——— (fl. 1694), 50
Martin, Abraham (fl. 1788-1834), 119
Martin & Son, 119
Mason, John, 114
——— Peter (1680-1730), 80, 81-2, 160, 164-6
Master(s), George (fl. 1717-28), 82
Mattheson, Messrs. 68
Maule, Alexander James (1820-1884), 102
——— James (fl. 1769-1811), 102
——— William (fl. 1815-50), 102
Meager, Leonard (c. 1625-c. 1700), 45, 93, 133
Menvell, Anthony (fl. 1590-1616), 59
Meracow, ———, 43
Middlewood, William (fl. 1776),

115
Millen, James (d. 1642), 44-5
——— John senior (fl. 1610-d. 1635), 44-5
——— John junior (c. 1610-1639), 44-5
Miller, John (fl. 1824-38), 102-3
——— Philip (1691-1771), 9, 65, 78, 79, 80, 82, 160, 171
Miller & Sweet, 102
Milne, Thomas (c. 1767-1838), 79, 80-1
Minier, 11, 200
——— Charles (c. 1710-1790), 47
Minier & Mason, 200
Minier, Minier & Nash, 114, 200
Minier, Teesdale, Minier & Oliver, 200
Mitchell, George (fl. 1786-98), 200
Mitchelson, George (fl. 1785-c. 1800), 198
——— James (fl. 1785-c. 1835), 198
Mollet, André (fl. 1639-61), 132
Moody, Thomas (fl. 1841-45), 101
'Mordan', ———, 49-50
Moullar (Moulart), James (fl. 1654-d. 1666), 43
'Mountain, Didymus' — see Hill, Thomas
Mounteyn, Richard (fl. 1545), 30
Mow, ———, 43
Mullock, Catharine (fl. 1828-34), 111
——— Isaac (fl. 1791-1805), 111
——— Peter (fl. 1800-24), 111
Murray, Robert (fl. 1807-23), 98
——— William (fl. 1780-1808), 105

Napier, ——— (fl. 1803-06), 130
Naylor, George (fl. 1716), 160
Neal(e), G. (fl. 1786-1802), 198
Newman, James & Co., 99

——— William senior (fl. 1784-d. 1789), 99
——— William junior (fl. 1789-1807), 99
——— William III (fl. 1789-1830), 99
Nickson, John (fl. 1759-d. 1809), 112-13
——— Joseph (d. 1755), 112
Nickson & Carr, 95, 108, 111, 112, 115, 119
Noble, Francis (fl. 1720-d. 1756), 68, 109, 132
——— John (fl. 1633-d. 1651), 48, 109, 132
——— Michael (fl. 1746-56), 68
North, Richard (fl. 1731-d. c. 1765), 87, 93
——— William (fl. 1788-1806), 198, 200
Notcutt, Messrs, 71

Oakley, ——— (fl. 1786-87), 200
Ordoyno, 11
——— Garrett (c. 1723-1795), 109
——— Jacob (c. 1734-1812), 109
——— Thomas (fl. 1810), 109-10
Ordoyno & Withers, 109
Osborn, Robert (fl. 1824-d. 1866), 79
——— Thomas (1819-1872), 10, 80
Outram, Joseph (fl. 1793), 108
Oxley & Scholey, 118

Page, 9
——— William Bridgewater (1790-1871), 99
Page & Toogood, 100
Palethorpe, Joseph (fl. 1832), 110
——— Thomas (fl. 1793-1807), 110
Pamplin, James (1785-1865), 87
——— William (1768-1844), 87
Park, John (fl. 1414), 26

——— William (fl. 1415), 26
Parkinson, John (1567-1650), 11, 37, 43, 44, 50, 51, 132, 140
——— John (fl. 1700-d. 1719), 86, 132
Pearson, ——— 5, 48
——— Alfred (fl. 1859), 109
——— George (fl. 1720), 48
——— James Royston (fl. 1859), 108-9
——— John I (fl. 1782-d. 1825), 108
——— John II (fl. 1807-32), 108
——— John III (1819-1876), 108
——— Powell (fl. 1716), 48
Pearson, John & Son, 109
——— J. R. & Co., 109
See also Peirson
Peirson, Samuel senior (fl. 1691-d. 1701), 48
——— Samuel junior (fl. 1700), 48
See also Pearson
Pendar, William (fl. 1766-71), 100-1, 194-5
Pennell, Charles (c. 1821-1896), 110
——— Richard (fl. 1820-d. 1869), 110
Pennell & Sons Ltd, 110
Perfect family, 95, 104, 109, 118
——— John (d. 1722), 66
——— John (c. 1700-d. 1764), 66, 68, 93
——— John (1717-1762), 66
——— John & William, 201-6
——— Noah (fl. 1708-d. 1723), 66
——— William (c. 1720-1785), 66-7, 202
Perkins, William (fl. 1776-1825), 198
Petrie, Robert (fl. 1795), 117
Philip, at Winchester (fl. 1410), 25
Philip 'le Fruter' (fl. 1336), 35
Philipson, Henry (fl. 1811-23), 119

––– John (fl. 1794-1807), 119

Philipson & Scales, 119

Picken, Joseph (c. 1806-1835), 113

Pince, Robert Taylor (c. 1804-1871), 72, 132

Pinkerton, William (fl. 1782-98), 116-17

Plant, Andrew (fl. 1791-1800), 112

––– Joseph (fl. 1820-39), 108

Pointer, 'Richard', 42

––– alias Corbet, Vincent (fl. 1597-d. 1619), 41-2, 45

Polwegge, John (fl. 1416-25), 26

Pontey, William (fl. 1782-d. 1831), 93-4

Poole, James (c. 1777-c. 1827), 103

––– William (fl. 1811), 103

Pope, Alexander (fl. 1837-d. c. 1853), 104

––– John (fl. 1818-72), 104

––– Luke (1740-1825), 95, 104

Post, Walter (fl. 1786-98), 200

Post & Hunt, 200

Powell, Nathaniel (fl. 1731-d. 1773), 47-8, 200

Pringle, William (d. 1813), 198

Prior, ––––– (fl. 1786), 198

Pullen, James (fl. 1726), 73

Pury, Robert (fl. 1528-32), 30

Quarton – see Wharton

Raby, Philip (fl. 1353), 16

Raffald, George (d. 1805), 116

––– John (d. 1790), 116

Ramann & Möhring, 8n.

Randoll, ––––– , 43

Rayner, John (fl. 1795-1805), 108

Rea, ––––– (fl. 1738), 85

––– John (fl. 1625-d. 1677), 5, 43, 69-70, 93, 116

Reid, Moses (fl. 1793-1834), 111

––– Thomas (fl. 1799), 111-12

Reigne, Reygny, John (fl. 1510), 29

Rench, Nathaniel (1682-1783), 37

––– Thomas (c. 1630-1728), 37, 50, 62

Renton, John (fl. 1780-d. 1810), 198

Richards, Thomas (fl. 1786), 198

Richmond, J. (fl. 1795), 117

Rickets, George (fl. 1665-d. 1706), 5, 43, 48, 51, 55, 56-7, 76, 145-9

––– James (fl. 1678-1711), 48, 76

Rigg, Ann (1786-1854), 131

––– John (1777-1833), 131

––– Thomas senior (c. 1746-1835), 131

––– Thomas junior (c. 1774-1811), 131

Robinson, William (1838-1935), 2

Robson, Adam (fl. 1771-1802), 200

Rocque, Bartholomew (fl. 1741-65), 67, 79, 93

Roger 'le Herberur' (fl. 1275-99), xiii, 40

Rogers, George (fl. 1781-d. 1799), 110-11, 169-70

––– John (1752-1842), 99

––– John (fl. 1781-1820), 111

––– Mary (fl. 1828-40), 111

––– William (fl. 1812-39), 99

Rogers, W. H. Ltd., 99

Rollisson, William (c. 1765-1842), 130

Ronalds, 200

––– Hugh senior (c. 1726-1788), 88, 198

––– Hugh junior (1759-1833), xiii, 88, 198

Rose, John (1622-1677), 5, 12, 46, 53, 54, 70, 93; Plate 1

Ross, John (fl. 1786-1837), 198

Rowse, ––––– (fl. 1658-61), 47,

53

Russell, Henry (fl. 1539-d. 1549), 27, 40, 167-8

——— John senior (c. 1731-1794), 88-9, 91, 124, 198

——— John junior (1766-1808), 89

——— Thomas (1777-1810), 89

Russell & Willmott, 198

Rutter, William (fl. 1530), 30

Salomon, at Havering (fl. 1130), 34

Sampson, John (fl. 1729-47), 77 See also Simpson

Sander, John (fl. 1790-1811), 117

Saxe, Philip (fl. 1790-94), 110

Scales, Robert (fl. 1793-98), 119

Scott, Henry (fl. 1738-60), 83, 86

——— James (fl. 1741-54), 83 84

——— John (fl. 1848), 71

Seabedge (Sebache), George (fl. 1617-25), 59

——— Walter (fl. 1595-1608), 59, 60

——— William (fl. 1628), 59

Seaman, William (fl. 1783-86), 200

Shailer, Henry senior (fl. 1775-1822), 202

——— Henry junior (fl. 1810-1852), 202

Shepherd, ——— (fl. 1786), 198

Shields (Sheilds, Shiells), James (fl. 1763-88), 87, 200

Shilling, John (fl. 1831-39), 100

Shuport, John (fl. 1786), 198

Shuttleworth, John (fl. 1722), 161

Siborn, Richard senior (fl. 1755-d. 1774), 87, 198

——— Richard junior (c. 1751-1821), 87

Sigston, Benjamin (fl. 1787-93), 69

——— John senior (fl. 1733-60), 69

——— John junior (fl. 1760), 69

——— Samuel (fl. 1767-91), 69

Silverlock, Henry (fl. 1798-1839), 99

Simpson, John (fl. 1733-40), 77 See also Sampson

——— John (fl. 1772-95), 95-6

——— Richard (fl. 1763-d. 1783), 95-6

Singleton, George (fl. 1730-d. 1735), 80

Small, Moses (fl. 1767-d. 1798), 99

Smith, Edward (fl. 1805-24), 88, 198

——— Samuel (c. 1695-d. 1757), 92

——— Samuel (fl. 1780-1825), 198

——— William (fl. 1697-1730), 10, 71

——— William (fl. 1790-1844), 108

Smiths, 88, 198, 200

Smyth, Richard (fl. 1418-19), 26

Speechly, William (c. 1734-1819), 96, 105, 108, 113, 118, 125

——— William (d. 1804), 109, 207

Spencer, William (fl. 1730), 80

Spier, Richard (fl. 1729), 81

Spires (Spyers), Joshua (fl. 1730-50), 81

Spiring, Edward (fl. 1793-1811), 102

——— William (fl. 1801-15), 102

Spiring, Mortimore & Co., 102

Spryngold, John (fl. 1404), 25

Squibb, R. W. (fl. 1839), 102

Stacy, Theophilus (fl. 1688-1719), 5, 47, 48

Stephens, Thomas (fl. 1835-41), 104

Stidolph, Godfrey (fl. 1768-1818), 198

Stow, Henry (fl. 1749-d. 1771), 71

——— John (fl. 1748), 71

Sutton, John (1777-1863), 100
Swallow, James (fl. 1767-1812),
    100
––– John (1779-fl. 1808), 100
Swallow & Son, 100
Swayne, John (fl. 1404), 25
Sweet, James (fl. 1798), 102
––– John (fl. 1795), 102
––– Robert (1783-1835), 88,
    102, 130, 133
Sweets & Miller, 102
Swinden, Nathaniel (fl.
    1768-1805), 198
Swinhoe, John (fl. 1735-56), 197
Swinton, ––––– (fl. 1786), 198
Switzer, Stephen (1682 ?-1745),
    47, 51-2, 53, 54, 56, 65, 66,
    77, 82, 83, 87, 91, 122, 171-2,
    180

Tagg Elizabeth (1696-1779), 62
––– James (fl. 1751-92), 62
––– Thomas senior (1695-d. c.
    1760), 36, 61, 62
––– Thomas junior (fl. 1806-d.
    1837), 36, 62
Talwyn (Tawvyn), Anthony (fl.
    1546), 29
Taylor & Smith, 115
Taylor, Weston & Co., 115
Taylor & Withington, 115
Teesdale, Robert senior (d. 1773),
    207-8
––– Robert junior (c.
    1740-1804), 38, 47, 207
Telford family, 11, 64-5, 72, 93,
    95, 104, 109, 121, 201
––– George (fl. 1684-d. 1704),
    64
––– George junior (1687-1711),
    64
––– George (1749-1834), 64-5
––– John I (1689-1771), 64-5
––– John II (1716-1770), 64
––– John junior (1744-1830),
    38, 64-5, 132

Thatcher, Samuel (fl. 1780-1831),
    200
Thoburn, Frank (fl. 1784-90),
    130, 198
––– & Whitley, 198
Thompson family, 120
––– Christopher (c. 1735-1782),
    95, 124
––– Christopher Masterman
    (1781-fl. 1849), 95
––– James (fl. 1757-58), 121
––– John (fl. 1730-58), 80, 91
––– William (1759-1811), 95
Thomson & Gordon, 198
Thoumbe, John (fl. 1419), 26
Tillforth, Tilford – see Telford
Tindall, George (fl. 1806-1830),
    119-20
––– William (fl. 1820-47), 120
Toogoods, 100
Totty, John (d. 1681), 101
Townly, E. W. (fl. 1786), 198,
    200
Tradescant, John senior (d. 1638),
    43, 44, 145; Plate 4
–––– John junior (1608-1662),
    43, 50, 145; Plate 5
Tuggie, Ralph (fl. 1621-d. 1633),
    42-3
––– Richard (1626-1670), 43,
    44
Turnbull, Robert (fl. 1812-25),
    105
Turner, John (d. 1662), 43
––– John (fl. 1695-1734), 47
––– Spencer (fl. 1751-d. 1776),
    87, 198

Veitch, John (1752-1839), 104
Verbadhome, Jan (fl. 1642), 133
Versprit, Anthony (fl. c.
    1680-1700), 49
Vickers, Thomas (fl. 1795), 112
––– William (fl. 1831), xiii

Walsh (Welsh), ––– (fl. 1530-37),

30

Warner, John (d. 1615), 41

――― William (d. 1628), 41

Warner & Seaman, 114, 200

Watson, George (fl. 1855-95), 115

――― James (fl. 1776-92), 129, 198

――― Thomas (fl. 1792-1821), 129-30, 198; Plate 16

――― William (fl. 1769-d. c. 1792), 129, 198

Watts, David (fl. 1786-88), 200

――― William (fl. 1786-1805), 198

Weare, James (fl. 1795-1830), 95

Webb, John (fl. 1753-63), 199

Webber & Pierce, 71

Welstead, William (fl. 1730), 80

Welton, Thomas (fl. 1827), 108

Weston, Francis (fl. 1688-1719), 5, 47

Whalley, John & Joseph 115

――― Thomas (fl. 1783-1815), 115

――― Thomas & Son, 115

Wharton, Jacob (1682-fl. 1726), 64

――― (Quarton), Matthew (fl. 1676-d. 1695), 63-4

――― Matthew (c. 1710-1784), 64

Wheeler, Alfred Cummins (fl. 1860-75), 103

――― Edward (fl. 1795), 103

――― Elizabeth (fl. 1814-20), 103

――― James (fl. 1763), 93, 103

――― James Cheslin (fl. 1841-d. 1860), 103

――― J. C. & Son, 103

――― James Daniel (fl. 1820-44), 103

――― & Son, 103

White, James (fl. 1785-97), 200

Whitley, Reginald (c. 1754-1835), 79, 130

Whitley & Brames, 114

Whitlock, John (fl. 1782-90), 198

Whitmill, Benjamin (fl. 1722-30),

49, 93

Whittingham, Charles (fl. 1783-93), 94-5

――― John (1696-fl. 1760), 74, 94

Whittingham & Weare, 95

Wilkinson, Thomas (fl. 1791-1815), 115

William, at Chester (fl. 1190), 16

―――, at London (fl. 1274-75), 40

―――, at Winchester (fl. 1400-08), 25

Williams, Richard (fl. 1791-1826), 84, 129; Plate 12

Williamson, John (fl. 1730-60), 78, 79, 197, 201

――― & Co., 78, 121, 197

Willmott, John (1775-1834), xiii, 89

Willmott & Co, 89

Willmott & Chaundy, 89

Wilson, James (fl. 1785-98), 200

――― Joseph (fl. 1798-1827), 69, 108

Wilson & Sanders, 199

Winter, John (fl. 1776), 68

Wise, Henry (1653-1738), 10, 51, 54, 55, 70, 71, 76, 93, 150; Plates 1, 6

Withers, George & Thomas, 109

Withers & Co., 109

Wolf (Le Leu, Le Loup), John (fl. 1538-1547), 28

Wood, Henry (fl. 1842), 110

――― James (1792-1830), 99

――― John (fl. 1767), 99

――― John (fl. 1795), xiii, 99

――― John (fl. 1795-1811), 110

――― William (fl. 1784-95), 110

――― William (fl. 1862), 110

Wood & Sons, 8-9

Woodman, Henry (c. 1698-1758), 82-3, 91, 122, 171-85

――― Henry junior (1732-1775), 83

Woods, John & William (fl. 1798), 71

—— Richard (fl. 1751-d. 1793), 97-8, 204-7
——— William (fl. 1749), 71
Woolley, Thomas (fl. 1729-33), 82, 122, 171, 174-80, 184
Wrench, Jacob (fl. 1715), 62-3
——— Jacob (fl. 1750-76), 63
——— Jacob & Sons, 63, 200
——— Thomas senior (fl. 1648-65), 5 61, 62
——— Thomas junior (fl. 1664-c. 1719), 36, 61
Wright, 12, 132
Wright & Beck, 199
Wynde John (fl. 1520), 35

Young John (c. 1790-1862), 103-4
——— Thomas (fl. 1605), 42

Gardeners to estates, 37, 92-3
Garlic, ix, 20, 26, 142
Gascoigne Sir Thomas, Bart., 85
Gateshead, Co. Durham, 3, 5, 36, 68, 106, 120, 121, 122-6, 171; Plate 8
——— Chapel lands, 36, 126
——— Park, 82, 93, 122, 171-85
Geekie, Joseph, 185
Gelder Rose, 147, 181, 182, 187, 205
Gelsemium sempervirens, 147
Genealogy of nurserymen, 9-12, 132-3
Genista Blue-flowered, 151
Genista monosperma, 151
Gentiana acaulis, 149
——— *amarella*, 142
——— *verna*, 149
Gentianella, 149
Gentlemen, gardeners as, 37, 38, 42, 45, 47, 50, 53, 69, 112
George I, king of England, Plate 6
——— II, 132, 171
——— III, 6, 88
Geranium, 2
——— nocte olens, 148

See also Pelargonium
Geranium robertianum, 142
Gerard of Bromley, lord, 69-70
Germany, 60, 110
Geum urbanum, 142
Gibson, Edmund, 65
Gilbert, Rev. Samuel, 69
Gill, Richard, glover, 168
Gilliflower, 20, 43, 148
Gilroy, Mr, 175, 179, 181
Gira solis, 19
Gladwin, 22, 142
Glasshouses, 88
See also Greenhouse
Glastonbury, Som., 49
Gleichenthal, Germany, 8n.
Globe-flower, 149
Gloucester, 34, 93, 103
——— Castle, 34
——— Llanthony priory by, 34
Glover, Moses, surveyor, 42
Glynde Place, Sussex, 23
Gnaphalion, Scarlet, 148
Goa, 52
Godfrey, Edward, 169
Goff, Robert, 170
Goldilocks, 151
Goldthorp, Richard, 63
Gooseberry, 37, 40, 44, 52, 56, 67, 101, 112, 116, 123, 141, 149, 165, 172, 178, 179, 182
——— meetings, 112, 113
Goosey, Berks., 62
Gorer, Mr Richard, xi
Gorton, John, 111
Gourd, 24, 173
Gower, earl, 94, 95
Grafting, 20, 21, 36; Plates 2, 3
Graham (Greyhome), Col. James, 57
Grantham, Lincs., 110
Grape, ix, 20, 21, 29, 34, 35, 40, 46, 67, 70, 85, 101, 116, 141, 149, 150, 165, 189, 201, 207
Grass, 67, 98
Green Fingers, Thumb, 14
Greenfield Hall, Flints., xiii

Greenhouse, 2, 46-7, 52, 75, 76, 97, 126, 176, 193
——— plants, 62, 83, 96, 103, 106, 109, 111, 125
See also Glasshouses, Hothouse
Greens — see Evergreens
Greenwich Palace, Kent, 27, 28-9, 30
Grimsby, Lincs., 110
Gromwell, 19, 142
Groundsel, 142
Guernsey Lily, 77
Guiting Power, Glos., 186n., 188, 189
——— Grange, 74, 186
Gurle, Joseph, 46
——— Martin, 46
——— William, 46

Hackney — see London
Hadfield, Mr Miles, xi, 18, 76, 92, 104, 116
Hadham, Little, Herts., 52, 53
——— Hall, 52
Hailstone, Samuel (1768-1851), botanist, 132
Hainault — see Jeanne de Valois, Philippa
Halesowen, Worcs. (formerly Salop), 104
Halifax, earls of, 5
Hallgarth, William, 123
Halnaby, Yorks., 123
Ham, Surrey, 167
——— Common, 130
Hamilton, Scotland, 126
Hammersmith — see London
Hampshire, 12
Hampton Court Palace, Middlesex, 27, 28, 30, 31, 206
Hanbury Trust, 96, 105
Handsworth, Staffs., 104, 118
Handsworth, Yorks., 104, 118-19
Hanmer, Sir Thomas, Bart., 43, 70, 145
Harewood, Yorks., 93
Harlington, Middlesex, 81

Harper, Rev. William, 37
Harrison, William, 23-4, 33, 58
Harrowby, lord, 193
See also Ryder, Nathaniel
Harrowby, earl of, 74
Hartburn, ? Northumberland, 124
Hartlepool, Co. Durham, 36, 120
——— Franciscan friary, 36, 120
Hartlib, Samuel, improver, 63
Hart's Tongue, 142
Hartwell, Bucks., 72, 97-8, 204
Hassendeanburn, Scotland, 117-18, 125
Hatfield, Herts., 30, 43, 52 & n., 132
Havering atte Bower, Essex, 34
Hawick, Scotland, 113, 118
Hawkshead, Lancs., 117
Hawkweed, Purple, 190
——— Scarlet, 190
——— Yellow, 190
Hawthorn, Quickset, 138, 195
Hazel, 138, 141
Hearne, Thomas, 36, 62
Heath (*Erica*), 2, 9, 72, 129, 130
Heath House, Staffs., 108
Heath, Mr, instrument maker, 175
Heaton, Northumberland, 123
Hebburn Quay, Co. Durham, 68, 95, 122-5
Hedging, xiii, 178
Helenium autumnale, 151
Helianthus, 19
Helichrysum orientale, 151
——— *sanguineum*, 148
Heliophila coronopifolia, xiii
Hellebore, 142
Helleborus niger, 18
——— *viridis*, 142
Hemp, ix, 35
Henbane, 142
Henley-on-Thames, Oxon., 100
Henley, Walter of (fl. 1250), ix, 14, 17
Henrietta Maria, queen, 133
Henry I, king of England, 15, 33, 34
——— III, 16, 40

—— IV, 24
—— V, 33
—— VII, 24
—— VIII, 9, 27-9, 30, 31, 32, 33,
39, 40, 112, 167
Hepatica triloba, 18, 143, 148, 172
Herb John — see St John's Wort
Herb Robert, 142
Herb Walter, 139, 140, 142
Herb Yve — see Wart Cress
Herbaceous plants, 2, 76, 96, 102,
103, 106, 109, 111, 115, 119,
148-9, 150
Herbals, 30, 37
'Herberur', xiii, 40
Herbs, 18-22, 24, 27, 29, 58, 138,
142-4
Hereditary factor, 10, 132-3
Hermodactylus tuberosus, 148
Hertford, 98
Hertford, William marquess of, 46
Hesperis matronalis, 148
Hewitt, Thomas, 86
Heworth, Co. Durham, 124
Hexham, Northumberland, 121, 123,
176
Hibiscus syriacus, 95, 134, 139n.,
147, 165
Hieracium pilosella, 143
Hindheal, 143
Hitchin Priory, Herts., 86
Hodsack Woodhouse, Notts., 68
Holland, 4, 75, 128
Holly, 31-2, 68, 73, 96, 100, 105,
141, 163-4, 165-6, 187, 190, 204,
205
—— striped and variegated, 49, 94,
108, 187, 188, 204, 205
Hollyhock, 18, 20, 139, 188, 190
Holywell, Flintshire, 112
Honey flower, 51
Honeysuckle (Woodbine), 20, 25, 46,
56, 57, 94, 143, 165, 172, 178,
182, 187, 188, 189, 202, 205
—— evergreen, 202
—— Trumpet, 94, 111, 202

—— Virginia Scarlet, 94
—— White, 147
Horehound, 143
Hornbeam, 68, 165, 178, 179, 182,
183, 184, 205, 206
Horncastle, Lincs., 110
Horseheath Hall, Cambs., 46
Horsel — see Elecampane
Horsley, West, Surrey, 29
Horsley, Benedict, surveyor, 63
Hothouse (Stove), 76, 88, 89, 110
—— plants, 103, 109
See also Glasshouses, Greenhouse
Houghton-le-Spring, Co. Durham,
120
Hoult, James, 115
Houseleek, Tree, 146
Howard, lord William, 60
Howden, Yorks., 59, 129
Hoxton — see London
Huddersfield, Yorks., 93
Huguenots, 11-12, 47, 83, 132-3
Hull, Yorks., 119, 120, 129
Hunstanton, Norfolk, 60
Huntingdon, 99
Hutchenson, Edward, master
mariner, 177
Hyacinth, 1, 115, 148, 188, 189
—— Blue Passetout, 151
Hyacinthus orientalis, 148
Hybridization, 15, 49, 76, 90, 130,
131
Hydrangea. 'Hydrangula', 203
Hyoscyamus niger, 142
Hypericum, 117
—— frutex, 147, 165, 203, 204
Hypericum androsaemum, 144
—— *perforatum*, 143
Hyssop, 18, 20, 27, 60, 143
Hyssopus officinalis, 143

Iberis semperflorens, 151
Idlicote, Warwicks., 193
Ilex, 147
Ilex aquifolium, 141
Immigrant gardeners, 132-3

Improvement, 1, 63, 65, 72, 75, 82, 107
Impyard (Impgarth), 22, 35
Indigo, Bastard, 205
——— Sweetmeats, 205
Industrial Revolution, 94
Ingram, Mr, 192
Insurance of plantations, 108
Introduction of plants, 1-2, *passim*
Inula helenium, 142
Inventories, 160-6
Ireland, 41, 72
Iris, 22, 148
——— English, 50
——— Persian, 172
——— *florentina*, 22
——— *foetidissima* 22
——— *germanica*, 22
——— *pseudacorus*, 22, 142
——— *xiphioides*, 148
Irregularity in garden design, 76
Isabell, John, cook, 35
Isham, Sir Justinian, 105
Isleworth, Middlesex, 80, 81, 88, 160
Islington - see London
Italy, 15, 60
Ivy, 165

Jacinth, 148
Jackson, Benjamin Daydon (1846-1927), botanist, 145
Jacobea Marina — see Ragwort
James II, king of England, 11
James, John (c. 1672-1746), 80
Jarrow, Co. Durham, 68, 122-5
Jasmine, 46, 178
——— Ilex-leaved, 151
——— Nettle-leaved, 151
——— Persian, 147, 172, 189, 203
——— Spanish, 77, 146, 187
——— Virginian, 147
——— White, 146, 165, 180, 182, 203
——— Winter, 51, 147
——— Yellow, 165, 181, 182, 189, 203, 205
——— Yellow Indian, 51, 146

Jasminum grandiflorum, 146
——— *odoratissimum*, 51, 146
——— *officinale*, 146
——— *sambac*, 51, 147
Jeanne de Valois, countess of Hainault, 17
Jenkins, Essex, 167
Jersey, earl of, 88
John, king of England, 34
Johnson, Thomas (c. 1605-1644), botanist, 11, 43, 44
Jones, Edward, 102
——— Samuel, 170
Jonquil, 56, 149
——— Campernelle, 56-7
Journals — see Books and Journals cited
Juglans regia, 141
Juniper, 32, 165, 194, 206
——— Swedish, 94, 105, 206
Juniperus bermudiana, 51
——— *sabina*, 147
Justice, James (1698-1763), 84

Kaempferia galanga, 19
Kale, 142
Kalm, Pehr, xiii
Keighley, Yorks., 117, 118
Kelshall, Herts., xiii
Kempton Park, Middlesex, 167
Kendal, Westmorland, 117
Kenilworth Castle, 33
——— 'Le plesans en marys', 33
Kent, William (1685-1748), architect, 11
Keswick, Cumberland, 113, 117, 118
Ketmia, 139 & n.
Kew, Surrey, 2, 67, 81, 160, 201
——— Gardens, xiii, 38, 81, 97, 99, 128, 129
——— Green, 50, 81, 164
——— New Garden, 81
Keyt, Sir Thomas Charles, Bart., 186, 191-2
——— Sir William, Bart., 73-4, 186 & n.

Kimbolton, Hunts., 99
Kings Lynn, Norfolk, 60
Kingston-upon-Thames, Surrey, 30, 55
Kinlet, Salop, 5, 69-70
Kiosk, 33-4
Kirkheaton, Yorks., 93
Kiveton Park, Yorks., 67, 160
Knaresborough, Yorks., xii-xiii, 95-6, 132
Kneller, Sir Godfrey, Plate 6
Knightsbridge — see London
Knots, 29, 35, 59; Plate 2
Knowsley, Lancs., 111, 112, 113, 114, 115, 116, 117
Knutsford, Cheshire, 105, 108, 111, 112-13, 116, 117, 118, 119

Laburnum, 146, 165, 181, 182, 183, 184, 187, 205
Laburnum alpinum, 146
——— *anagyroides,* 146
Lactuca sativa, 143
Ladyholt, Sussex, 85
Lakenham, Norfolk, 98
Lambeth — see London
Lamesley, Co. Durham, 127
Lamotte, Rev. Charles, 37
Lamport Hall, Northants., 105
Lancashire, 37, 107, 110, 112, 116
Lancaster, 117
Landscape gardeners, 1, 11, 97, 204
——— gardening, 24-5, 57, 76
Langley, Herts., 34
Langley, Batty (1696-1751), architect etc., 81, 165
Langton, Church, Leics., 96, 105
Langue de boeuf, 'Langdebefe', 140, 143
Lantana aculeata, 151
——— *camara,* 151
Larch, 68, 94, 102, 111, 119, 187, 194, 195
Larkspur, 173, 188
——— double, 190
Lascelles, Edward, 93

Lathom, Lancs., 113
Lathyrus vernus, 147
Lauderdale, duchess of, 167
Laurel, 51, 105, 141, 147, 163-4, 165, 187, 188, 194, 206
——— Portugal, 105, 194, 205
——— striped, 205
——— Tongue, 204
  See also Bay, Spurge Laurel
Laurence, Mr, 175, 176
Laurus nobilis, 141, 147
Laurustinus, 46, 73, 105, 147, 164, 165, 181, 182, 188, 194, 203
——— striped, 205
Lavandula spica, 143
Lavatera, 190 & n.
Lavatera trimestris, 190n.
Lavender, 20, 27, 135, 136, 143
——— spike, 27
Lavorgne, John, artist, Plate 2
Lawrence, Anthony, 63, 70, 71, 101
Lawson, William (fl. 1570-1618), Plate 3
Leasehold ground, 36, 73, 88, 89, 97, 101, 112-13, 114, 119-20, 122-3, 124, 130, 168, 170
Le Blond (A. J. Dézallier d'Argenville), 80
Lee, Sir William, Bart., 72, 97, 204, 207
Leeds, Yorks., 64, 93, 95, 106, 121
Leeds, duke of, 160
Leek, 20, 30, 32, 142, 173
Leek, Staffs., 108
Leicester, 6, 38
——— Society of Florists, 38
Leigh, Lancs., 112
Leith, Scotland, 126
Leland, John (1506 ?-1552), 59, 112
Le Leu, Le Loup — see Wolf, John
Lemmon, Mr Kenneth, xi
Lemon, 146
Lentiscus, 51, 146
Leopard's Bane, 146
Lepidium latifolium, 139
——— *sativum,* 139, 142

Le Strange family, 60
Lettuce, 20, 143, 173, 182, 183, 184
Leucojum aestivum, 149
—— *autumnale*, 149
—— *vernum*, 149
Levens, Westmorland, 11, 56-7, 76, 105, 126
Lewisham, Kent, 88-9
Lexden, Essex, 71
Leyden, Holland, 78
Leyton, Essex, 97
Leytonstone, Essex, 81, 87, 128
Liddell, Colonel, 181
Lignum vitae, 79, 194
Lilac, 1, 146, 165, 181, 182, 204
—— Persian, 46, 205
   See also Jasmine, Persian
Lilies of the field, 15
Lilium, 148
—— *candidum*, 18, 143
—— *martagon*, 57, 148
Lily, 18, 20, 25, 33, 40, 56, 139, 143, 172
—— of Constantinople, 56, 57
—— Martagon, 22, 56, 148
—— White, 77, 190
   See also Atamasco Lily
Lime, 56, 67, 68, 95, 119, 141, 148, 163-4, 165-6, 190, 194
—— Dutch, 46
Limonium minutum, 151
—— *sinuatum*, 151
Linaria repens, 140
Lincoln, 6, 69, 110
Lincoln, earl of, ix, 35
Lincolnshire, 11, 52
—— Archives Office, 110
Linconia, 151
Lindley, John (1799-1865), botanist, 93
Linnaeus, Carl von (1707-1778), 104, 190n.
Lionel, duke of Clarence, 17
Liquidamber, 203
Liquorice, 66, 118
Liriodendron tulipifera, 51

Litchfield, earl of, 62
Lithospermum officinale, 19, 142
Liverpool, Lancs., 11, 113
Liverwort, 18, 143
Llandovery, Carmarthenshire, 102
Lloyd, Richard, 169
Lobelia cardinalis, 148
—— *syphilitica*, 51, 148
Lolium perenne, 139
Londesborough, Yorks., 84, 167
London, x, 3, 6, 32, 36, 37, 44, 45, 52, 58, 60, 68, 71, 74, 75, 76, 83, 93, 96-7, 98, 101, 106, 114, 121, 122, 128, 131, 145, 150, 167, 188, 189, 193, 196-200
Battersea, 80
Bear Quay, 177
Bishopsgate, 5, 47, 48, 146
Brompton, 66, 110, 114, 128, 130
—— Old, 114
—— Park, 5, 6, 10, 37, 43, 44, 50, 51-6, 66, 71, 76, 93, 114, 128, 131, 133, 150, 160, 167, 168
Camberwell, 129, 130
Chelsea, 38, 40, 44, 80, 91, 129, 130, 133, 135
—— Manor, 27, 40
—— Physic Garden, 78, 129
Chiswick, 82, 171
—— House, 83
City New Road, 88
Clerkenwell, 42, 133
Covent Garden, 4, 129, 130
Dalston, 88
Essex House, 47
Fenchurch Street, 84
Fleet Street, 91
Fulham, 10, 37, 50, 55, 62, 67, 78-80, 85, 91, 93, 128
—— Palace, 54, 68
Gardeners Company, 6, 42
Hackney, 87, 88, 89, 128
Hammersmith, 50, 84-5, 91, 93, 99-100, 128, 130, 131, 132

Holborn, ix, 5, 35, 47, 145
Horsleydown, 41, 42
Hoxton (Hogsden), 5, 45, 48, 49, 76, 81, 93, 132, 145, 146, 150
Hyde Park Corner, 80
Islington, 45, 129-30
Kennington, 88, 129
Kensington, 44, 55, 78, 93, 114, 121, 128, 129, 131, 133-4
King William Street, 63
Kingsland, 130
Knightsbridge, 50
Lambeth, 44, 49, 78, 82, 86, 87, 93, 129, 132, 145
Leicester Fields, 184
Lewisham, 88-9, 124, 128
Lombard Street, 4
Maps and plans of — see Cary, Milne, Rocque
Mile End, 5, 36, 49, 84, 114, 128, 131
Minories, 132-3
New Cross, 130
Newington, 129
Old Street, 44-5
Putney, 50, 78, 80, 128
Ranelagh, 130
St Giles without Cripplegate, 45, 49, 76
St Katherine's by the Tower, 31
St Leonard Shoreditch, 76
St Luke Old Street, 88
St Paul's Cathedral, 82, 171
Shoreditch, 45, 48, 114
Southwark, 41, 43, 46
Spitalfields, 5, 43, 45
Stepney, 43
Stockwell, 88, 114, 129
Strand, 5, 47, 58, 70, 91
Thames Street, Lower, 53, 63
Tooting, Upper, 130
Tottenham, 130
Tower of, 18, 40, 41, 42
Turnham Green, 84, 97, 129
Vauxhall, 49, 130
Walworth, 12, 80, 112, 129

Whitechapel, 5, 42, 45, 50
   See also Westminster
London, George junior, 54-5
——— Henrietta (Mrs Peachy), xiii, 54; Plate 9
——— John junior, 55
Longevity, 2, 10, 37, 72, 96, 99, 101, 129
Long Newton Hall, Co. Durham, 95
Lonicera, 147
——— *caprifolium*, 147
——— *periclymenum*, 143
Loudon, John Claudius (1783-1843), x, 8, 37, 71, 87, 88, 101, 104, 111, 112, 113, 119, 128, 133
Louis XIV, king of France, 75
Love in a Mist, 190
Love lies Bleeding, 190
Loversall, Yorks., 96
Lowgin, Robert, master mariner, 183
Lucerne, 68, 93
Luckombe, John (1653-1758), 72
Lucy, George, 80
Lupin, 18, 173
Lupinus albus, 18
Lychnis chalcedonica, 148
Lydgate, John, 24-5, 33
Lysons, Daniel, 8
Lyte, Henry (1529-1607), botanist, 12
Lytes Cary, Som., 12

Machinery, 125-6
McNiven, Charles, 116
Maghull, Lancs., 115
Magnolia, 87
Maidenhead, Berks., 100
Mainwaring, Edward, 70
Mallow, 139
——— Venetian, 190
Malpas, Cheshire, 37
Malus pumila, 141
Mamhead, Devon, 72
Manchester, Lancs., 113
Mangles, James (1786-1867), 8, 9, 99, 100, 102, 104, 111, 119, 132

––– Robert, 8
Mansfield, Notts., 5, 68
Manure, 21, 123, 137
Maple, 96, 141, 165
––– Ash-leaved, 205
––– Norway, 94
––– Scarlet, 205
––– Sir Charles Wager's, 94
––– Sugar, 94, 205
––– Virginian, 205
March (*Apium*), 139, 140, 143
Maresfield, Sussex, 9
Marguerite, 25
Marigold, African, 183, 184, 188, 190
––– French, 183, 184, 188, 190
Marjoram, 20, 173, 183, 184
Market gardeners, 1, 11, 30, 35, 36, 37, 49, 61, 131
Market Harborough, Leics., 105
Marlborough, Wilts., 194
Marrubium vulgare, 143
Marsh Mallow, 139
Marsh, Salt, 52
Martagon – see Lily
Marum syriacum, 146
Marvel of Peru, 190
Mary I, queen of England, 29
Mason, William, 208
Mass production, 32
Massachusetts, 4
Matthew Paris, chronicler, 16
Maud, Rev. Mr, 94
Maund, Benjamin (1790-1864), botanist, 112
Meakin (Meekin), 173
Medicago arborea, 146
Medical gardens, 44
Mediterranean, 19
Medlar, 18, 21, 73, 101, 141, 165, 179, 182
––– Dutch, 178
Melandrium rubrum (*dioicum*), 142
Melford, Long, Suffolk, 99
Melia azedarach, 51
Melianthus major, 51

Melksham, Wilts., 101
Melon, 4, 24, 30, 126, 173, 175, 182, 183, 184
'Menagier de Paris, Le', 19-22, 135
Mentha spicata, 143
Mercantilism, 43, 75
Merian, Maria, 54
Mersey valley, 112
Mespilus germanica, 141
Methley, Yorks., 22-3
Mexico, 100
Mezereon, 147, 165, 187, 190, 203
––– White, 205
Michaelmas Daisy, 188
Micklewright, C. & Co., printers, 101
Middlewich, Cheshire, 111
Midlands. 11, 69, 94-6, 104-6, 113
Mignonette, 112, 190
Mile End – see London
Milford, Wilts., 101, 102
Milkwort, Tree, 151
Milne, Thomas, surveyor, 7
Mimms, South, Middlesex, 86
Mint, 143
Monasteries, x, 59 & n.
Monastic precincts, gardens in, 35-6, 39, 58
Money, value of, 31-2
Monkton Farleigh, Wilts., 101
Montagu, George, 79
Montbray, Geoffrey de, bishop of Coutances, 15
Moors in Spain, 34
Mordaunt, lord, 50
More, Sir Thomas, 135
Morgan, Edward (fl. 1638-78), botanist, 44
––– M., printer, 108
Morland, Mrs, 117
Morley, Lancs., 112
Morpeth, Northumberland, 5, 68
Morrice, Henry, spurrier, 168
Mortlake, Surrey, 48
Morus nigra, 141
Mosley, Thomas, 63
Motherwort, 143

Mounts, garden, 59
Mouse-ear, 143
Mulberry, 21, 56, 67, 70, 87, 101,
   138, 164, 165
—— Black, xiii, 87, 138, 141
—— White, 87
Muncaster, lord, 120
Muscari, 148
Mustard, 143
Myrtle, 146
—— Candleberry — see Candleberry
   Myrtle
Myrtus communis, 146
Mytton, Richard, 170

Nantwich, Cheshire, 11, 111
Napoleonic Wars, 7, 91
Narcissus. 115
—— Polyanthus, 189
Narcissus jonquilla, 149
—— *odorus,* 57
—— *pseudonarcissus,* 142, 148
—— *tenuior,* Plate 13
Nasturtium, 173, 190
—— Small, 188
'Navewe', (swede Turnip), 24
Naworth Castle, Cumberland, 60
Naylor, William, 160
Nectarine, 41, 44, 45, 46, 50, 56, 62,
   67, 73, 83, 101, 103, 116, 145,
   149, 163, 165, 172, 179, 180,
   182, 187, 189
Nemesia strumosa, xiii; Plate 9
Nepeta cataria, 143
Nepp, 143
Nerium oleander, 146
New Cross — see London
New Hall — see Beaulieu
New Holland — see Australia
Newark-upon-Trent, Notts., 5, 11,
   68, 83, 106, 109-10, 113
Newby Hall, Yorks., 68
Newcastle-upon-Tyne, 121, 122,
   125-7, 172, 174-5, 178, 179, 181
—— Literary and Philosophical
   Society of, 127

Newspapers, 91-2
Nicholas the Fruiterer, 16
Nickson, Joseph, 112
Nightshade, striped, variegated, 187,
   203
Nomenclature, scientific, 11, 89, 90
Nonconformists, nurserymen as, 115,
   124, 126
   See also Quakers
Nonsuch Palace, Surrey, 18, 33
Norman Conquest, 15, 23, 35
Normans, 15, 34
Normanton Hall, Rutland, 105, 110
North of England, 2-3, 11, 68-9, 72,
   106, 107-27, 129
—— definition of, 107
Northallerton, Yorks., 65
Northumberland, dukes of, 59, 78,
   88
—— Henry Percy, 9th earl of, 59
—— Henry Algernon Percy, 5th earl
   of, 59
Northumbria, 11
Northwich, Cheshire, 118
Norton — see Burnt Norton
Norwich, 30, 37, 60, 93, 98
Nostell Priory, Yorks., 66
Nottingham, 108, 109
Nottinghamshire, 11, 160
Numbers of firms, 6-9
Nuneham, lord, 72
Nuphar, 140
Nurseries, private, 1, 67-8
—— provincial, xiii, 5, 58-74,
   94-127
—— size of, 45, 88, 89, 120, 125-6,
   129
—— value of, 89, 96, 105, 114,
   123-4, 126
Nurseries (main references only;
   places within a radius of 20 miles
   are entered under London):-
   Addlestone, Surrey, 97; Plate 11
   Ampthill, Beds., 98
   Ashley, Staffs., 70
   Barnet, Herts. — see London

Barton-upon-Irwell, Lancs., 115
Beverley, Yorks., 69, 119-20
Birmingham, 104-5, 201
Blyth, Notts., 68, 161-4
Brampton, Hunts., xiii
Bridlington, Yorks., 120
Bristol, 102-3
Bromley, Kent — see London
Burslem, Staffs., 108
Cambridge, 99
Campden, Chipping, Glos., 73-4, 186-91
Carlisle, Cumberland, 117
Catton, Norfolk, 93, 98
Cheadle, Staffs., 108
Checkley, Staffs., 108
Chertsey, Surrey, 97-8, 204
Cheshunt, Herts. — see London
Chester, 110-11, 169-70
Chichester, Sussex, 99
Colchester, Essex, 71
Cottingham, Yorks., 119
Coventry, Warwicks., 74, 94-5
Creake, Norfolk, 60
Crewkerne, Som., 71
Daventry, Northants., 105
Derby, 69
Doncaster, Yorks., 96
Dorking, Surrey, 97
Exeter, 71-2, 104
Gateshead, Co. Durham, 68, 121-6; Plate 8
Gloucester, 103
Grantham, Lincs., 110
Handsworth, Staffs., 104
Handsworth, Yorks., 118-19
Hartlepool, Co. Durham, 120
Hassendeanburn near Hawick, 117-18
Hawkshead, Lancs., 117
Hertford, 98
Holywell, Flints., 112
Horncastle, Lincs., 110
Houghton-le-Spring, Co. Durham, 120
Huntingdon, xiii, 99

Keighley, Yorks., 118
Kendal, Westmorland, 117
Keswick, Cumberland, 117
Kinlet, Salop, 69-70
Knaresborough, Yorks., 95-6
Knowsley, Lancs., 113
Knutsford, Cheshire, 112-13
Lancaster, 117
Langton, Church, Leics., 96
Leek, Staffs., 108
Lewisham, Kent — see London
Lincoln, 69, 110
Liverpool, 114-15
London region:
  Barnet, 86, 197
  Battersea, 80
  Bethnal Green, 197
  Bow, 197
  Brentford, 88, 198, 200
  Bromley, Kent, 198
  Brompton, 85, 98, 130, 197, 198
  Brompton Park, 51-5, 167, 168; Plates 6, 9
  Camberwell, 129, 130
  Chelsea, 80, 130, 197, 201; Plate 14
  Cheshunt, 86
  Dalston, 88, 198
  East Sheen, 197
  Fulham, 50, 78-9, 196, 198
  Hackney, 89, 197, 198
  Ham Common, 130
  Hammersmith, 50, 84-5, 197; Plate 10
  Hampstead, 196
  Hampton Court, 197
  Highgate, 196
  Homerton, 198
  Horsleydown, 41, 42
  Hoxton, 48-9, 55-7, 76-7, 145-6, 150-9, 196, 197, 198; Plate 7
  Isleworth, 81, 88, 160, 164-6
  Islington, 129-30, 197, 198; Plate 16

Kennington, 88, 197, 198
Kensington, 78, 85, 197, 201
Kent Road, 197, 198
Kew, 67, 81
Kingsland, 130, 197, 198
Kingston Wick, 197
Knightsbridge, 50, 87, 198
Lambeth, 49, 80, 86, 87, 197,
    198, 199, 200; Plate 5
Lewisham, 88-9, 198
Leyton, 198
Leytonstone, 81, 87, 197
Mile End, 49, 84, 197
Neat Houses, 80
New Cross, 130, 196
Newington Butts, 196, 197,
    198
Old Street, 44-5
Paddington, 196, 197, 198
Putney, 50, 197
Ranelagh, 130
Richmond, 197
Shoreditch, 45, 196, 197
Southwark, 197, 198, 199, 200
Spitalfields, 43
Stepney, 197
Stockwell, 88
Stoke Newington, 198
Strand-on-the-Green, 82-3, 171
Sydenham, 198
Tooting, Upper, 130, 197
Tothill Street, 40-1, 42
Tottenham, 130, 196
Turnham Green, 84; Plate 12
Twickenham, 41-2, 50, 81, 89
Vauxhall, 130
Walworth, 80, 129, 196, 198,
    200; Plate 13
Westminster, 42-3, 167-8, 197
Weybridge, 83
Whitechapel, 45-6, 196, 199,
    200
Loversall, Yorks., 96
Maidenhead, Berks., 100
Manchester, 115
Mansfield, Notts., 68

Market Harborough, Leics., 105
Melford, Long, Suffolk, 99
Merriott, Som., 71
Middlewich, Cheshire, 111
Milford, Wilts., 101
Morpeth, Northumberland, 68
Nantwich, Cheshire, 111
Newark-upon-Trent, 68, 109-10
Newcastle-upon-Tyne, 121
Norwich, 98
Ormskirk, Lancs., 115
Oundle, Northants., 106
Oxford, 61-3
Perry Hill, Worcs. (Salop), 104
Pickhill, Yorks., 95
Pontefract, Yorks., 66-8, 118, 201
Reading, Berks., 100
Ripon, Yorks., 69
Rochford, Essex, 99
Rothwell, Yorks., 132
Rugeley, Staffs., 107-8
Salford, Lancs., 116
Salisbury, Wilts., 101
Small Heath, Warwicks., 105
Smethwick, Staffs., 104
Southampton, 71, 99-100
Stockport, Cheshire, 112
Taunton, Som., 103-4
Tinwell, Rutland, 105
Tytherington, Glos., 73
Wakefield, Yorks., 131-2
Waltham, Lincs., 110
Warnborough, North, Hants., 100;
    Plate 15
Wavertree, Lancs., 114
Wells, Som., xiii, 104
Weybridge, Surrey — see London
Wigan, Lancs., 116
Woodbridge, Suffolk, 71
Woolhampton, Berks., 100-1, 194
Worcester, 103
Workington, Cumberland, 117
Worksop, Notts., 68
York, 63-6, 131, 201
Nursery, xiii, 4-5
——— cost of running, 114, 133

Nurserymen as a class, 9-12, 132-3
––– as authors, 93-4, 133
––– scope of their work, 90-1, 120
––– wills of – see Wills
    for individuals, see Gardeners etc.
Nut, 18, 21, 29
Nutmeg, 18, 52
Nymphaea alba, 140, 144
Nynehead, Som., 101

Oak, 15, 23, 31, 67, 68, 74, 96, 117,
    119, 141, 163, 165, 190, 205, 206
––– American, 87
––– Champion, 205
––– Cork – see Cork Tree
––– evergreen, 50, 72, 94, 100,
    105, 165, 194, 206
––– Lucombe, 72
––– North American, 74
––– Red, 87, 205
––– Scarlet, 87, 205
––– striped, 205
––– Turner's, 87
Oakspring, 23
Oats, ix
Ockendon, North, Essex, 97
Oculus Christi – see Clary, Wild
Odiham, Hants., 100
Oftia (Spielmannia) africana, 151
Oleander, 146
Oleaster, 146, 203, 205
Oliver, George, 120
Onion, ix, 21, 25, 26, 30, 32, 142,
    173, 176
Ophioglossum vulgatum, 139, 142
Opuntia vulgaris, 146
Orach, 143
Orange, 21, 47, 95, 146
Orchards, 16, 29, 58, 59, 98, 112
Orchids, 89, 102, 130
Orchis, Spotted, 19
Orchis maculata, 19
Ordoyno, Charles, 109
––– Thomas (fl. 1792-1812),
    botanist, 109, 110
Origanum dictamnus, 139, 142

––– *maru*, 146
Ormskirk, Lancs., 113, 115
Ornithogalum, 149
Orobus venetus, 147
Orpine, 143
Orwell, Cambs., 49
Osier, 23, 25, 40, 110
––– matting, 110
Oundle, Northants., 93, 106
Ovingham, Northumberland, 123
Oxalis acetosella, 144
––– *Deppeii*, 108
––– *versicolor*, 117
Oxford, 5, 6, 36, 61, 70, 106
––– Botanic Garden, 61
––– Franciscan friary, 36
––– Magdalen College, 63
––– Paradise Gardens, 5, 36, 61-3
Oxford, countess of, 68, 201, 202
Oxford and Banbury Canal, 6
Oxlip, 149

Paeonia officinalis, 143, 148
Paeony, 18, 20, 40, 143, 148
Paliurus spina-Christi, 147
Palma Christi, 19
Pansy, 131
Paradise stock – see Apple
Pardus (Pardalianches) Theophrasti,
    145, 146
Parietaria officinalis, 140, 143
Paris, France, 20-2, 27, 60, 135, 138,
    139
––– Goodman of – see Menagier
Parish registers, 39
Parkinson, John (fl. 1838), 100
Parks, 1, 15, 22, 35
Parlington House, Yorks., 85
Parsley, 18, 20, 21, 30, 126, 140,
    143, 184
Parsnip, 20, 24, 138, 173
Parsons, John, 186
Parthenocissus, 147
Passetout – see Hyacinth
Passiflora incarnata, 147
Passion Flower, 147

Pea, ix, 20, 39, 64, 67, 82, 126, 138, 142, 176, 191
  See also Sweet Pea
Peach, 18, 21, 40, 41, 44, 46, 50, 56, 62, 65, 67, 73, 83, 98, 101, 103, 116, 141, 145, 149, 163-4, 165, 172, 178, 179, 180, 182, 187, 189
——— double, 205
Peachy, John, 54
——— Mrs — see London, Henrietta
Peacock, George, printer, 112
Pear, ix, 18, 21, 29, 31, 41, 44, 46, 56, 64, 65, 67, 68, 73, 101, 111, 116, 123, 138, 141, 145, 149, 164, 165, 172, 177, 178, 179, 182, 187, 189
——— double, 205
——— stocks, 68, 108, 163, 165
——— Williams' Bon Chretien, 84
Pearson, Edward, 48
——— Richard, 48
Pelargonium, 2
——— *quinquevulnerum*, 100; Plate 15
Pellitory of the wall, 140, 143
Pendarves, Mrs — see Delany
Pennicott, Rev. William (c. 1726-1811), rector of Long Ditton, Plate 1
Pepys, Samuel, 37, 52
Percivalle, John, 41, 45
——— Samuel, 45
Percy family — see Northumberland, dukes of
Periploca graeca, 147, 203
Periwinkle, 20, 143, 204
——— silver, 188
Perry Hill, Worcs. (Salop), 95, 104
Persia, 34, 139
Persimmon ('Percemian Plumb'), 206
Petasites albus, 151
Petre, lord, 84
Petroselinum crispum, 143
Petworth, Sussex, 59
Peucedanum graveolens, 18

Peyvre, Paulin (d. 1251), 16
Philadelphus, 1
——— *coronarius*, 147
Philip, king of England and Spain, 29
Philippa of Hainault, queen of England, 17, 135
Philips, John, 108
Phillips, John, 189
Phillyrea, 105, 146, 147, 164, 165, 188, 194, 204, 206
Phillyrea angustifolia, 147
Phlomis, 204, 206
Phyllitis scolopendrium, 142
Physic gardens, 16, 80
Picea abies, 141, 147
Pickhill, Yorks., 95, 113, 114, 120, 122, 124
Picris echioides, 140, 143
Pimpernel, 140, 143
Pinaster, 147, 195, 205
Pine, 68, 94, 105, 141
——— Aleppo, 57
——— Cluster, 206
——— Foxtail, 206
——— Jersey, 206
——— Mountain, 147
——— Scots (Scotch Fir), 18, 56, 57, 62, 94, 102, 111, 118, 119, 147, 163, 165, 187, 189, 190, 191
——— Weymouth, 94, 205
  See also Pinaster
Pineapple, 4, 83, 84, 101, 110, 201, 206, 207-8; Plate 1
Pinery, 97
Pink, 1, 129, 139
——— China, 190
——— Fairchild's Mule, 76
Pinus halepensis, 57
——— ——— *brutia*, 57
——— *hispanica*, 57
——— *pinaster*, 147
——— *pinea*, 147
——— *pyrenaica*, 57
——— *sylvestris*, 57, 141, 147
Pistacia lentiscus, 51, 146
——— *terebinthus*, 51

Pisum sativum, 142
Plane, 68, 141, 164, 165, 194, 195, 206
––– American, 2, 148
––– London, 2, 99
––– Oriental, xiii, 2, 18, 148, 194
Plantago lanceolata, 143
––– *major*, 144
Planting, 63, 65, 95, 106, 108, 117, 118
Plants, numbers cultivated, 128
Plantsmanship, 14-26, 128, 130
Platanus occidentalis, 148
––– *orientalis*, 141, 148
Plough, iron, 125-6
See also Breast ploughing
Plum, 18, 20, 41, 44, 46, 60, 65, 67, 73, 98, 101, 116, 141, 149, 163, 165, 172, 173, 177, 178, 179, 182, 187
––– Cambrian, 112
––– stocks, 165
See also Bullace
Pocock, Mr Hugh S., xiii
Polyanthus, 1, 149, 172, 190
Polygala chamaebuxus purpurea, 151
Polygonum hydropiper, 139, 143
Polypodium vulgare, 143
Polypody, 143
Pomegranate, 18, 21, 146, 178, 180, 182, 205
––– double, 205
Pontefract, Yorks., 23, 95, 104, 106, 122
Pope, Alexander, 89
Poplar, 62, 68, 141, 165
––– abele, 62, 68, 148, 190
––– Black, 62, 148
––– Carolina, 87, 205
––– Taccamahacca, 205
––– White, 62
See also Aspen
Poppy, 188, 190
Populus, 141
––– *alba*, 148
––– *nigra*, 148

––– *tremula*, 141
Port Antonio, Jamaica, 119
Portland, earl of, 75
Potatoes, 119
Poterium sanguisorba, 140
Pots, flower, 30, 49, 79, 117
Potters Bar, Middlesex, 107
Poulson, George, 120
Powderham, Devon, 72
Pratt, Sir Roger, 46
Price, Sir Carbury, 55
Price-cutting, 3, 118, 125
Prices, 25-6, 27, 29, 30, 31-2, 40, 41, 46, 59-60, 68, 74, 85, 94, 95, 99, 100, 101, 105, 106, 108, 118, 125, 134
––– excessive, 82
––– high, 81
Primrose, 20, 143, 149
Primula auricula, 148
––– *farinosa*, 151
––– x *variabilis*, 149
––– *veris*, 142
––– *vulgaris*, 143, 149
Prince's Feather, 190
Privet, 165, 205
––– evergreen 203
Prizes, 91
Profits of nurseries, 105, 113
Protestant refugees, 30
Prunus cerasus, 141, 147
––– *communis*, 147
––– *domestica*, 141
––– *insititia*, 141
––– *laurocerasus*, 147
––– *persica*, 141
––– *tenella*, 147
Psoralea pinnata, 151
Pumpkin, 20, 24, 138
Punica granatum, 146
Purslane, 182, 183
––– Seagreen, 204
Putney – see London
Pyracantha, 117, 147, 165, 204
Pyracantha coccinea, 147
Pyrus communis, 141

Quakers, 12, 103, 129, 132, 133
Quercus ilex, 147
——— *petraea*, 141
——— *robur*, 141
——— x *Turneri*, 87
Quickset — see Hawthorn
Quince, 18, 21, 40, 46, 67, 101, 116, 141, 163, 165
Quinton, Worcs. (Salop), 104

Radcliffe, John, 86
Radish, 20, 24, 143, 183, 184
Radix cava, 151
Ragwort, Sea (Jacobaea marina), 146
Railways, 2, 6, 106, 120, 131
Raisin, 21
Ramsey, Joseph, 123
Ranulph III, 6th Earl of Chester, 16
Ranunculus, 1, 56, 92, 115, 148, 172, 175
Ranunculus asiaticus, 148
——— *flammula*, 143
Ranworth Hall, Norfolk, 55
Raphanus sativus, 143
Raspberry, 20, 101, 113, 165, 172
——— Virginian, 187, 205
——— White, 172
'Rauscorth', 23
Raynham, Edward, 71
Reading, Berks., 100, 101
'Redenay', 138-9, 143
Red knees, 139
Red Ray grass, 139
Reed for thatching, 40
Reed, Mr, 176
Reformation, 35
Rents for nursery ground, 36, 114, 122, 126-7
'Restingtre' (? stock tree), 16
Restoration, 37, 145
Revesby Abbey, Lincs., 66
Revolution of 1688, 75
Rhamnus alaternus, 146, 147

——— *catharticus*, 141
Rhododendron, 109, 119
Rhododendron campanulatum, 111
——— *luteum*, Plate 16
Rhus, 146
Ribes grossularia, 141
——— *sanguineum 'coccinea'*, 132
Ribston, Yorks., xiii
Ribwort, 143
Richard I Coeur de Lion, king of England, 16
——— II, 34
Richardson, Ralph, xiii
Richmond, Surrey, 27, 29, 34, 42, 99, 125
Ricinus communis, 19
Ripley Castle, Yorks., 68
Ripon, Yorks., 69
Roberts, Rev. James Foulkes, 99
——— William, 120
Robinia pseudacacia, 146
Rochford, Essex, 99
Rock, Northumberland, 65
Rock gardens, 2
    See also Alpine plants
Rocket, double, 95, 174
——— Purple, 148
——— White, 148
Rocque, John, surveyor, 79, 84
Romsey Abbey, Hants., 16
Ronalds, Elizabeth, 88
Roncesvalles, 39
Rosa x alba, 143
——— *gallica*, 143
Rosamund's Bower, 25-6, 33
Rose, 9, 16, 20, 25, 29, 33, 56 57, 68, 86, 96, 106, 109, 110, 165, 181, 182, 187, 194, 201
——— American, 204
——— Damask, 29, 172
——— Moss, 78, 108, 188, 201
——— named varieties of, 187-8, 195, 201-2, 203-4
——— Red, 22, 29, 31, 143
——— Unique or White Provence, 106, 201-2

—— White, 22, 143
  See also Sweet Briar
Rose Bay, 151
Rose, Stephen (c. 1563-1638), 46
Rosemary, 17, 19, 20, 27, 34, 135-7, 143
—— striped, 205
Rosmarinus officinalis, 143
Rothwell, Yorks., 132
Rounceval pea, 39
Roxwell, Essex, 55
(Royal) Horticultural Society, xi, 38
Royal Society, 77
(Royal) Society of Arts, 118
Rudley, Thomas, vintner, 168
Rue, 18, 143
Rugeley, Staffs., 107-8
Runcorn, Cheshire, 113
Rural culture, 12
Rushton, Northants., 167
Russell family — see Bedford, earls of
Ruta graveolens, 143
Rutter, Mrs, 191
Ryder, Sir Dudley, 74, 186n., 191-3
—— Nathaniel, 74, 193
Rye, ix
Ryston Hall, Norfolk, 46

Safflower, Bastard Saffron 19
Saffron, 18, 20, 21, 143
Sage, 20, 27, 30, 143
—— Tree (Phlomis), 203
St John's Wort (Herbe Ion), 143, 181, 182, 187
St Peter's Wood, Wort, 187, 205
St Thomas's, Devon, 72
Salads, 4, 24, 35, 36, 142-4
Salford, Lancs., 116
Salisbury, Wilts., 70, 101, 102
Salisbury, earl of, 30, 52
Salix, 141
Salkeld, John, 65
—— Samuel, 65
Salsify, 173
Salvia officinalis, 143
—— *patens*, 100

—— *sclarea*, 142
—— *verbenaca*, 142
Sambucus ebulus, 140, 144
Sand, 'Calesse', 27
Sanderson, Charles, 185
Sandy, Beds., 98
Sanicle, 143
Sanicula europaea, 143
Sarracenia, 84
Satureia montana, 143
Savernake, Wilts., 88, 100, 194
Savin, 147, 204
Savory, 18, 20, 143
Savoy — see Cabbage
Saxifraga umbrosa, 151
Saxon gardening, 16, 34
Scabiosa succisa, 140, 143
Scabious, 20, 140, 143
—— Sweet, 190
Scallion, 142
Scarborough, Yorks., 120
—— Vauxhall Gardens, 120
Scilla, 148
Scorpion Senna — see Senna
Scorzonera, 173
Scotland, 3, 7, 9, 11, 12, 66, 69, 83, 84, 89, 121
Scottish gardeners, 83-4
Seaton Delaval, Northumberland, 87, 121
Sedum, Yorkshire, 151
Sedum rhodiola, 151
—— *telephium*, 143
Seed, ix, 3, 25, 36, 40, 46, 49, 52, 60, 65, 68, 70, 82, 83, 86, 94, 95, 96, 100, 101, 106, 108, 109, 114, 115, 117, 125, 128, 173, 175, 176, 177, 182-4, 185, 188, 190
—— flower, 88, 128
—— growers, 112
—— saving of, ix, 21-2
—— tree, 87
—— vegetable, 173
Seedsmen, 3, 4, 5, 12-13, 31, 47, 51, 67, 70, 80, 86, 91, 93, 99, 100, 103, 108, 109, 110, 111, 113,

115, 117, 119, 120, 121, 128, 145, 199-200
for individuals, see Gardeners etc.
Selby, Yorks., 22
Selim II, Sultan (1566-74), 15
Selkirk, Scotland, 116
Senecio cineraria, 146
––– *vulgaris*, 142
Senna, 146
––– Bladder, 165, 181, 182, 202, 205
––– Scorpion, 147, 165, 181, 182, 203
Service Tree ('Aleys'), 18, 50, 141, 165
Shallot, 20, 142
Shaw, Wilts., 101
Sheffield, Yorks., 104, 108, 118, 119
––– Horticultural Society, 119
Shefford, Beds., 50
Shepherd, Thomas, 77n.
Sherard, Dr James, 84
Shields, South, Co. Durham, 123
Shifnal, Salop, 95
Shincliffe Park, Co. Durham, 35
Shottery, Warwicks., 192
Shrewsbury, 60, 95
Shrubs, ornamental, 2, 50, 62, 68, 76, 79, 81, 82, 83, 87, 96, 99, 101, 102, 106, 108, 111, 115, 119, 150, 178, 180-2, 194, 201
Shutt, John, 181
Sible Hedingham, Essex, 53
Sicily, 15, 34
Side-saddle Flower, 84
Silverlock, Nevill, 99
Sisson, Thomas, 171, 177, 179, 181, 183, 184, 185
Skirret, 24, 138
Skreens, Essex, 55
Smallage, 140
Smallwood, Robert, brewer, 167
Smartweed, 139
'Smerewort', 19
Smethwick, Staffs., 95, 104
Smith, Thomas, 101

Smyrnium olusatrum, 142
Snell, Powell, 74, 186
Snowdon, Johnson, master mariner, 174
Snowdrop, 172
Societies, 91
Society or Club of Florists, 4, 37, 38
––– of Gardeners, 5, 38, 50, 77, 78, 80, 82, 91
Sodbury, Chipping, Glos., 102
Soil, 14, 36, 60, 98
Solanum pseudocapsicum, 146
Somerset, duke of, 46
––– duchess of, 46-7
Sorbus, 205
Sorbus domestica, 141
Sorrel, 20
––– Wood, 20, 144
Southampton, 9, 71, 99-100, 106
––– Avenue, 71
Southernwood, 18, 143
Southwark, Surrey, 29
Sowerby, Yorks., 64
Spade cultivation, 120, 126
Spain, 34, 60
Sparsholt (Spersholt), Berks., 62
Spartium junceum, 147, 151
Spearwort, 143
Spence, Rev. Joseph, 80, 83
Spielmannia – see *Oftia*
Spinach, 20, 138, 140, 143
Spinacia oleracea, 140, 143
Spinoke, 140
Spiraea hypericifolia, 147, 165
––– *salicifolia*, 147, 165
Spirea Frutex, 147, 165, 181, 182, 203, 204
Spring (Plantation), 23
Spruce – see Fir
––– Norway, 18
Spurge (Catapuce), 140, 143
––– evergreen, 151
––– Laurel, 143, 203
Stachys officinalis, 142
Stafford, 193
Stafford, marquess of, 108

Staines, Middlesex, 175
Stamford, Lincs., 38, 93, 106, 107
Stamford Baron, Northants., 38
Stanhope, Sir William, 85
Starwort, Virginian, 151
Steele, Richard, 112, 119, 125
Stellaria holostea, 143
Stephenson, Richard, 121
Stitchwort, 143
Stock, Brompton, 190
——— Queen's, 190
Stockport, Cheshire, 112, 116
Stockton, Co. Durham, 95
Storax, 203
Stove — see Hothouse
Stowell, Glos., 73
Strand-on-the-Green, Middlesex, 48, 82
Strandwick, John, master mariner, 177
Stratford-on-Avon, Warwicks., 192
Strawberry, 29, 50, 143
——— Hautboy, 172, 174, 175
Strawberry Hill, Middlesex, 79, 81, 89
Strawberry Tree, 96
Studley Royal, Yorks., 66, 85, 132
Sumach, 146, 165, 181, 182, 194, 205
——— myrtle-leaved, 203
——— shining-leaved, 194
——— Stag's Horn, 187
Sunflower, 190
Surinam, 54
Surveyors, 7, 25, 42, 63, 79, 80, 81, 87, 97, 113, 116, 125
Swallowfield, Berks., 167
Swede Turnip — see 'Navewe'
Sweet, William, 102
Sweet Briar, 178, 180, 182, 194, 203, 205
——— Gum, 205
——— Pea, 93, 173, 188, 190
——— William, 76, 190
Sycamore, 56, 67, 96, 119, 165, 190
Symphytum officinale, 142

——— *tuberosum*, 151
Syon House, Middlesex, 43, 59, 78
'Syringa' (*Philadelphus*), 1, 147, 165, 181, 182, 203, 204
Syringa persica, 147
——— *vulgaris*, 146

Taccamahacca — see Poplar
Talman, William (1650-1719), architect, 55
Tanacetum vulgare, 143
Tansy, 143
Taunton, Som., 103-4, 193
Taxus baccata, 141
——— ———*fastigiata*, 115
Teasel, Wild, 144
Tees valley, 120
Temple, Mr, 72
Temple Newsam, Yorks., 67
Terebenthus, 51
Teucrium fruticans, 151
——— *scorodonia*, 143
Tewkesbury, Glos., 186
Thames valley, 50, 97, 106
Thirkleby, Yorks., 69
Thirsk, Yorks., 95
Thomson, Miss G. Scott, 53
Thorn, 141
——— Cockspur, 205
——— Double-blossomed, 94, 205
——— Egyptian, 165-6
——— evergreen, 94
——— Glastonbury, 49, 94, 205
——— Lord Ely's, 205
——— Yellow-berried, 205
See also Hawthorn
Thorn Daisy, 151
Thornbury Castle, Glos., 35
Thorndon Hall, Essex, 84
Thrift a northern virtue, 69
Thunbergia alata, 103
Thyme, 27, 30, 144
Thymus serpyllum, 144
Tilia, 141
——— x *europea*, 148
Timber, 53

Time-lag after introduction, 51
Timothy grass, 67
Tinwell, Rutland, 105, 107
Titumallus, 140
Toddington, Beds., 16
Toddington, Glos., 186n.
Tools, cost of, 25-6, 30, 31, 162
Tooting — see London
Topiary, 59
Torch-thistle, 49
Torquay, Devon, 102
Tottenham — see London
Tours by nurserymen, 53-4, 103,
    110, 115
Town-planning, horticultural, 49
Townsend, Benjamin, 82
Toxicodendron, 203, 205
——— Wing-leaved, 205
Tracy, viscount, 186 & n., 192
Transport, 6-7, 60, 71, 72, 82-3, 97,
    101, 102, 106, 122, 126, 172-85,
    188-90, 191-3, 206, 207-8
Travel, 53, 72, 85, 90, 97, 103, 175,
    191-3, 206-7
Traveller's Joy, 203
Treacher, Alderman, 62
Trees, 50, 62, 65, 68, 71, 76, 78, 79,
    81, 82, 83, 85, 89, 93-4, 105,
    106, 108, 115, 117, 118, 119,
    133, 150, 177, 180, 185, 193
——— ornamental, 50, 76, 117, 118,
    146-7, 148
    See also Forest Trees, Fruit Trees
Trent, river, 107
Trentham,
    Staffs., 94, 95, 104, 108
Trollius europaeus, 149
Tropaeolum, 100
Tuberose, 188
Tulip, 1, 2, 15, 56, 71, 92, 109, 115,
    129, 148, 172
Tulip Tree, 51, 194
——— Carolina, 205
Tulipa, 148
Tuncarse, 139
Turkey, 2, 34, 44

Turner, William (c. 1508-1568),
    botanist, 11, 68
Turnham Green — see London
Turnip, 20, 24, 138, 173, 183, 184
    See also 'Navewe'
Tutsan, 96, 144, 203, 204
Tweed, river, 124
Twickenham, Middlesex, 41-2, 50,
    81, 82, 89
Tyne, river, 107, 122
Tytherington, Glos., 5, 73
Tythimals, Aizoid, 151

Uddingston, Scotland, 126
Uffenbach, Zacharias Conrad von, 61
Ulmus, 141
——— *glabra exoniensis*, 104
Uttoxeter, Staffs., 108
Uxbridge, earl of, 81

Vaccinium amoenum, Plate 11
Valerian, 144
Valeriana officinalis, 144
Van Blach', painter, Plate 7
Vandenancker, Peter, 4
Vane, Lionel, 95
Vegetables, 21, 22, 24, 35, 36, 40,
    58, 82, 110, 117, 121, 138,
    141-2, 173
Venus' Looking Glass, 173, 188, 190
Verbena melindris, 103
——— *officinalis*, 144
Vermuyden, Sir Cornelius, 11
Versailles, France, 75
Vervain, 144
Viburnum opulus, 147
——— *tinus*, 147
Vicia faba, 141
Victoria, Queen, 2, 7, 8, 9, 128, 131
Vinca major, 143
——— *minor*, 143
Vine — see Grape
Vineyards, 15, 16, 35, 52, 65
Viola odorata, 144
Violet, 20, 144
——— Armenian, 22

——— March, 22
Virgin's Bower, 117, 147
Virginian Climber, Creeper, 147, 202
Virgultum, 23
Vitis vinifera, 141

Wages and fees of gardeners, 25-6, 28, 29, 30, 31, 32-3, 36, 59-60, 89, 97
Wakefield, Yorks., 131
Wales, 7, 55, 72
Wales, Augusta Princess of (1719-1772), 2, 85, 97, 201
Wales, Frederick Louis, Prince of, 37-8, 81
Walker, James, 120
Wall, hollow, 99
Wallflower, 20, 187, 188
Wallwort, 140, 144
Walnut, 23, 62, 67, 68, 73, 141, 163-4, 165
——— Virginian, 206
Walpole, Horace, 79, 81, 89, 91; Plate 1
Walsham, North, Norfolk, 129
Waltham, Lincs., 110
Walworth — see London
Wanstead, Essex, 30, 81
Ward, Ann, printer, 96
Warkworth, Northants., 85
Warnborough, North, Hants., 100
Warrington, Lancs., 12, 116, 129
Wars of the Roses, 24
Wart Cress (Herb Yve), 144
Warter Hall, Yorks., 120
Warwick, 95
——— Castle Park, 74, 94
Warwick, earl of, 74
Water in gardens, 15, 16
Water Pepper, 139
Waterlily, 20, 140, 144
Watford, Herts., 52
Watson, Hewett Cottrell (1804-1881), botanist, 11
——— Richard, bishop of Llandaff, 117

Wavertree, Lancs., 114
Waybread, 144
Wearmouth, Co. Durham, 176
Weaverham, Cheshire, 118
Webb, Daniel, 101
Webber, Mr Ronald, 116
Welbeck Abbey, Notts., 68, 201
Welby Mason, Lincs., 86
Weldon, John, master mariner, 179
Wellington, Som., 101
Wells, Som., xiii, 104
Welton, Northants., 94
Wentworth Woodhouse, Yorks., Plate 2
Wentworth, Thomas (d. 1587), Plates 2, 3
West Bromwich, Staffs., 81
West Country, 71-4, 102-4
Westminster, 27, 39-41, 44, 45, 58, 97, 167-8
——— Abbey, 18, 27, 34, 39
——— ——— Infirmary Garden, 44
——— Charing Cross, 39
——— Neat Houses, 80
——— Palace, 34, 39-40
——— St James's, 30
——— ——— ——— Park, 46; Plate 1
——— St Margaret's, 40, 41, 42, 55
——— St Martin's in the Fields, 55, 82, 168-9
——— St Mary Rounceval, 39
——— St Mary Savoy, 169
——— Tothill Street, 40, 41, 42
——— Whitehall Palace, 28, 40
——— York Place, 30, 40
Weston, Richard, 112, 129
Weybridge, Surrey, 83, 86
Wheat, ix
Wheatcroft, Francis, 193
Whig oligarchy, 75
Whitebeam (Aria Theophrasti), 95
Whitehall Palace — see Westminster
Whiteside, Mr, 62
Whitingham, John, 95
Whitmore, Staffs., 70
Whitton, Middlesex, 42

Whixley, Yorks., 69
Wigan, Lancs., 101, 113, 116
Wilderness Quarters, 96
Willesden, Middlesex, 60
William Rufus, king of England, 15
――― III, 75
Willis, T., 115
Willmott, Dr A. J., xiii
Willow, 40, 87, 141
――― Norfolk, 87
Wills of nurserymen, 167-70
Willson, Miss E. J., xi, 84, 131
Wilmington, lord, xiii, 84
Wilson, J., printer, 113
Wilson-Cracroft, Robert, 110
Wilton, Wilts., 70
Wiltshire, 102
――― apprentices, 101
――― Horticultural Society, 101-2
Wimbledon, Surrey, 98n., 132, 133
Winchester, Hants., 32
――― College, 25, 33, 99, 100
Windsor, Berks., 30
Wine, 16
Winthrop, John junior, 4
Wippeltree – see Cornel
Woburn, Beds., xiii, 45, 47, 53, 58
――― abbot of, 28
Wolsey, Cardinal Thomas, 30, 32, 33
Women weeders, 31
Wood Sorrel, 144
Woodbine – see Honeysuckle
Woodbridge, Suffolk, 71
Woodham Walter, Essex, 46
Woodruff, 144
Woodstock, Oxon., 15, 33
――― Everswell, 33
Woodward, Charles, 54
――― George, 55
――― Richard, 54, 55
Wooler, Northumberland, 124
Woolhampton, Berks., 100-1, 194
Woolridge (Worlidge), John (fl.
    1669-98), 5, 47, 51, 145
Woolton Hall, Lancs., 118
Worcester, 103

Workington, Cumberland, 117
――― Agricultural Society, 117, 118
――― Hall, 117
Worksop, Notts., 68
Worlidge – see Woolridge
Wormwood, 144
Worts – see Colewort
Wressle Castle, Yorks., 59
Wrest Park, Beds., 50
Wycombe, Bucks., 167
Wykeham, William of, bishop of
    Winchester, 25
Wyndham, Wadham, 101

Yarrow, 144
Yew, 32, 56, 61, 68, 73, 75, 141,
    163-4, 165-6, 189, 191, 204
――― Florence Court, 115
――― Irish, 115
York, 5, 35, 36, 60, 61, 63-6, 69, 72,
    92, 93, 95, 96, 104, 106, 112,
    113, 114, 121, 122, 131, 132,
    138, 141
――― Ancient Society of Florists, 38,
    69, 96
――― archbishops of, 40
――― Clementhorpe priory, 63
――― Dominican friary (Blackfriars),
    35-6, 63
――― Fishergate, 36, 131
――― Franciscan friary (Greyfriars),
    36, 64
――― Friars' Gardens, 5, 36, 63, 131
――― Knavesmire, 65
――― Micklegate Bar, 63, 92
――― New Walk, 64
――― St Andrews priory, 36, 63, 131
――― St Martin-cum-Gregory, 63, 64
――― St Mary's abbey, 36
York, Richard duke of, 35
Yorkshire, 12, 89, 95, 104, 105, 106,
    108, 118, 131, 160
Youmen, Thomas, master mariner, 176
Yucca (Jucca), Indian, 146

Zephyranthes atamasco, 150